elements
of
calculus
for
technical
students

———————————————

elements
of
calculus

for

technical
students

---

by
Lee W. Davis

CANFIELD PRESS · San Francisco

A DEPARTMENT OF HARPER & ROW, PUBLISHERS, INC.

NEW YORK · EVANSTON · LONDON

Editor: *Gerald T. Curtis*
Basic Book Editor: *Kenneth R. Burke*
Production Manager: *Christine Schacker*
Designer: *Kenneth R. Burke*

ELEMENTS OF CALCULUS FOR TECHNICAL STUDENTS
Copyright © 1971 by Lee W. Davis

Standard Book Number: 06-382540-6
Library of Congress Catalog Card Number: 71-148576

Preface

This book seeks to present elementary calculus as a tool to the technical student in today's expanding junior colleges and technical institutes.

It is assumed that the student will have successfully completed a course in technical algebra and trigonometry before starting this book. It is recognized, however, that the student will need some help in recalling many important precalculus mathematics ideas. To this end a precalculus mathematics review section is presented first. It should be covered thoroughly before proceeding further into the text. This review section should also become a ready reference for any point in the text where mathematics trouble is encountered.

Many examples are presented and for the most part no step is omitted, no matter how elementary it may seem. It is hoped that those students with good mathematics backgrounds will pass over these elementary steps gracefully when they realize what a help they are to others.

Since the text has as its purpose to make calculus a tool, theory and proofs are kept to a minimum or presented intuitively. Many proofs from the section on differentiation are presented in the appendix.

The structure of the book is such that its use can cover a wide variety of course requirements. For maximum coverage with minimum time, most application discussion and problems can be omitted. For a particular discipline, application discussions and problems can be selected. And for an all-inclusive course, the entire text can be covered.

L.W.D.

Miami, Florida
February 1971

Contents

Precalculus
Mathematics Review

SYMBOLS

$>$	is greater than.		$\triangle$	triangle.
$<$	is less than.		$\measuredangle$	angle.
$\neq$	is not equal to.		$\odot$	circle.
$\sim$	is similar to.		$\perp$	is perpendicular to.
$\approx$	is approximately equal to.		$\parallel$	is parallel to.
$\cong$	is congruent to.		$f(x)$	function of x.
$\equiv$	is identically equal to.		$f[x]$	functional value at x.
$\rightarrow$	approaches.		$\overline{ab}$	line segment ab.
$\Rightarrow$	then, or implies.		$\int$	indefinite integral sign.
$\Leftrightarrow$	if and only if, double implication.		$\int_a^b$	definite integral sign.
$\therefore$	therefore.		Σ	sigma (sum of).
$n!$	factorial; $n(n-1)(n-2)(n-3)\ldots(1)$.		$\ln$	natural logarithm (base e).
$\lvert n \rvert$	absolute value.		$\log$	common logarithm (base 10).

THE COMPLEX NUMBERS CHARTED

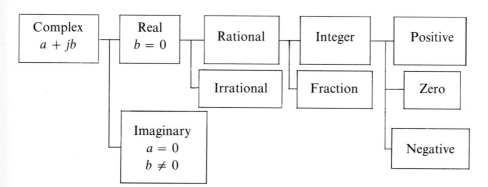

ALGEBRA

Powers and Roots

$$a^n \cdot a^m = a^{n+m} \qquad\qquad a^n \div a^m = a^{n-m}$$

$$a^0 = 1 \quad (a \neq 0) \qquad\qquad (a/b)^n = a^n/b^n$$

$$(a^n)^m = a^{nm} \qquad\qquad a^{n/m} = \sqrt[m]{a^n}$$

$$\sqrt[n]{ab} = \sqrt[n]{a} \cdot \sqrt[n]{b} \qquad\qquad \sqrt[n]{\sqrt[m]{a}} = \sqrt[nm]{a}$$

$$\sqrt[n]{a/b} = \sqrt[n]{a}/\sqrt[n]{b} \qquad\qquad a^{-n} = 1/a^n$$

$$j = \sqrt{-1} \qquad j^2 = -1 \qquad j^3 = -j \qquad j^4 = 1$$

Expansions

$$(a + b)(a - b) = a^2 - b^2$$

$$(a + jb)(a - jb) = a^2 + b^2$$

$$(a + b)^2 = a^2 + 2ab + b^2$$

$$(a + b)^n = a^n + na^{n-1}b + \frac{n(n-1)}{2!}a^{n-2}b^2 + \frac{n(n-1)(n-2)}{3!}a^{n-3}b^3$$

$$+ \cdots + b^n$$

$(a - b)^n$: use $[a + (-b)]^n$ in above expansion

$(r + 1)$st term of $(a + b)^n$ is:

$$\frac{n(n-1)(n-2)(n-3)\ldots(n-r+1)}{r!}a^{n-r}b^r$$

SERIES

Exponential

$$e = 1 + \tfrac{1}{1} + \tfrac{1}{2}! + \tfrac{1}{3}! + \tfrac{1}{4}! + \cdots$$

$$e^x = 1 + x + x^2/2! + x^3/3! + x^4/4! + \cdots$$

$$a^x = 1 + x \ln a + \frac{(x \log a)^2}{2!} + \frac{(x \log a)^3}{3!} + \cdots$$

Trigonometric

$\mathrm{Sin}\, x = x - x^3/3! + x^5/5! - x^7/7! + \cdots$

$\mathrm{Cos}\, x = 1 - x^2/2! + x^4/4! - x^6/6! + \cdots$

Sigma Notation

$$\sum_{i=1}^{n} x_i y_i = x_1 y_1 + x_2 y_2 + x_3 y_3 + \cdots + x_n y_n$$

$$\sum_{i=1}^{n} x_i y = x_1 y + x_2 y + x_3 y + \cdots + x_n y$$

$$\sum_{i=1}^{n} x y_i = x y_1 + x y_2 + x y_3 + \cdots + x y_n$$

TRIGONOMETRY

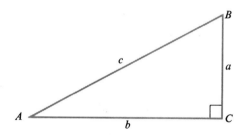

Figure 0.1

Fundamental Relations (Figure 0.1)

$\mathrm{Sin}\, A = a/c = \cos B$

$\mathrm{Cos}\, A = b/c = \sin B$

$\mathrm{Tan}\, A = a/b = \cot B$

$\mathrm{Cot}\, A = b/a = \tan B$

$\mathrm{Sec}\, A = c/b = \csc B$

$\mathrm{Csc}\, A = c/a = \sec B$

Reciprocals   Reciprocals

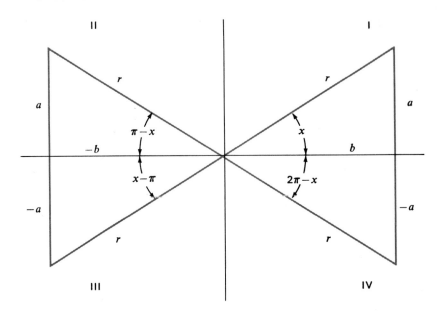

Figure 0.2

Functional Values in Any Quadrant (Figure 0.2)

$\pi/2 < x < \pi$
(Second Quadrant)

$\text{Sin } x = \sin(\pi - x)$
$\text{Cos } x = -\cos(\pi - x)$
$\text{Tan } x = -\tan(\pi - x)$
$\text{Cot } x = -\cot(\pi - x)$
$\text{Sec } x = -\sec(\pi - x)$
$\text{Csc } x = \csc(\pi - x)$

$\pi < x < 3\pi/2$
(Third Quadrant)

$\text{Sin } x = -\sin(x - \pi)$
$\text{Cos } x = -\cos(x - \pi)$
$\text{Tan } x = \tan(x - \pi)$
$\text{Cot } x = \cot(x - \pi)$
$\text{Sec } x = -\sec(x - \pi)$
$\text{Csc } x = -\csc(x - \pi)$

$3\pi/2 < x < 2\pi$
(Fourth Quadrant)

$\text{Sin } x = -\sin(2\pi - x)$
$\text{Cos } x = \cos(2\pi - x)$
$\text{Tan } x = -\tan(2\pi - x)$
$\text{Cot } x = -\cot(2\pi - x)$
$\text{Sec } x = \sec(2\pi - x)$
$\text{Csc } x = -\csc(2\pi - x)$

Functions Plotted (Figures 0.3–0.6)

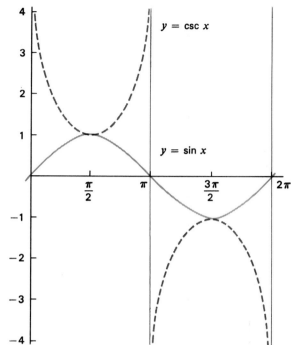

Law of Sines

$$\frac{a}{\sin A} = \frac{b}{\sin B} = \frac{c}{\sin C}$$

Law of Cosines

$$c^2 = a^2 + b^2 - 2ab \cos C$$

$$a^2 = c^2 + b^2 - 2cb \cos A$$

$$b^2 = a^2 + c^2 - 2ac \cos B$$

Figure 0.3

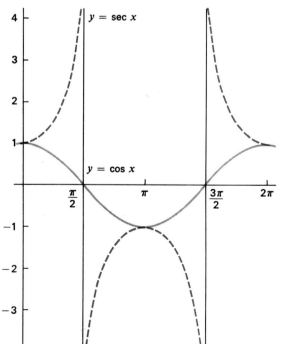

Law of Tangents

$$\frac{a - b}{a + b} = \frac{\tan \frac{1}{2}(A - B)}{\tan \frac{1}{2}(A + B)}$$

$$\frac{b - c}{b + c} = \frac{\tan \frac{1}{2}(B - A)}{\tan \frac{1}{2}(B + A)}$$

Figure 0.4

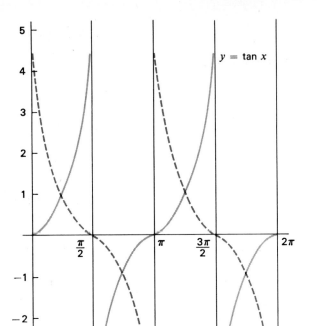

Figure 0.5

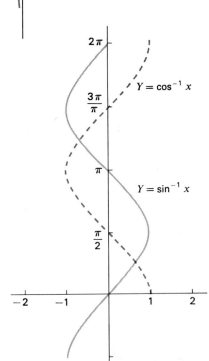

Figure 0.6

Harmonics (Figure 0.7)

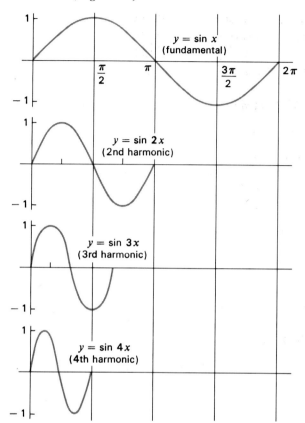

Figure 0.7

Identities Charted (Figure 0.8)

Function	Reciprocal	Ratio	Ratio	Product	Pythagorus
$\sin A = \dfrac{y}{r}$	$\dfrac{1}{\csc A}$	$\dfrac{\cos A}{\cot A}$	$\dfrac{\tan A}{\sec A}$	$\cos A \cdot \tan A$	$\sin^2 A = 1 - \cos^2 A$
$\cos A = \dfrac{x}{r}$	$\dfrac{1}{\sec A}$	$\dfrac{\cot A}{\csc A}$	$\dfrac{\sin A}{\tan A}$	$\sin A \cdot \cot A$	$\cos^2 A = 1 - \sin^2 A$
$\tan A = \dfrac{y}{x}$	$\dfrac{1}{\cot A}$	$\dfrac{\sin A}{\cos A}$	$\dfrac{\sec A}{\csc A}$	$\sin A \cdot \sec A$	$\tan^2 A = \sec^2 A - 1$
$\cot A = \dfrac{x}{y}$	$\dfrac{1}{\tan A}$	$\dfrac{\cos A}{\sin A}$	$\dfrac{\csc A}{\sec A}$	$\cos A \cdot \csc A$	$\cot^2 A = \csc^2 A - 1$
$\sec A = \dfrac{r}{x}$	$\dfrac{1}{\cos A}$	$\dfrac{\tan A}{\sin A}$	$\dfrac{\csc A}{\cot A}$	$\csc A \cdot \tan A$	$\sec^2 A = \tan^2 A + 1$
$\csc A = \dfrac{r}{y}$	$\dfrac{1}{\sin A}$	$\dfrac{\sec A}{\tan A}$	$\dfrac{\cot A}{\cos A}$	$\cot A \cdot \sec A$	$\csc^2 A = \cot^2 A + 1$

Figure 0.8 Trigonometric Identities

Troublesome, Similar Combinations

$2 \sin x$ means: Two times the sine of x or $2(\sin x)$.
Sin $2x$ means: The sine of two times x or $\sin(2x)$.
Sin x^2 means: The sine of the square of x or $\sin(x^2)$.
Sin$^2 x$ means: Square the sine of x or $(\sin x)^2$.

LOGARITHMS

$\text{Log } 100 \ = 2 \Leftrightarrow 10^2 = 100$

$\text{Log}_A B \ \ = C \Leftrightarrow A^C = B$

$\text{Log } MN = \log M + \log N$

$\text{Log } M/N = \log M - \log N$

$\text{Log } M^n \ \ = n \log M$

To change base:

$$\text{Log}_A B = \frac{\log_c B}{\log_c A}$$

VECTORS

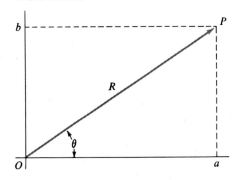

Figure 0.9

Ordered-pair notation: $\mathbf{OP} = (a,b)$
Complex notation: $\mathbf{OP} = a + jb$
Polar notation: $\mathbf{OP} = R \underline{/\theta}$
Exponential notation: $\mathbf{OP} = R\, e^{j\theta}$

Conversions:

If $\mathbf{OP} = (a,b) \Rightarrow \mathbf{OP} = \sqrt{a^2 + b^2}\underline{/\tan^{-1} b/a}$

If $\mathbf{OP} = (a,b) \Rightarrow \mathbf{OP} = a + jb$

If $\mathbf{OP} = (a,b) \Rightarrow \mathbf{OP} = \sqrt{a^2 + b^2}\, e^{j\tan^{-1} b/a}$

If $\mathbf{OP} = R\angle \Rightarrow \mathbf{OP} = (R\cos\theta, R\sin\theta)$

If $\mathbf{OP} = R\angle^\theta \Rightarrow \mathbf{OP} = R\cos\theta + jR\sin\theta$

If $\mathbf{OP} = R\angle^\theta \Rightarrow \mathbf{OP} = Re^{j\theta}$

ANALYTIC GEOMETRY

Straight Line (Figure 0.10)

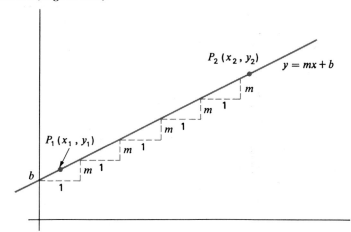

Figure 0.10

Slope-intercept form: $y = mx + b$

Slope $m = \dfrac{y_2 - y_1}{x_2 - x_1}$ and y intercept is b

Quadratics

General form: $ax^2 + bx + c = 0$ where $a \neq 0$

Quadratic formula for evaluating x: $x = \dfrac{-b \pm \sqrt{b^2 - 4ac}}{2a}$

Conic Sections

Parabola: $y = (x - a)^2 + b$ (see Figure 0.11)

Circle: $(x - a)^2 + (y - b)^2 = R^2$ (see Figure 0.12)

Ellipse: $\dfrac{(x - a)^2}{c^2} + \dfrac{(y - b)^2}{d^2} = 1$ (see Figure 0.13)

Hyperbola: $\dfrac{(x - a)^2}{c^2} - \dfrac{(y - b)^2}{d^2} = 1$ (see Figure 0.14)

$$xy = k$$

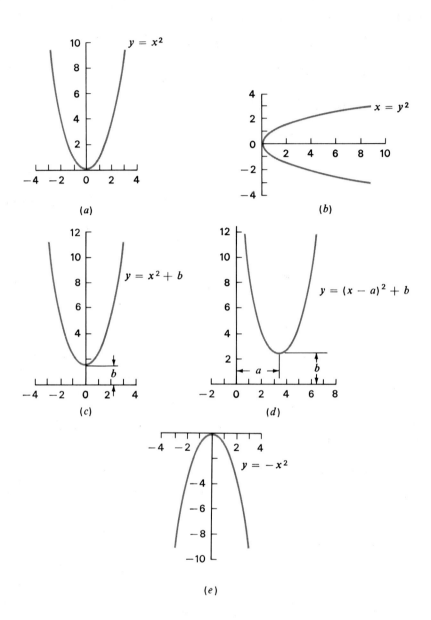

Figure 0.11

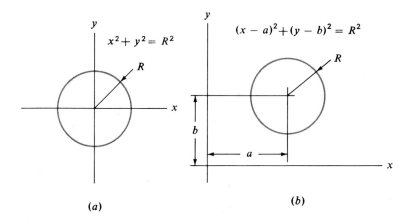

Figure 0.12

Figure 0.13

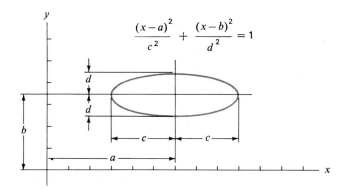

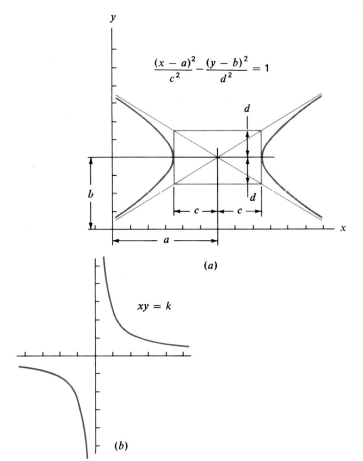

Figure 0.14

$$\frac{(x-a)^2}{c^2} - \frac{(y-b)^2}{d^2} = 1$$

(a)

$xy = k$

(b)

FUNCTION NOTATION

$y = f(x)$ is read: y is a function of x, thus $f(x)$ represents a *function*.
$y = f[x]$ is read: The functional value of y at x, thus $f[x]$ represents a *number*.
Figure 0.15 schematically shows the concept of a function.

1. The *domain* is a set of elements "x."
2. The *rule*, $y = f(x)$, picks an element "x" from the *domain*, assigns it a value $f[x]$ and places this value, or maps it, into the *range*.
3. The *range* is a set of elements "$f[x]$."
4. For the function to be "*single valued*", the rule must map each element from the domain to one and only one element in the range.

If $y = f(x)$ is the notation of a function as pictured in Figure 0.15, then the inverse function is denoted by $x = f^{-1}(y)$. Figures 0.3 and 0.4 illustrate the plots of the two functions $y = \sin x$ and $y = \cos x$. Figure 0.6 illustrates the plots of the inverse functions $y = \sin^{-1} x$ and $y = \cos^{-1} x$.

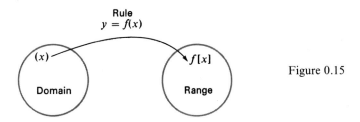

Figure 0.15

If when a function is plotted there are no breaks or abrupt jumps, the function is said to be continuous.

Figure 0.16 is the plot of a function that shows a break at x_1 and an abrupt jump at x_2. This is not a continuous function. Unless stated, all functions in this book will be single valued and continuous.

Figure 0.16

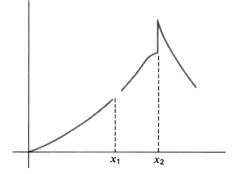

1

What Calculus
Is All About

1.1 WHAT IS CALCULUS?

Most mathematics prior to calculus concerns either nonchanging situations or changes that are constant. Much is made of the "average change" in precalculus mathematics. Calculus deals with the rate of change or, more precisely, the "instantaneous" rate of change.

The most important thing to remember is that calculus will be new to you and that new things often seem difficult. Calculus is not difficult if it is approached systematically, step by step as it is presented here. You will find that a good background in the basic principles of algebra and trigonometry is most important. Many students really learn to appreciate algebra for the first time as they proceed through a course in calculus.

Excluding the practical applications of this course we shall be interested in four basic things:

1. Slope of a straight-line segment.
2. Slope of a curved-line segment.
3. Area under a straight-line segment.
4. Area under a curved-line segment.

The slope of a straight line, you will recall from previous study, is constant.* Since it is constant, it is not directly a part of calculus but leads us indirectly into an important concept of calculus.

The slope of a curved line is a definite concept of calculus and will form a basis of a good portion of our thinking in the study of derivatives. It should be further noted that it is necessary to define the slope of a curved line before any study can be made of it.

The area under a straight line, as it is so often called, should be the area under a straight-line segment. Although calculating the area under a straight-line segment is a problem for geometry, it gives us an insight into a similar situation that requires calculus.

The area under a curve is a concept of calculus that is closely associated with integration. It is necessary to consider only a portion of a curve as with the straight-line segment, although we may choose to introduce the end points in a slightly different manner. We will also need to define area under a curve.

---

*See the Precalculus Mathematics Review.

1.2 SLOPE OF A STRAIGHT LINE

If we desire to plot a straight line whose equation is $y = 2x + 3$, we must first plot some points on this line—namely, those points that satisfy the equation of the line.

Letting $x = 1$ we get a corresponding $y = 2 \cdot 1 + 3$ or 5 and (1,5) is a point on the line.

Should we increase our $x = 1$ by 4 we get an x equal to $1 + 4$ or 5. The y corresponding to this $x = 5$ is $y = 2 \cdot 5 + 3 = 13$. Thus the point (5,13) is also on the required line. Figure 1.1 shows the two points plotted and the line in question passing through them.

The slope of a straight line is constant and is defined as the ratio of the rise over the run. From Figure 1.1 and the coordinates of the two points, we see that the rise is $13 - 5$ or 8 and the run is $5 - 1$ or 4. Thus the slope must be 8/4 or 2.

Recall from past mathematics that our line $y = 2x + 3$ is in the slope-intercept form $y = mx + b$, where $m =$ slope and b is the y intercept, and our calculation of the slope is correct. Note from Figure 1.1 that our line did in fact intercept the y axis at $y = 3$, so we have a further check on the plot of our line.

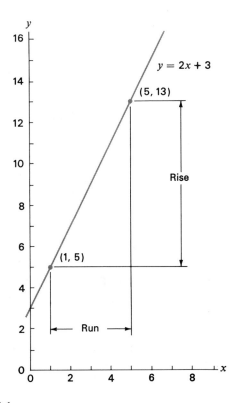

Figure 1.1

Had we recalled our slope-intercept information, we could have plotted our line in a slightly different manner. From $y = 2x + 3$ we see that the y intercept is 3, so we plot that point (0,3). Since the slope is 2 or 2/1, we can start at (0,3), increase x by 1, the run, and then increase y by 2, the rise, yielding the new point (1,5). (See Figure 1.2.) Repeating this process of adding the run to the x coordinate

Figure 1.2

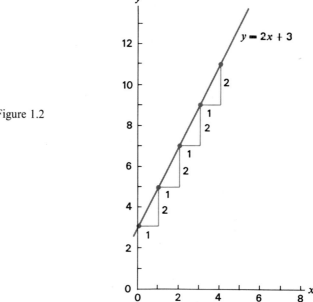

and the rise to the y coordinate produces point (2,7). A similar addition of a run of 1 and a rise of 2 yields point (3,9). The line through these points is the plot of $y = 2x + 3$.

Consider now the plot of $y = -2x + 3$. Here we see the y intercept is 3 or the point (0,3) and the slope is negative 2 or $-2/1$. Now we start at the y intercept (0,3) and add the run of 1 to 0 yielding 1. Adding the rise of -2 to 3 we get 1. Thus we see the next point is (1,1). Repeated additions of run and rise produce points $(2,-1)$, $(3,-3)$, and $(4,-5)$, all on our line $y = -2x + 3$. See Figure 1.3.

From what we have done so far we can come to some intuitive conclusions. First we conclude that two lines with the same slope are parallel. Second, if as a line is scanned from left to right it appears to go up, it has positive slope. And, conversely, if the line appears to go down as it is scanned from left to right, it has negative slope.

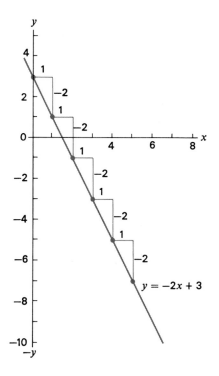

Figure 1.3

We can also see that since a horizontal line has no rise, the slope must be zero because slope equals rise/run equals 0/run which equals 0. Likewise, vertical lines have no run and so have no slope because slope = rise/run = rise/0 which is undefined.

In summary then, vertical lines have no slope, but all other lines do have slope, which may be positive, zero, or negative.

Suppose now instead of plotting a line whose equation is given we are asked: "What is the slope of a line that passes through the two points (2,1) and (6,7)?" Here we calculate run as $6 - 2 = 4$ and rise as $7 - 1$ or 6. Thus slope = rise/run $= 6/4 = 3/2$. Note that run could have been thought of as $2 - 6$ or -4 and rise as $1 - 7$ or -6, which would produce a slope = rise/run $= -6/-4 = 3/2$.

In the study of calculus we normally do not use the terms *rise* and *run*. Instead of rise we use Δy, which represents "change in y" and is called or read "delta y." Instead of run we use Δx, which represents "change in x" and is called or read "delta x." From all of this we can say

$$\text{Slope} = \frac{\text{rise}}{\text{run}} = \frac{\Delta y}{\Delta x}$$

If we now set up a general situation for any line passing through any two points (x', y') and (x'', y'') as pictured in Figure 1.4, we have

Figure 1.4

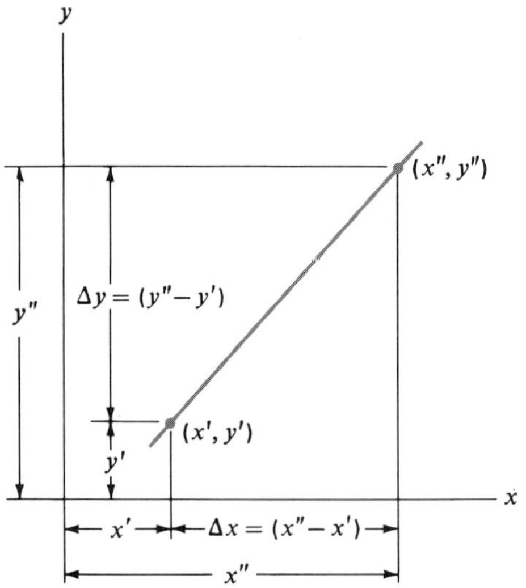

$$\text{Slope} = \frac{y' - y''}{x' - x''} = \frac{y'' - y'}{x'' - x'} = \frac{\Delta y}{\Delta x} \qquad (1.1)$$

Exercise 1.1

1. Define the slope of a straight line.

   For problems 2 through 7, calculate the slope of the line passing through the given points.

2. $(1,2)$ and $(3,7)$ 3. $(-2,3)$ and $(3, -5)$
4. $(-3,5)$ and $(2,4)$ 5. $(0,0)$ and $(3,3)$
6. $(-5, -5)$ and $(0,0)$ 7. $(-3,3)$ and $(2, -5)$
8. What is the slope of a line whose equation is $y = 3x + 1$? $y = (\frac{1}{2})x + 2$?

1.3 AVERAGE SLOPE OF A CURVED LINE

Average slope or average rate of change of slope is an important concept of calculus. Intuitively, if the temperature rises 20 degrees in five hours, we say the average rate of change in temperature is 4 degrees for each hour of change in time. This does not mean that the temperature changed 4 degrees each hour, or 2 degrees each half-hour, or 1 degree each quarter-hour. But rather it means that, on the average, the temperature changed 4 degrees per hour over this particular five-hour interval. If this thinking is now applied to calculus, we must think of the average rate of change of slope between two points on a curve which implies that the slope of a curve is constantly changing from point to point. Now if two points on a curve are being considered, and the slope is continuously changing between them, then the average slope will be the average rate of change of slope between these two points.

Definition:

The average slope of a curve between two points on that curve is the slope of the straight line through those points.

Or:

The average slope of a curve between two points on that curve is the slope of the secant passing through those points.

In Figure 1.5 we have two points P_1 (x_1, y_1) and P_2 (x_2, y_2) on the curve $y = f(x)$.

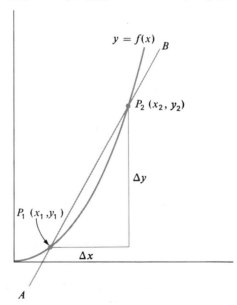

Figure 1.5

Line *AB* is passed through the two points and these calculations made:

$$\Delta y = y_2 - y_1$$

$$\Delta x = x_2 - x_1$$

and

$$\text{Average slope} = \frac{\Delta y}{\Delta x}$$

Exercise 1.2.   Use the information in Figure 1.6 to calculate the average slope between the following list of given points.

1. $P_1 P_2$ 2. $P_2 P_3$
3. $P_1 P_3$ 4. $P_3 P_4$
5. $P_2 P_4$ 6. $P_4 P_5$
7. $P_3 P_5$ 8. $P_5 P_6$
9. $P_4 P_6$ 10. $P_5 P_7$
11. $P_1 P_7$ 12. $P_2 P_6$

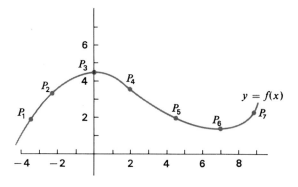

Figure 1.6

1.4 INSTANTANEOUS SLOPE OF A CURVED LINE

Definition:

The instantaneous slope of a curve at a given point is the slope of the straight line tangent to the curve at that point.

Figure 1.7 shows the line *CD* tangent to the curve at point P_1—that is, line *CD* touches the curve at the one point, P_1, only. The slope of the line *CD* is the slope of the curve at P_1.

Note also that line *EF* is tangent to the curve at point P_2, and that the slope of the curve at point P_2 is not the same as the slope at P_1. It is the changing slope, of course, that makes the line a curve. If the slopes were the same throughout or were constant, it would be a straight line. In Figure 1.7 then,

$$\frac{\Delta y_1}{\Delta x_1} \neq \frac{\Delta y_2}{\Delta x_2}$$

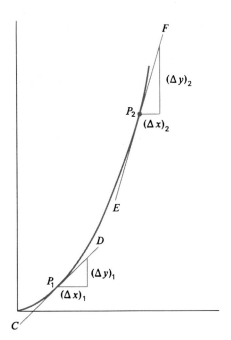

Figure 1.7

Exercise 1.3. With a straightedge attempt to draw the tangent and then calculate the instantaneous slope of the curve at the given points in Figure 1.8. Do you find this a satisfactory method of establishing the instantaneous slope of a curve at a point? Why?

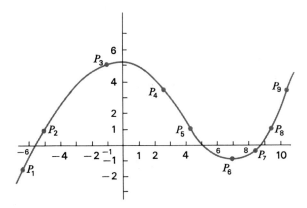

Figure 1.8

1.5 AREA UNDER A STRAIGHT-LINE SEGMENT

Definition:

The area under a straight-line segment is the area between the line segment and the *x* axis. The area above the *x* axis is positive; the area below the *x* axis is negative.

A look at Figure 1.9*a* shows that the area under a straight-line segment is really the area of a trapezoid.

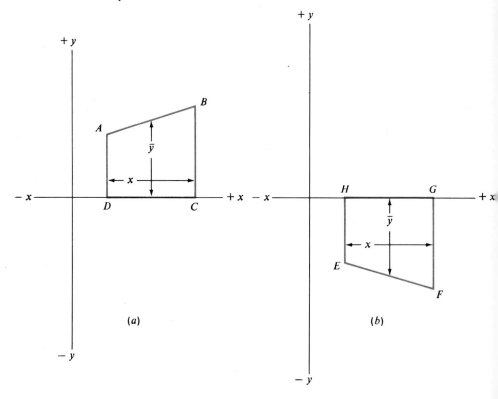

Figure 1.9

Area $ABCD = \bar{y}x$

where
$$\bar{y} = \frac{\text{line } AD + \text{line } BC}{2}$$

and
$$x = \text{line } DC$$

Figure 1.9*b* shows an area below the *x* axis. Let us see why it is negative.

Area $EFGH = \bar{y}x$

where
$$x = \text{line } HG$$

and
$$\bar{y} = \frac{\text{line } HE + \text{line } GF}{2}$$

Since lines HE and GF are both negative, their sum will be negative and, as a result, $\bar{y}$ will be negative. If $\bar{y}$ is negative then the area $EFGH$ must be negative.

This problem of calculating the area under a straight-line segment can be asked in a different manner: Calculate the area under $y = \frac{1}{2}x + 2$ between $x = 1$ and $x = 4$.

In Figure 1.10 the line $y = \frac{1}{2}x + 2$ is plotted as line AB and the required area is shaded.

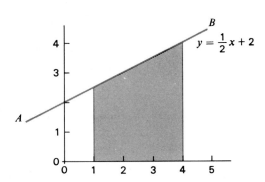

Figure 1.10

Required area $= x\bar{y}$

where
$$x = 4 - 1 = 3$$

and
$$\bar{y} = \frac{(2.5 + 4.0)}{2} = 3.25$$

Thus the required area $= 3 \cdot 3.25 = 9.75$ square units.

Exercise 1.4. In each of the following make an appropriate sketch and:

1. Find the area under $y = x$ between $x = 1$ and $x = 5$.
2. Find the area under $y = -x$ between $x = 1$ and $x = 5$.
3. Find the area under $y = 2x + 1$ between $x = 0$ and $x = 2$.
4. Find the area under $y = -2x + 1$ between $x = -5$ and $x = -2$.
5. Find the area under $y = 4$ between $x = 1$ and $x = 5$.
6. Find the area under $y = 4$ between $x = -5$ and $x = -1$.
7. Find the area under $y = 4$ between $x = -5$ and $x = 5$.
8. Find the area under $y = x/3$ between $x = 3$ and $x = 4$.

1.6 AREA UNDER A CURVED LINE

Definition:

The area under a segment of a curve is the area between the curve segment and the x axis. The area above the x axis is positive; the area below the x axis is negative.

The area under $y = f(x)$ between $x = 1$ and $x = 5$ is shaded in Figure 1.11 and marked A_1. Area A_2, which is negative, is that area under $y = f(x)$ between $x = 8$ and $x = 11$ in Figure 1.11.

Figure 1.11

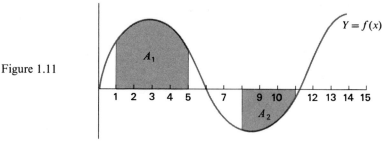

Exercise 1.5.   In problems 1 through 9 find the area under $y = f(x)$ as plotted in Figure 1.12 between the limits given by counting and summing all square and partial square units.

1. $x = 1, x = 7$ 2. $x = 3, x = 8$
3. $x = 2, x = 5$ 4. $x = 9, x = 10$
5. $x = 9, x = 14$ 6. $x = 10, x = 14$
7. $x = 2, x = 13$ 8. $x = 7, x = 10$
9. $x = 6, x = 8$

10. How does this method of finding area under a curve impress you? Why?

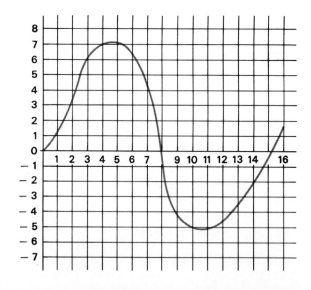

Figure 1.12

1.7 SUMMARY

We have now found that what we will really be interested in is:

1. Instantaneous slope of a curve.
2. Area under a curve.

Note further that we have been able to approximate these two requirements graphically by first plotting the curve of the function and then attempting to establish the tangent to that curve at a specific point. For the area we must count up unit squares or partial unit squares. Although the graphic approach gives us an intuitive idea of what we will be doing in calculus, it leaves much to be desired as an acceptable method. For one thing it requires that the curve of our function be plotted, and this in itself is sometimes quite time consuming. Next, accuracy requires extreme care in the plotting of the curve of the function as well as a large-scale drawing.

Deciding the exact position of the tangent to a curve at a given point is not precise, as you must have found even with your limited exposure to the process this far. In counting and adding unit squares you must also have found the partial squares exasperating as well as practically impossible to handle with any degree of accuracy.

After this brief introduction to our problems we shall take the next two units to devise mathematical processes that will quickly and accurately establish instantaneous slope and area under a curve without even a plot of the curve. It should be noted, however, that a sketch (not an accurate plot) of the curve is suggested for every problem to help analysis of the situation. This sketch suggestion applies to any and all technical problems.

Exercise 1.6

1. Define the slope of a straight line.
2. Define average slope of a curved line.
3. Define the instantaneous slope of a curved line.
4. Define the area under a straight-line segment.
5. Define the area under a curved line.
6. Think about the average and instantaneous slopes of a curved line. If you wanted the average slope to be as near equal to the instantaneous as possible, how would you locate the second point with respect to the first?
7. Think about finding the area under a curved line by first carefully plotting the curve and then counting unit squares. What would you do to make this operation as accurate as possible?

2

Differential Calculus

In this unit we shall pursue the problem of finding the instantaneous slope of a curve by mathematical methods. Usually the instantaneous slope is called simply "slope," so we shall use the terms interchangeably.

The formula for the slope of a curve is the derivative of the function of that curve.

2.1 AVERAGE SLOPE

It has been established in Unit 1 that the average slope between two points on a curve is the slope of the secant through those points. In Figure 2.1 we see a secant passing through two points P_1 and P_2 on the curve. The slope of that secant is $\Delta y/\Delta x$.

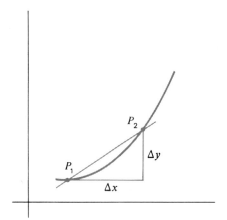

Figure 2.1

Intuitively looking at Figure 2.1 and recalling Unit 1, we see that the closer we place P_2 to point P_1 the closer the secant will come to matching the position of the tangent at point P_1.

Figure 2.2a illustrates the plot of a curve $y = f(x)$ with a secant passing through points P_1 and P_6. Figure 2.2b shows the same curve with a new secant passing through P_2 and P_6. Figure 2.2c shows the same curve with a secant through P_3 and P_6. Figure 2.2d pictures a secant through P_4 and P_6, and Figure 2.2e a secant through P_5 and P_6.

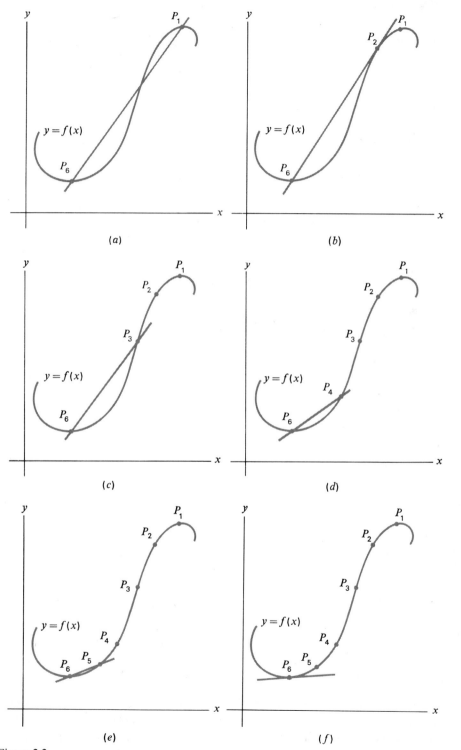

Figure 2.2

In each instance shown, the secant passed through point P_6. The other point of secant-curve intersection started at P_1 and moved successively to P_2, P_3, P_4, and P_5. Each new point was closer to P_6 than the last. An analysis of the secants in each figure mentioned shows average slope changing.

Figure 2.2f pictures the tangent to the curve at point P_6. The slope of the tangent is the slope of the curve at point P_6.

Each move along the curve from P_1 to P_2 to P_3 to P_4 to P_5 produced a Δx smaller than the last and a Δy smaller than its predecessor. Note further that, as Δx diminished in size, the slope of the secant approached the slope of the tangent at P_6.

From all this then we conclude that as Δx gets smaller Δy gets smaller and the secant approaches the tangent as a limiting position. In summary, as Δx approaches zero the secant approaches tangency as a limiting position.

The tangent at point P_6 in Figure 2.2f is the limiting position of all secants through P_6 and points approaching P_6. This statement tells us that we could approach point P_6 from the left and still arrive at the same limiting position. Figure 2.3 pictures secants $P_7 P_6$ and $P_8 P_6$ with P_8 closer to P_6. Once again Δx is decreasing and the secant is approaching the tangent at P_6 as a limiting position.

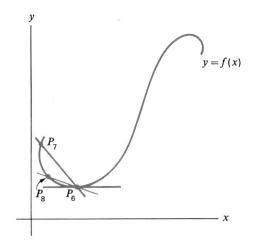

Figure 2.3

We have now discussed a tangent line as the limiting position for a line or lines that behave according to some prearranged instructions. This idea of limit is extremely important to calculus and will be pursued mathematically.

2.2 LIMITS

In our real number system, zero divided by any real number except zero produces the real number zero. Since division by zero is undefined in the real number system, however, the result of dividing by zero is either undefined or meaningless.

Since division by zero is meaningless, the mathematical combination of such a meaningless entity with a real number must also be meaningless. From this then $(25/0) + 50$ is meaningless.

Exercise 2.1. In each of the following, state a value if it exists; otherwise state that no value exists.

1. $5 - 0$ 2. $0/5$
3. $(5)(0)/2$ 4. $5 + 4/0$
5. $5/0$ 6. $(2)(3)/0$
7. $0 + 0/0$ 8. $(0)(0)/0$
9. $0 \div 3/2$ 10. $3/2 \div 0$
11. $5/(0/2)$ 12. $5/(2/0)$
13. $(2/0) + 5$ 14. $(0/2) + 5$
15. $(0/2)/5$

Continuing our pursuit of the limit idea we will intuitively look at some limit concepts before a formal definition is made.

If x is a number close to 2, then the number $4x + 3$ is close to 11. The following table shows our contention to be true.

x	$4x + 3$
1.8	10.2
1.9	10.6
1.95	10.8
1.999	10.996
2.001	11.0004
2.1	11.4
2.2	11.8

The fact that $4x + 3$ equals 11 when x is 2 is not important to us now. What is important is that $4x + 3$ is close to 11 when x is close to 2 (but not equal to 2), which allows us to say: The limit of $4x + 3$ as x approaches 2 is 11. In mathematical symbolism we write:

$$\lim_{x \to 2} 4x + 3 = 11$$

Here $x \to 2$ means "as x approaches 2."

It is also true that:

$$\lim_{x \to -1} \frac{3x}{x+2} = -3$$

An example that cannot be so easily evaluated is:

$$\lim_{x \to 0} (1/2)^{1/x^2}$$

If we let $x = 0$ our exponent will be meaningless, that is $1/0$, so we are forced to make a table using values of x close to zero, but not equal to zero.

x	$(1/2)^{1/x^2}$
± 1	$1/2$
$\pm 1/2$	$1/16$
$\pm 1/3$	$1/512$
$\pm 1/4$	$1/65536$
$\pm 1/n$	$1/2^{n^2}$

Thus we say:

$$\lim_{x \to 0} (1/2)^{1/x^2} = 0$$

These have been examples of the limit of a function. We say then: The limit of a function of x, as x approaches a, equals b. In mathematical symbolism:

$$\lim_{x \to a} f(x) = b$$

Example 2.1. Calculate the limit of

$$\frac{1/x - 1/2}{x - 2} \qquad \text{as } x \text{ approaches 2.}$$

Here $f(x) = (1/x - 1/2)/(x - 2)$ and if $x = 2$ the denominator will be zero and the function undefined. We therefore must declare $x \neq 2$ and the problem becomes:

$$\lim_{x \to 2} \frac{1/x - 1/2}{x - 2}$$

and $f(x) = \dfrac{1/x - 1/2}{x - 2} = \dfrac{2/2x - x/2x}{x - 2}$

$$= \dfrac{(2 - x)/2x}{x - 2} = \dfrac{(2 - x)}{(x - 2)2x}$$

$$= -\dfrac{x - 2}{(x - 2)2x} = -\dfrac{1}{2x}$$

This tells us that $-1/2x$ is close to $-1/4$ when x is close to 2. Therefore:

$$\lim_{x \to 2} \frac{1/x - 1/2}{x - 2} = \frac{-1}{4}$$

Example 2.2.   Calculate

$$\lim_{x \to 1} \frac{\sqrt{x} - 1}{x - 1}$$

Here the function $f(x) = (\sqrt{x} - 1)/(x - 1)$ where $x > 0$ and $x \neq 1$.

$$f(x) = \frac{\sqrt{x} - 1}{x - 1} = \frac{\sqrt{x} - 1}{(\sqrt{x} - 1)(\sqrt{x} + 1)} = \frac{1}{\sqrt{x} + 1}$$

when $x \neq 1$.

This tells us that $1/(\sqrt{x} - 1)$ is close to $1/2$ when x is close to 1. Therefore:

$$\lim_{x \to 1} \frac{\sqrt{x} - 1}{x - 1} = \frac{1}{2}$$

Limit Theorems

Having found some limits let us now try to systematically formalize our concept of a limit.

If we are discussing the function $y = f(x)$, let the limit of $f(x)$ be b, and we write:

$$\lim_{x \to a} f(x) = b$$

or $f[x] \to b$ as $x \to a$

Then from Figure 2.4 we say: As x gets closer to a, the functional value $f[x]$ gets closer to b. This then becomes our intuitive definition of a limit. It should be noted that if the distance from a to x is Δx, then instead of stating "as x approaches a," we could make the equivalent statement "Δx approaches zero."

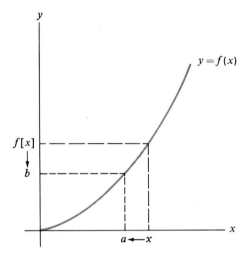

Figure 2.4

Theorem:

The limit of a sum is the sum of the limits:

$$\lim_{x \to a} \left[f(x) \pm g(x) \right] = \lim_{x \to a} f(x) \pm \lim_{x \to a} g(x)$$

In words this theorem says: The limit of the sum of two functions f of x and g of x as x approaches a equals the limit of the function f of x as x approaches a plus the limit of the function g of x as x approaches a.

Theorem:

The limit of a product is the product of the limits:

$$\lim_{x \to a} \left[f(x) \cdot g(x) \right] = \lim_{x \to a} f(x) \cdot \lim_{x \to a} g(x)$$

Theorem:

The limit of a quotient is the quotient of the limits, provided that the limit of the denominator is not zero:

$$\lim_{x \to a} \left[\frac{f(x)}{g(x)} \right] = \frac{\lim_{x \to a} f(x)}{\lim_{x \to a} g(x)} \qquad \text{if } \lim_{x \to a} g(x) \neq 0$$

Exercise 2.2.   Calculate the following limit values.

1. $\text{Lim} (x^3 - 5x^2 - 1)$ as $x \to 2$
2. $\text{Lim} (x^2 - 4)/(x - 2)$ as $x \to 2$
3. $\text{Lim} (x^2 - 9)/(x + 3)$ as $x \to -3$
4. $\text{Lim} (1/x - 1/3)/(x - 3)$ as $x \to 3$
5. $\text{Lim} 1/(2 - x)$ as $x \to 2$
6. $\text{Lim} 3/(1 - x)$ as $x \to 1$
7. $\text{Lim} 2/(x^2 - 4)$ as $x \to -2$
8. $\text{Lim} 100/x^2$ as $x \to 0$
9. $\text{Lim} 1/(x - 4)$ as $x \to 4$
10. $\text{Lim} 25/(27 - x^3)$ as $x \to 3$
11. $\text{Lim} 5/(1 + x)$ as $x \to -1$

2.3 AVERAGE SLOPE OF A CURVE

We shall now try to establish a mathematical system for arriving at the average slope of a curved line.

Looking at Figure 2.5 we see a portion of the graph of the function $y = x^2$. Now let us pick two points on the curve—that is, points P_1 and P_2. Let P_1 be the point $(1,1)$ and P_2 the point $(2,4)$. Here we have $\Delta x = 2 - 1 = 1$ and $\Delta y = 4 - 1 = 3$, so $\Delta y/\Delta x = 3/1 = 3 =$ average slope between P_1 and P_2.

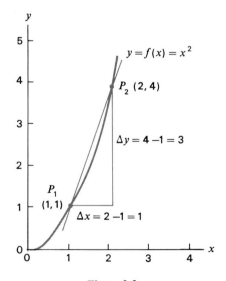

Figure 2.5

Let us now try to generalize this for any two points P_1 and P_2 instead of two specific points as above.

We will pick point P_1 as (x_1, y_1) and point P_2 as (x_2, y_2), but we see from Figure 2.6 that $x_2 = x_1 + \Delta x$ and $y_2 = y_1 + \Delta y$, so P_2 is the point $(x_1 + \Delta x, y_1 + \Delta y)$. Now if $y_1 = (x_1)^2$ then $y_2 = (x_2)^2$ or by substitution:

$$y_1 + \Delta y = (x_1 + \Delta x)^2$$

or   (1) $y_1 + \Delta y = x_1^2 + 2x_1(\Delta x) + (\Delta x)^2$

(2) $y_1 = x_1^2$

-----

(3) $\Delta y = 2x_1(\Delta x) + (\Delta x)^2$

(4) $\Delta y / \Delta x = 2x_1 + (\Delta x)$

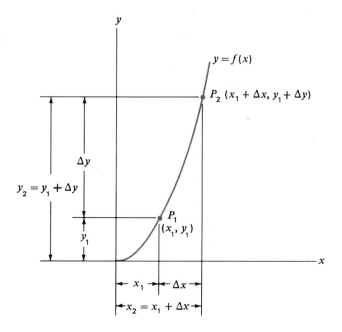

Figure 2.6

Equation (3) is obtained by subtracting equation (2) from equation (1). Dividing through by Δx produces equation (4), which is the general equation for the average slope through (x_1, y_1) and any other point on the curve.

Checking our problem in Figure 2.5 with this equation we find $x_1 = 1$ and $\Delta x = 1$, therefore $\Delta y / \Delta x = 2(1) + 1 = 2 + 1 = 3$.

Example 2.3. Calculate the general equation for average slope between any two points on the curve $y = x^3 + 2$.

Assume one point to be $P_1 = (x_1, y_1)$ and the other $P_2 = (x_1 + \Delta x, y_1 + \Delta y)$. Then:

$$y_1 + \Delta y = (x_1 + \Delta x)^3 + 2$$

or

$$y_1 + \Delta y = x_1^3 + 3x_1^2(\Delta x) + 3x_1(\Delta x)^2 + (\Delta x)^3 + 2$$

$$\underline{y_1 = x_1^3 \qquad\qquad\qquad\qquad\qquad\qquad\qquad + 2}$$

$$\Delta y = 3x_1^2(\Delta x) + 3x_1(\Delta x)^2 + (\Delta x)^3$$

and

$$\Delta y / \Delta x = 3x_1^2 + 3x_1(\Delta x) + (\Delta x)^2$$

Thus we have a general equation for the average slope between any P_1 and P_2 on $y = x^3 + 2$.

Example 2.4. If $y = f(x) = x^3 + 2$, what is the average slope between $x = 2$ and $x = 2.5$?

Here $x_1 = 2.0$ and $x_2 = 2.5$ so $\Delta x = 2.5 - 2.0 = 0.5$. Substituting these values into the equation from Example 2.1, we have:

$$\Delta y / \Delta x = 3(2)^2 + 3(2)(0.5) + (0.5)^2$$

$$= 3 \cdot 4 + 3 + 0.25$$

$$= 15.25$$

This method of calculating the equation for the average slope of a curve is known as the *delta method* and is here outlined:

1. Add an increment (Δx) to x.
2. Add the corresponding increment (Δy) to y.
3. Place this new point ($x + \Delta x, y + \Delta y$) in the given equation and expand.
4. Subtract the original equation from the expansion.
5. Divide through by Δx.

Example 2.5. If $y = f(x) = \sqrt{x}$, what is the equation for the average slope?

Here $y = \sqrt{x} = x^{1/2}$ and adding Δx to x along with the corresponding Δy to y, we have:

$$y + \Delta y = (x + \Delta x)^{1/2}$$

or $y + \Delta y = x^{1/2} + \frac{1}{2}x^{-1/2}(\Delta x) - \frac{1}{8}x^{-3/2}(\Delta x)^2 + \frac{1}{16}x^{-5/2}(\Delta x)^3$

$$- \frac{5}{128}x^{-7/2}(\Delta x)^4 + \cdots$$

Subtracting $y = x^{1/2}$ yields:

$$\Delta y = \frac{1}{2}x^{-1/2}(\Delta x) - \frac{1}{8}x^{-3/2}(\Delta x)^2 + \frac{1}{16}x^{-5/2}(\Delta x)^3 - \frac{5}{128}x^{-7/2}(\Delta x)^4 + \cdots$$

Then dividing through by Δx:

$$\frac{\Delta y}{\Delta x} = \tfrac{1}{2}x^{-\frac{1}{2}} - \tfrac{1}{8}x^{-\frac{3}{2}}(\Delta x) + \tfrac{1}{16}x^{-\frac{5}{2}}(\Delta x)^2 - \tfrac{5}{128}x^{-\frac{7}{2}}(\Delta x)^3 + \cdots$$

This then simplifies to:

$$\frac{\Delta y}{\Delta x} = \frac{1}{2x^{\frac{1}{2}}} - \frac{\Delta x}{8x^{\frac{3}{2}}} + \frac{(\Delta x)^2}{16x^{\frac{5}{2}}} - \frac{5(\Delta x)^3}{128x^{\frac{7}{2}}} + \cdots$$

It should be noted that the preceding expansion will have an infinite number of terms but we are justified in dropping all but the first four or five because some power of Δx always shows up in the numerator, and we have seen that we shall want to keep Δx small. Consequently all terms dropped will be small and their effect on the average slope will be negligible.

Exercise 2.3. Calculate the equation for the average slope of the following functions using the delta method.

1. $y = x^2 + 3$ 2. $y = x^3 + 2$
3. $y = 2x^2$ 4. $y = x^3 - 2x$
5. $y = x/(x + 3)$ 6. $y = 1 + 2x - 1/x$
7. $y = 6\sqrt{x}$ 8. $y = \sqrt{6x}$
9. $y = 3/x$ 10. $y = x^2 - 3x - 18$
11. $A = \pi r^2$
12. In problem 11 calculate the change in area (ΔA) if r increases from 4.0 to 4.2.

2.4 THE DERIVATIVE—INSTANTANEOUS SLOPE

We are now ready to put all that has been said thus far into proper focus, arriving at the instantaneous slope formula which is the *derivative*.

In order to fit our current thinking into accepted notation, we must change our slope symbol to dy/dx, which is the universal symbol for slope or derivative. Figure 2.7*b* shows the accepted derivative notation in proper perspective.

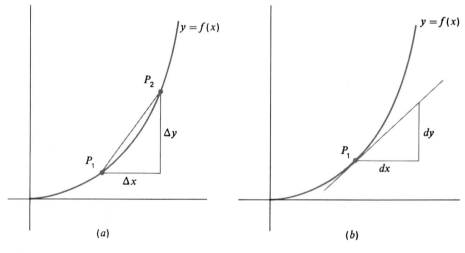

(*a*)   (*b*)

Figure 2.7

Figure 2.7a shows the average slope between two points to be $\Delta y/\Delta x$, the slope of the straight line through those points. Figure 2.7b shows the calculus concept of the instantaneous slope of a curve at a point. This is the slope of the tangent to the curve at that point, and this slope dy/dx is known as the derivative.

The relation between Figures 2.7a and b is made by the basic derivative equation:

$$\lim_{\Delta x \to 0} \frac{\Delta y}{\Delta x} = \frac{dy}{dx}$$

This basic formula states in mathematical symbolism that, given the average slope of a curve with the limit taken as Δx approaches zero, the instantaneous slope dy/dx results. Recall that previously we found by the delta method that if $y = x^2$ then $\Delta y/\Delta x = 2x + \Delta x$, so to arrive at the derivative of $y = x^2$ we have but to take the limit of $\Delta y/\Delta x$ as Δx approaches zero:

$$\frac{dy}{dx} = \lim_{\Delta x \to 0} (2x + \Delta x) = 2x$$

Thus the derivative or slope of $y = x^2$ at any point is $2x$. What is the slope of $y = x^2$ when $x = \frac{3}{2}$?

$$\frac{dy}{dx} = 2x = 2(\tfrac{3}{2}) = 3$$

See Figure 2.8.

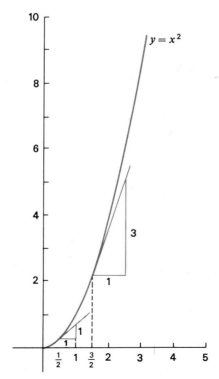

Figure 2.8

What is the derivative or slope of $y = x^2$ at $x = \frac{1}{2}$? $dy/dx = 2x = 2(\frac{1}{2}) = 1$. See Figure 2.8.

Now to obtain the derivative of a function, calculate the average slope by the delta method, and then take the limit of the average slope as delta x approaches zero. To find the slope of a function at a specific point or value of x, substitute this value of x into the derivative formula.

> **Exercise 2.4.**   Calculate the derivative of the functions given in Exercise 2.3, problems 1 through 10. Then calculate the slope at the value of x as specified below.
>
> 1. $x = 3$ 2. $x = 2$
> 3. $x = 1$ 4. $x = 2$
> 5. $x = 1$ 6. $x = 2$
> 7. $x = 4$ 8. $x = 4$
> 9. $x = 2$ 10. $x = 1$

You now know enough about differentiation to calculate the derivative of most power functions. If you set out to calculate the derivative of a good number of power functions, two things would soon become apparent:

1. The delta method, though precise and straightforward, often becomes complicated and time consuming.
2. Many problems would seem very similar and you would have the feeling that you had worked this problem before.

Both of these observations would be correct. To overcome this we shall take a certain "type" function and calculate a formula that will produce the derivative for that "type." After calculating derivative formulas for several different types of functions, we will probably have trouble deciding which formula to use for the particular problem at hand. This may seem trivial but from actual experience with many students it becomes their number one stumbling block. You should recognize that this will be a trouble spot and stay alert.

2.5 THE DERIVATIVE OF A POWER FUNCTION

A power function is one of the type: $y = kx^n + C$, where k is the multiplicative constant, n the exponent, and C the additive constant.

Letting n be positive or negative, integral or fractional, rational or irrational, we can show that calculating the average slope by the delta method and then taking the limit as delta x approaches zero yields: nkx^{n-1}.

This brings us to our first type:

$$\text{If } y = kx^n + C \Rightarrow \frac{dy}{dx} = nkx^{n-1} \tag{2.1}$$

Proof for (2.1) will not be given herein, since our needs can be best served by acceptance without proof.*

Example 2.6. Differentiate $y = 5x^3$.

$$\frac{dy}{dx} = y' = 3(5)x^2 = 15x^2$$

By now you will no doubt be glad to use y' for the instantaneous slope, or first derivative instead of dy/dx simply because it means less writing. From here on we shall use either interchangeably as we desire.

Example 2.7. Find the instantaneous slope of $y = 5x^{-3}$.

$$\frac{dy}{dx} = y' = -3(5)x^{-3-1} = -15x^{-4}$$

Example 2.8. Calculate the first derivative of $y = -5x^{-3}$.

$$\frac{dy}{dx} = y' = -3(-5)x^{-3-1} = 15x^{-4}$$

Example 2.9. Differentiate $y = 5x^{3/4}$

$$\frac{dy}{dx} = y' = 5(\tfrac{3}{4})x^{(3/4)-1}$$

$$= (\tfrac{15}{4})x^{-1/4}$$

Example 2.10. Differentiate $y = 3x^{-1/2}$

$$y' = 3(-\tfrac{1}{2})x^{(-1/2)-1}$$

$$= (-\tfrac{3}{2})x^{-3/2}$$

Example 2.11. Differentiate $y = x^\pi$.

$$y' = \pi x^{\pi-1}$$

Example 2.12. Differentiate $y = 3\sqrt{x}$.

This does not appear to fall into type (2.1), but closer inspection shows that it can be rewritten so that it does:

$$y = 3\sqrt{x} = 3x^{1/2}$$

and
$$y' = 3(\tfrac{1}{2})x^{(1/2)-1}$$

$$= \tfrac{3}{2}x^{-1/2} = \tfrac{3}{2}(x^{1/2})$$

$$= \frac{3}{2\sqrt{x}}$$

*See Appendix.

Example 2.13. Differentiate $y = 3(5x)^2$.

Since our type (2.1) applies to the raising of only x to a power, it would appear that since in this function $5x$ is raised to a power we cannot use (2.1). A closer examination shows that the function can be rewritten so that (2.1) applies:

$$y = 3(5x)^2 = 3(5)^2 x^2 = 75x^2$$

and

$$y' = 2(75)x^{2-1} = 150x$$

Example 2.14. Differentiate $y = 3/x$.

This function must be rewritten so that (2.1) applies.

$$y = \frac{3}{x} = \frac{3}{x^1} = 3x^{-1}$$

$$y' = -1(3)x^{-1-1} = -3x^{-2}$$

$$= \frac{-3}{x^2}$$

Example 2.15. Differentiate $y = x$.

In order to make this fit our type (2.1) we write x with its understood exponent 1.

$$y = x = x^1$$

$$y' = (1)x^{1-1} = 1x^0 = 1(1) = 1$$

A little thought about the delta method along with the process of taking the limit as Δx approaches zero should make it obvious that the derivative of a constant is zero. Thus:

$$\text{If } y = C \Rightarrow y' = 0$$

As here used $\Rightarrow$ means "then."

Exercise 2.5. Differentiate the following functions.

1. $y = x^2 + 3$
2. $y = x^3 + 2$
3. $y = 2x^2$
4. $y = x^6$
5. $y = \sqrt{6x}$
6. $y = 6\sqrt{x}$
7. $y = 3/x$
8. $y = 7$
9. $y = 3x^{k+1}$
10. $y = x^{-1.3}$
11. $y = 2x^7$
12. $y = ex^\pi$
13. $y = 5\sqrt[5]{x}$
14. $y = 6x^{-15}$
15. $y = \pi/\sqrt[3]{x^4}$
16. $y = 5/(8\sqrt[8]{x^5})$
17. $y = -4/\sqrt{x}$
18. $y = C/dx$
19. $y = 2x^{-4/3}$
20. $y = \frac{4}{3}\pi x^3$

2.6 THE DERIVATIVE OF A SUM OR DIFFERENCE

Using the delta method let us calculate the derivative of the sum: $y = 3x + 2x$.

$$y + \Delta y = 3(x + \Delta x) \quad + 2(x + \Delta x)$$

$$= 3x + 3(\Delta x) + 2x + 2(\Delta x)$$

$$y = 3x \qquad\qquad + 2x$$

$$\overline{\qquad\qquad\qquad\qquad\qquad\qquad\qquad}$$

$$\Delta y = \qquad 3(\Delta x) \qquad + 2(\Delta x)$$

$$\Delta y/\Delta x = 3 + 2$$

Since 3 is the average slope of $3x$ and 2 is the average slope of $2x$, we conclude that the average slope of a sum must be the sum of the average slopes. Taking the limit as Δx approaches zero produces:

> The derivative of a sum is the sum of the derivatives.

> *and* (2.2)

> The derivative of a difference is the difference of the derivatives.

At first reading this sounds like double talk when in reality it is most profound and makes differentiation of some complicated functions quite simple.

> ***Example 2.16.***   Differentiate $y = x^3 + x^2 + x + 1$. Applying (2.2): $y' = 3x^2 + 2x + 1$.

> ***Exercise 2.6.***   Differentiate the following functions.

> 1. $y = Ax^2 + Bx + C$
> 2. $y = x^2 + 5x$
> 3. $y = 7x^5 - 20x^3 + 12$
> 4. $y = 7x^3 + 2x$
> 5. $y = \sqrt{x} + 12$
> 6. $y = 3x^5 - 5x$
> 7. $y = x^2 - x$
> 8. $y = x^{3/2} + \sqrt{x} + 10$
> 9. $y = (4x^3 - 7x + 8)/x$
> 10. $y = (2x - 5)(3x - 1)$
> 11. $y = (4/\sqrt{x}) - 4\sqrt{x}$
> 12. $y = \frac{1}{3}x^2 - \frac{5}{2}x$
> 13. $y = 4x^{-3} + \pi$
> 14. $y = \sqrt[n]{x^{n+1}}$
> 15. $y = (26/x^4) - 3$
> 16. $y = kx^{-3} + e$
> 17. $y = (\pi/2x^3) - 26$
> 18. $y = e^2 + 5x^3 - 2x$
> 19. $y = x^2 - 3x$
> 20. $y = (e/x^3) - (\pi/x^2)$

2.7 THE DERIVATIVE OF A FUNCTION OF A FUNCTION

If we are given $y = ku^n$ where u is some function of x, k is a constant, and n the exponent of the function u, and we wish to differentiate y with respect to x, we use:

$$\text{If } y = ku^n + C \Rightarrow y' = nku^{n-1}\frac{du}{dx} \ ^* \tag{2.3}$$

Note that in this style problem we are not differentiating x raised to a power but rather a function of x raised to a power.

Example 2.17. Differentiate $y = (x^2 + 1)^2$. We must now decide whether we have an "x^n" or a "u^n" type problem. Since $(x^2 + 1)$ does not equal x, we conclude that we have a u^n type. As obvious as this conclusion may seem, it is not always easy for the uninitiated. The problem is to decide whether we have a u^n or an x^n. This choice is made by looking at the base which is being raised to the power n. If the base is other than x then a u^n type exists. When faced with this decision some assume all power functions to be of the u^n type. This is not a bad system for one never misses a u^n, and if it is an x^n it turns out that the du/dx is one, which does not affect the result anyway.

The equation $y = (x^2 + 1)^2$ is a $y = u^n$ type where $u = x^2 + 1$ and $du/dx = 2x$. Therefore:

$$y' = nu^{n-1}\frac{du}{dx}$$

$$= 2(x^2 + 1)(2x)$$

$$= 4x(x^2 + 1)$$

$$= 4x^3 + 4x$$

We can check this solution by noting that

$$y = (x^2 + 1)^2 = x^4 + 2x^2 + 1 \qquad \text{and} \qquad y' = 4x^3 + 4x$$

Exercise 2.7. Calculate the derivative of each of the following.

1. $y = 6(5 - x^2)^2$
2. $y = (3x^2 + 2x + 5)^4$
3. $y = 2\sqrt[3]{x^2 + 9}$
4. $y = (3x^4 - 2x^3 + x^2)^{-2/3}$
5. $y = 5\sqrt{100 - x^2}$
6. $y = \sqrt[4]{6 - 7x^2}$
7. $y = 17/\sqrt{6 - x^2}$
8. $y = (x - x^2)^4$
9. $y = 4(x^2 + 16)^{2/3}$
10. $y = \frac{1}{8}(3 - x^2)^2$

2.8 MAXIMA AND MINIMA—CRITICAL POINTS

By definition the function $y = f(x)$ has a relative or local maximum at $x = b$ if there is an interval or neighborhood $x_1 < b < x_2$ in which the ordinal value $y = f[b]$ is greater than the value of $f[x]$ for any other values of x in the interval.

The words *relative* or *local* must be carefully noted. They tell us that $f[b]$ need not be the greatest value the function can have—they tell us that $f[b]$ is the greatest value in a small localized interval on the x axis.

*For proof see Appendix.

The function $y = f(x)$ has a relative or local minimum at $x = b$ if there is an interval or neighborhood $x_1 < b < x_2$ in which the ordinal value $y = f[b]$ is less than the value of $f[x]$ for any other values of x in the interval.

In Figure 2.9 a relative maximum occurs at $x = -2$ because $y = f[-2] = 20$ which is greater than any other $f[x]$ in a small interval around $x = -2$. A relative minimum occurs at $x = 1$ because $y = f[1] = -7$ which is less than any other $f[x]$ in a small interval around $x = 1$.

Figure 2.9 further reveals that the slope of the curve at $x = -2$ is zero, and the slope of the curve is zero at $x = 1$ also. This leads us to our next definition.

The point on a curve at which the slope is zero, or the point on a curve where the slope does not exist, is called a *critical point* or *critical value*.

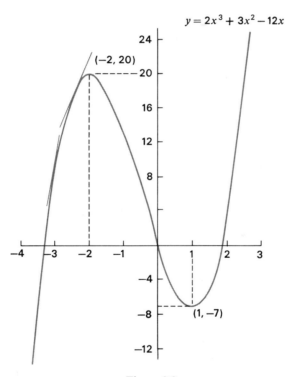

Figure 2.9

In Figure 2.9 the slope of the curve is zero at $x = -2$ and $x = 1$, therefore $x = -2$ and $x = 1$ are critical points.

The trial-and-error method can be used to identify a suspected critical point. Suppose that for $y = 2x^3 + 3x^2 - 12x$ we suspect that $x = 1$ is a critical point. We calculate $f[x]$ for $x = 1$ the suspected critical point, and then for values of x a little less than 1 and then a little more than 1. Making a chart we have:

x	$y = f[x]$
0.98	−6.9964
0.99	−6.9991
1.00	−7.0000
1.01	−6.9991
1.02	−6.9964

Thus we have shown that our suspected critical point probably is a critical point because a re tive minimum apparently exists there.

A more precise mathematical method for locating critical points presents itself when we recall that the first derivative of a function is the equation for the slope at any point satisfying that function, and that the slope of a curve is zero at a critical point. The method then is to equate the derivative of a function to zero and solve for the values of x that make the derivative or slope zero.

Looking again to $y = 2x^3 + 3x^2 - 12x$ as plotted in Figure 2.9, let us use this method to locate the critical points.

If $y = 2x^3 + 3x^2 - 12x$, then $y' = 6x^2 + 6x - 12$, and $6x^2 + 6x - 12 = 0$ or $x^2 + x - 2 = 0$ or $(x - 1)(x + 2) = 0$ from which $x = 1$ and $x = -2$.

Thus we see we have mathematically located the critical points. All we know now though is that the slope at these two points is zero. Our next project is to identify the critical points—that is, to decide whether a maximum or a minimum occurs at each.

In Figure 2.9 we see that at the critical point $x = -2$ our curve is at a relative maximum. We further note that all slopes a little to the left of $x = -2$ are positive and all slopes a little to the right of $x = -2$ are negative. We conclude then that, if the slope of a curve changes from positive to zero to negative as we move along the curve from left to right, we have passed a maximum.

A similar observation at $x = 1$ shows that, if the slope of a curve changes from negative to zero to positive as we move along the curve from left to right, we have passed a minimum.

Thus if $x = 1$ is a critical point for $y = 2x^3 + 3x^2 - 12x$, we will pick points a little to the left and a little to the right of $x = 1$, say $x = 0.99$ and $x = 1.01$ and substitute these into the slope function $y' = 6x^2 + 6x - 12$.

If $x = 0.99 \Rightarrow y' = 6(.99)^2 + 6(.99) - 12 = -0.1794$

If $x = 1.00 \Rightarrow y' = 6(1.0)^2 + 6(1.0) - 12 = 0.0000$

If $x = 1.01 \Rightarrow y' = 6(1.01)^2 + 6(1.01) - 12 = 0.1800$

Thus we see that at the critical point $x = 1$ the curve is at a minimum. A similar procedure identifies the critical point $x = -2$.

$$\text{If } x = -2.01 \Rightarrow y' = 6(-2.01)^2 + 6(-2.01) - 12 = 0.1800$$

$$\text{If } x = -2.00 \Rightarrow y' = 6(-2.00)^2 + 6(-2.01) - 12 = 0.0000$$

$$\text{If } x = -1.99 \Rightarrow y' = 6(-1.99)^2 + 6(-1.99) - 12 = -0.1800$$

At the critical point $x = -2$ the curve is at a maximum.

Figure 2.10 shows both $y = 2x^3 + 3x^2 - 12x$ and its derivative $y' = 6x^2 + 6x - 12$ plotted. From Figure 2.10, when $x = -2$, $y = +20$ and $y' = 0$. Also when $x = 1$, $y = -7$, and $y' = 0$. Thus the two critical points show up graphically at each intersection of the x axis and the curve y', for it is at these intersections that $y' = 0$.

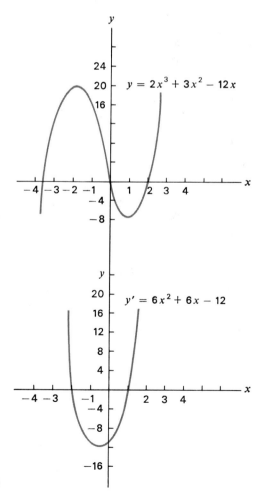

Figure 2.10

Before we draw any conclusions with respect to critical points and maxima and minima, let us look at another function, $y = x^3$. The graph of $y = x^3$ is shown in Figure 2.11. By observation no maximum or minimum exists. But regardless let us follow out previous procedure.

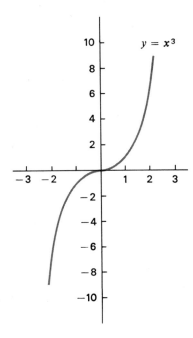

Figure 2.11

If $y = x^3$ then $y' = 3x^2$, and if $y' = 0$ then $3x^2 = 0$ from which $x = 0$. Mathematically then $x = 0$ is a critical point and by observations neither a maximum nor a minimum exists. From this then we conclude that something other than a maximum or a minimum can exist at a critical point.

By definition a smooth curve is concave upward on an interval $x_1 < a < x_2$ if y' increases as x increases on the interval. Or, the tangent line turns counterclockwise as the curve is traversed from left to right. Or, the curve lies above its tangent for all values of x on the interval. See Figure 2.12a.

Similarly a smooth curve is concave downward on an interval $x_1 < a < x_2$ if y' decreases as x increases on the interval. Or, the tangent line turns clockwise as the curve is traversed from left to right. Or, the curve lies below its tangent for all values of x on the interval. See Figure 2.12b.

Definition:

A function has an inflection point at a, if there is an interval $x_1 < a < x_2$ where the curve is concave upward on $x \leq a$ and concave downward on $a \leq x$. See Figure 2.13a.

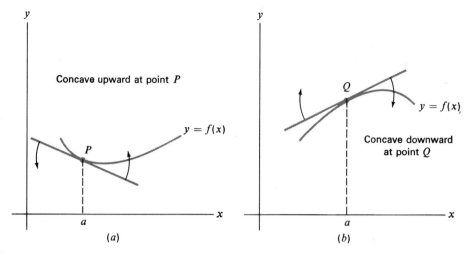

Figure 2.12

Or:

Is concave downward on $x \leq a$ and concave upward for $a \leq x$. See Figure 2.13b.

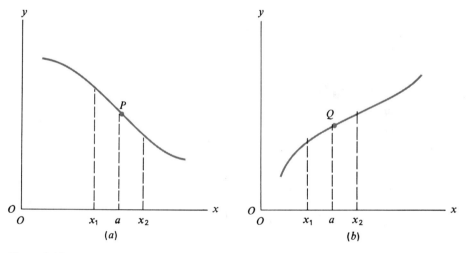

Figure 2.13

In Figure 2.13a point P is an inflection point as is point Q in Figure 2.13b. By observation the slope of the curve on either side of point P is negative and is positive on either side of point Q.

If we look now to Figure 2.11 where we have plotted $y = x^3$, we see that we not only have an inflection point at $x = 0$, but the slope at that point is zero, so we conclude that it is possible to have an inflection point as well as a maximum or minimum at a critical point.

Let us check the critical point $x = 0$ for the function $y = x^3$. If $y = x^3$ then $y' = 3x^2$ and by taking points close to and on either side of $x = 0$ we obtain:

If $x = -0.01 \Rightarrow y' = +.0001$

If $x = 0.00 \Rightarrow y' = .0000$

If $x = 0.01 \Rightarrow y' = +.0001$

The slopes on either side of the critical point are positive, which shows us that the critical point $x = 0$ is an inflection point.

Most technical problems will be concerned with maxima and minima and not much with inflection points. We must mention them in passing, however, for they will be present whether we are interested or not.

Example 2.18.   If $y = 3x^4 - 8x^3 + 6x^2$, locate and identify all critical points.

$$y = 3x^4 - 8x^3 + 6x^2 \qquad \text{so} \qquad y' = 12x^3 - 24x^2 + 12x$$

And if $y' = 0$ then $12x(x - 1)(x - 1) = 0$ and the critical points are $x = 0$ and $x = 1$.

If $x = -0.01 \Rightarrow y'$ is $-$

$x = 0.00 \Rightarrow y'$ is 0

$x = 0.01 \Rightarrow y'$ is $+$

From this, a minimum exists at $x = 0$.

If $x = 0.99 \Rightarrow y'$ is $+$

$x = 1.00 \Rightarrow y'$ is 0

$x = 1.01 \Rightarrow y'$ is $+$

From this, an inflection point exists at $x = 1$.

Recall that in the definition of a critical point we mentioned that either the slope had to be zero or it did not exist. Since the only line that has no slope is a vertical line, we look at Figure 2.14 which shows relative maxima and relative minima as ordinary, and then shows cusp maxima and minima which have vertical tangents or no slope.

We will not be too concerned with cusp maxima and minima but they must be mentioned in passing to complete the information needed to define critical point.

In review, then, to identify critical points: If as we scan the curve from left to right the slope changes:

$$+ \to 0 \to - \quad \text{Maximum}$$

$$- \to 0 \to + \quad \text{Minimum}$$

$$\left.\begin{array}{c} + \to 0 \to + \\ - \to 0 \to - \end{array}\right\} \text{Inflection}$$

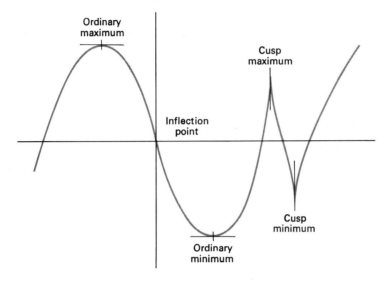

Ordinary maximum

Cusp maximum

Inflection point

Cusp minimum

Ordinary minimum

Figure 2.14

Exercise 2.8

1. What do we mean when we say a function $y = f(x)$ has a maximum at $x = 2$?
2. What are the three possible conditions under which the graph of a function might have a horizontal tangent line?
3. What are the three possible conditions under which the graph of a function might have an instantaneous slope of zero?
4. Given $y = f(x)$, outline the method for locating the critical points.
5. Given the critical points of a function $y = f(x)$, outline the method for identifying them.

In problems 6 through 17 locate and identify all critical points.

6. $y = (x^3/3) + (x^2/2) - 6x + 8$
7. $y = x^4 + 2x^3 - 3x^2 + 4$
8. $y = x^3 - 12x^2 + 36x - 25$
9. $y = x^3 - 3x^2 - 9x + 10$
10. $y = x^3 - 6x^2 + 12x - 20$
11. $y = \sqrt{3x^3 - 16x + 20}$
12. $y = x + (9/x)$
13. $y = -x^4 + 24x^2 + 2$
14. $y = (x^3 - 16)/x$
15. $y = (x^2 + 4)/x$
16. $y = \sqrt{3x^3 - 4x + 11}$
17. $y = 5/(2x^4 - 9x^2)$
18. The sum of two numbers is 12. Find the numbers whose product is a maximum. Use calculus.

19. Find the length and width of the largest rectangle that can be inscribed in a circle of diameter 10 inches.
20. Three towns, *A*, *B*, and *C*, are to be served by a high-tension line. The towns are located as shown in Figure 2.15. You are to locate pole *D* so as to make the total wire used a minimum.
21. From the discussion in the text we can say a critical point indicates either a maximum or a minimum or an inflection point Looking closely at the definition of inflection point, do you conclude that all inflection points occur at critical points? Why?

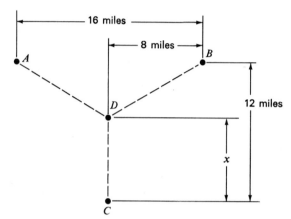

Figure 2.15

2.9 APPLICATIONS

2.9.1 Motion

It is interesting to note that calculus was developed by two men at about the same time, each being completely ignorant of the other's efforts. Wilhelm von Leibniz approached this new mathematics from the standpoint of slopes of tangents to curves much as we have discussed so far. Sir Isaac Newton developed a calculus also, but his approach was involved with velocities and accelerations of moving bodies. Thus we shall see that the derivative underlies the motion of bodies.

2.9.2 Linear Motion

Motion is defined as a continuing change of place or position. Linear motion is motion in a straight line. Thus we see that when a body moves from point *A* to point *B*, the body is displaced as a result of motion.

2.9.3 Linear Velocity

If you should travel from Miami to Tampa, a distance of about 260 miles, in $6\frac{1}{2}$ hours, you would say your average speed was 260/6.5 or about 40 miles per hour. This "everyday" term *speed* is really the magnitude of the vector quantity *velocity*, or time rate of change in distance. Or we say, the average velocity (V_{av}) equals the change in distance (Δs) or displacement divided by the change in time (Δt), thus:

$$V_{av} = \frac{\Delta s}{\Delta t} \qquad (2.4)$$

Velocity is expressed in any units indicating time rate of change in distance. Some typical units are miles per hour, feet per second, centimeters per second, and millimeters per microsecond.

We can readily see that average velocity is an arithmetic calculation and not one requiring calculus because all that is involved is a ratio of two differences.

Should we desire to know an instantaneous velocity at an exact given time we must resort to our limit concepts and calculus. We obtain instantaneous velocity by taking the limit of $\Delta s/\Delta t$ as Δt is allowed to approach zero, or:

$$V = \lim_{\Delta t \to 0} \frac{\Delta s}{\Delta t} = \frac{ds}{dt} \qquad (2.5)$$

Therefore instantaneous velocity is the first derivative of the distance s with respect to time t.

Example 2.19. An object in free fall, neglecting air resistance and other external variables, falls a distance approximately equal to $s = 16t^2$. Calculate the instantaneous speed when $t = 2$ seconds.

If $s = 16t^2$ then $V = ds/dt = 32t$, and when $t = 2$, $V = 32(2) = 64$ feet per second.

Exercise 2.9

1. Calculate the average speed of an object that moves from A to B in a straight line a distance of 175 centimeters if the total time taken was 25 seconds.

2. An automobile is equipped with what is commonly called a speedometer, which indicates two things by two separate mechanisms. One mechanism (the odometer) indicates total miles traveled with no regard to time. The other mechanism is really a machine that differentiates. Vindicate this last statement.

3. Three towns are located on a straight stretch of highway. Town B is 25 miles from town A and town C is 50 miles from town B. If it takes a car $\frac{1}{2}$ hour to go from A to B and $1\frac{1}{4}$ hours to go from B to C, what is the average speed from A to C?

4. Calculate a formula for instantaneous velocity of an object that moves a distance s according to: $s = 15t + 2t^2$.

5. Calculate the instantaneous velocity of the object in problem 4 when $t = 1$; when $t = 2$; when $t = 10$.

6. In free fall an object falls according to $s = \frac{1}{2}gt^2$, with g approximately 32. Calculate s and v for $t = 0, 1, 3, 4, 5, 10$.

7. If a test rocket on rails moves according to $s = 400t + 300t^2$, calculate the formula for the instantaneous velocity.

8. If $s = kt$ is plotted, the plot would be a straight line going through the origin with slope k. Describe the plot of v. (See Figure 2.16a.)

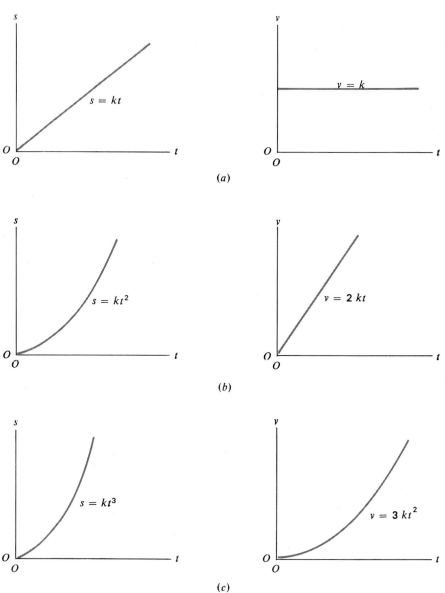

Figure 2.16

9. If $s = kt^2$ is plotted, the plot would be the right half of a parabola with the minimum point at the origin. Describe the plot of v. (See Figure 2.16b.)
10. If $s = kt^3$ plots as shown in Figure 2.16c, describe the plot of v.
11. A block that weighs 1000 pounds rests on a horizontal surface for which the coefficient of friction is μ. A force of P pounds acts on the block as shown in Figure 2.17. The force just necessary to put this block in motion is:

$$P = \frac{1000\mu}{\cos \theta + \mu \sin \theta}$$

If $\mu = 0.2$, determine the largest and smallest values of P.

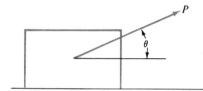

Figure 2.17

2.9.4 *Instantaneous Current—Electronics*

The rate of flow of electrons is called an *electric current*. The unit of electric current is one ampere and represents a net flow of one coulomb ($6.242 \cdot 10^{18}$ electrons) in one second. Actually current and electron flow are the same thing but because of incorrect early electron theories we treat them as being different now.

It is generally accepted practice to think of current flowing from positive to negative, which was the original incorrect theory. If actual electron movement—which is from negative to positive—is desired, it is called *electron flow*.

Instantaneous current at any point in a circuit is the coulombs-per-second rate at which electric charge is transmitted past that point. Therefore:

$$i = \frac{dq}{dt} \tag{2.6}$$

where $i = $ current in amperes, $q = $ charge in coulombs, and $t = $ time.

> **Example 2.20.** The charge transferred in a certain circuit varies according to $q = 3t^2 + 4t$. Derive a formula for current flow.
>
> $$i = \frac{dq}{dt} = 6t + 4 \text{ amp}$$

2.9.5 *Induced Voltage*

When a wire is physically moved through a magnetic field or lines of a magnetic field move past a wire, voltage is induced in that wire. The induced voltage varies with the number of turns of wire in the coil or the change in flux density of the magnetic field. If we consider a coil with a fixed number of turns N, then the induced voltage will vary only by the change in flux. From all this then we have:

$$e_{ind} = -N\frac{d\phi}{dt} \tag{2.7}$$

Where e_{ind} is the induced voltage, N the number of turns of wire, ϕ the flux density in webers, and t the time. The negative sign is a result of Lenz's law showing that current resulting from induced voltage moves in a direction opposing the flux change.

> **Example 2.21.** If the flux density varies according to $\phi = 5t^3 + 10$ past a coil of 100 turns, what voltage is induced when t is 0.2 seconds?
>
> From $\phi = 5t^3 + 10$, $d\phi/dt = 15t^2$ webers per second change in flux. From (2.7):
>
> $$e_{ind} = -N\frac{d\phi}{dt} = -100(15)(0.2)^2 = -60 \text{ volts}$$

2.9.6 Instantaneous Power

A volt is defined as a unit of work per unit charge and current as the rate of flow of charge per unit time. The product EI then must be units of work per second, because:

$$EI = \frac{work}{charge} \cdot \frac{charge}{second} = \frac{work}{second}$$

Work per second is by definition power. Note further that voltage is defined as joules per coulomb and current as coulombs per second, so

$$EI = \frac{joules}{coulomb} \cdot \frac{coulomb}{second} = \frac{joules}{second}$$

Now if the current is one amp and voltage one volt, the power is one joule per second. One joule per second is called one watt, therefore

$$P = EI \quad \text{in watts}$$

Instantaneous power in a circuit is by definition the rate of change of work at a given instant, thus

$$P = \frac{dw}{dt} \tag{2.8}$$

where P is power in watts, w is work in joules, and t is time.

Example 2.22.   A resistor in a circuit dissipates energy according to $w = 5t^2 + 2t$. What is the power at 1.2 seconds?

$$P = \frac{dw}{dt} = 10t + 2$$

$$= 10(1.2) + 2$$

$$= 12 + 2$$

$$= 14 \text{ watts}$$

2.9.7 Capacitance

A combination of conducting plates separated by an insulator is known as a *capacitor* and is used to store an electric charge. The extent to which a capacitor is capable of being charged is constant for any particular capacitor and is known as its *capacitance* (C).

Capacitance is the ratio of the charge on either plate of a capacitor to the potential difference between the plates, thus $C = Q/E$ or $Q = CE$.

Since any change in voltage will produce a corresponding change in charge, we say the rate of change with respect to time is equal, therefore

$$\frac{dq}{dt} = C \frac{de}{dt}$$

But from (2.6), $i = dq/dt$, so

$$i = C \frac{de}{dt} \tag{2.9}$$

where i is current in amperes, C is capacitance in farads, e is voltage, and t is time.

2.9.8 Induced Voltage

By definition the product of the inductance of a coil and the current in that coil equals the product of the number of turns in the coil and flux density, or $Li = N\phi$.

Now assuming the inductance L and the number of turns N are constant, then any change in current will produce a corresponding change in flux. By differentiation then, $L\, di/dt = N\, d\phi/dt$, but since from (2.7), $e_{ind} = -N\, d\phi/dt$, we have:

$$e_{ind} = -L \frac{di}{dt} \tag{2.10}$$

2.9.9 Mutual Inductance

Figure 2.18 shows coil 1 with N_1 turns and i_1 current flowing, and coil 2 with N_2 turns being cut by flux field ϕ_2, inducing voltage e_2. If M is the mutual inductance in henrys, then we have $N_2\phi_2 = M i_1$, and differentiating with respect to time, $N_2\, d\phi_2/dt = M\, di_1/dt$, and using (2.7), we have:

$$e_{2\text{ ind}} = -M \frac{di_1}{dt} \qquad\qquad (2.11)$$

where $e_{2\text{ ind}}$ is the voltage induced in coil 2, M is the mutual inductance in henrys, i_1 the current in coil 1 in amperes, and t is the time.

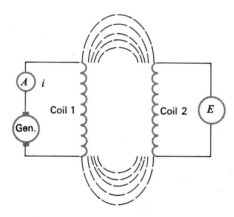

Figure 2.18

Exercise 2.10

1. Calculate the formula for the current in a capacitor if the charge varies as $q = 3t^2$. What current flows at $t = 0.01$? At $t = 0.03$? At $t = 0.05$?
2. Calculate the formula for the current in capacitor if the charge varies as $q = 2t^3/3 - t^2 + 0.001$. What current flows at $t = 0.01$? At $t = 0.03$? At $t = 0.05$?
3. Calculate the voltage induced in a 100-turn coil being cut by a magnetic field that changes according to $\phi = 0.003t$, when $t = 0.01$.
4. Calculate the voltage induced in a 250-turn coil being cut by a magnetic field that changes according to $\phi = 0.05t - t^3 + 0.05$, when $t = 0.02$.
5. Calculate the power in a circuit when $t = 0.02$ if the work done varies according to $w = 2t^3 + 3t$.
6. Calculate the power in a circuit when $t = 0.01$, if the work done varies according to $w = 5t^2 + 2t$.
7. Calculate the formula for the current flowing in a 2-microfarad capacitor if the voltage varies according to $e = 300t^3$.
8. Calculate the formula for the current flowing in a 0.5-microfarad capacitor if the voltage varies according to $e = 75t^{2/3}$. What is the current flowing when $t = 1$?

9. Calculate the formula for induced voltage in a 20-henry coil if the current flowing is $4t^{1/2}$.
10. Calculate the formula for induced voltage in a 5-henry coil if the current is 0.4 amp.
11. Calculate the induced voltage in coil number 2 if the mutual inductance is 0.3 henrys, time is 1 second, and the current in coil 1 is $i_1 = 12t^{2/3}$.
12. Calculate the induced voltage in coil number 2 if the mutual inductance is 0.2 henrys, time is 0.001 seconds, and the current in coil number 1 is $i_1 = \frac{1}{3}t^3$.

2.9.10 Kirchhoff's Current Law

Kirchhoff's current law states that the currents entering a junction must equal the currents leaving that junction.

$$\sum I = 0 \tag{2.12}$$

In Figure 2.19 current i flows toward point A and currents i_1 and i_2 flow away from point A, so according to Kirchhoff's law $I = i - (i_1 + i_2) = 0$.

If we look to Figure 2.20 we see a similar situation but one that approaches a

Figure 2.19

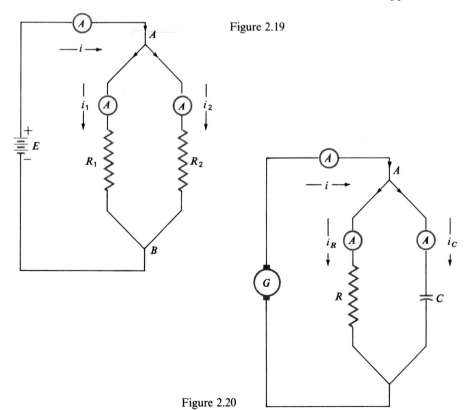

Figure 2.20

practical condition. As before, $I = 0$ here at point A, but $i_R = e/R$ and $i_C = C\,de/dt$, so if $I = i - i_R - i_C = 0$, then $I = i - (e/R) - C\,de/dt = 0$ or

$$C\frac{de}{dt} + \frac{e}{R} - i = 0 \tag{2.13}$$

Example 2.23.   Calculate i in Figure 2.20 if $C = 10$ microfarads, $R = 100{,}000$ ohms, and $e = 2t^3 + 544$, when $t = 12$ seconds.
   If $e = 2t^3 + 544$ then $de/dt = 6t^2 = 6(12)^2 = 864$ volts at $t = 12$.

$$e = 2(12)^3 + 544 = 4000 \text{ volts} \qquad \text{at } t = 12$$

Therefore

$$\frac{6(12)^2}{100000} + \frac{4000}{100000} = i = 0.40864 \text{ amp}$$

2.9.11 *Kirchhoff's Voltage Law*

   Kirchhoff's voltage law states that the source or impressed voltage equals the sum of the voltage drops of the several elements of a series circuit.

$$\sum E = 0 \tag{2.14}$$

In Figure 2.21 a circuit is shown with a resistor R in series with an inductance coil L. Here

$$e_R + e_L - e = 0 \tag{2.15}$$

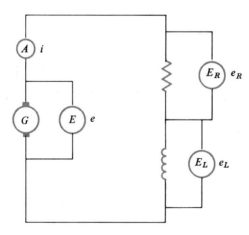

Figure 2.21

The voltage drop across the resistor is Ri while that across the coil is $L\,di/dt$, so

$$Ri + L\frac{di}{dt} - e = 0 \tag{2.16}$$

Example 2.24. Calculate the formula for the voltage output of the generator shown in Figure 2.21 if the current output of the generator is $i = \frac{1}{3}t^3 + \frac{1}{2}t^2 - \frac{1}{4}$, the inductance is 10 henrys, and the resistance is 12 ohms.

If $i = \frac{1}{3}t^3 + \frac{1}{2}t^2 - \frac{1}{4}$, then $di/dt = t^2 + t$ amp per second and, according to (2.16),

$$e = 10(t^2 + t) + 12\left(\frac{t^3}{3} + \frac{t^2}{2} - \frac{1}{4}\right)$$

$$= 10t^2 + 10t + 4t^3 + 6t^2 - 3$$
$$= 4t^3 + 16t^2 + 10t - 3$$

Example 2.25. Calculate the voltage output of the generator in Figure 2.21 if $t = 1$.

$$e = 4t^3 + 16t^2 + 10t - 3$$
$$= 4(1) + 16(1) + 10(1) - 3$$
$$= 4 + 16 + 10 - 3$$
$$= 27 \; volts$$

The student should note that the preceding type of problem is not solvable with elementary impedance formulas or ordinary vector approaches.

Exercise 2.11

1. Calculate the formula for the current in a circuit where a resistor of 200,000 ohms is in parallel with a capacitor of 10 microfarads and the voltage varies as $e = \frac{1}{3}t^3 + 1000$.
2. Calculate the formula for the current in a circuit where a resistor of 100,000 ohms is in parallel with a capacitor of 15 microfarads and the voltage varies as $e = t^3 + t^2 + 2000$.
3. Calculate the plate current of an amplifier tube with a plate-load resistance of 100,000 ohms if the shunt capacitance is 100 microfarads and the voltage varies as $e = 8(10)^6 t + 100$.
4. Calculate the voltage across a circuit where a resistance of 1000 ohms is hooked in series with an inductance of 10 henrys, if the current varies as $i = 3t^{2/3} - 5$ when $t = \frac{1}{27}$ second.
5. Calculate the voltage across a circuit when a resistance of 500 ohms is hooked in series with an inductance of 100 henrys if the current varies as $i = t^2 + 2$ when $t = 0.2$ second.
6. What is the voltage across a coil with an inductance of 1 henry and a resistance of 500 ohms if the current flow varies as $i = \sqrt{t} + 1$, when $t = 0.02$ second?
7. What is the voltage across a coil with an inductance of 5 henrys and a resistance of 100 ohms if the current flow varies as $i = \frac{1}{2}t^2 + 0.02$ when $t = 0.01$ second?

8. What is the voltage across an inductance of 100 henrys in series with a 25-microfarad capacitor if the voltage across the capacitor varies as $e = 900(t^3 + t^2 + 1)$ when $t = 1$ second?

2.9.12 The RC Differentiating Circuit

In Figure 2.22 we have a capacitor in series with a resistor being fed by a low plate-resistance tube. If the resistance is ignored the current flowing would be, from (2.9), $i_C = C\,de/dt$. Then the voltage drop across the resistor (output) is:

$$e_R = Ri_C = RC\frac{de}{dt} \qquad\qquad (2.17)$$

This is called a *differentiating circuit* because the output voltage is proportional to the derivative of the input voltage.

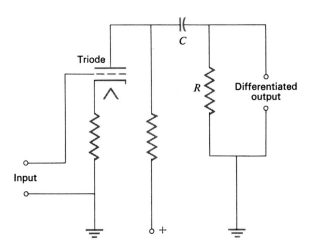

Figure 2.22

2.9.13 The L Differentiating Circuit

Figure 2.23 shows another circuit whose output is proportional to the derivative of the input voltage. This too is a differentiating circuit. Here the inductance coil is being fed by a tube with a high-resistance plate. No coil is resistance free but to consider it theoretically resistance free we show the resistance (R_L) as a separate portion of the circuit.

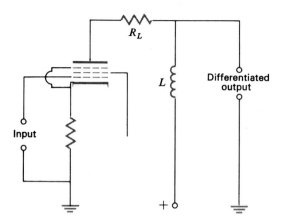

Figure 2.23

The voltage drop across the inductance coil is, according to (2.10), $e_L = -L \, di/dt$.

If the input voltage to a differentiating circuit has a rectangular waveform as shown in Figure 2.24a, the voltage is zero between t_1 and t_2. At t_2 the voltage goes to maximum instantaneously and remains at maximum between t_2 and t_3. At t_3 the voltage drops instantaneously to zero and remains at zero between t_3 and t_4. Figure 2.24b shows the resulting differentiated output voltage. Note that between t_2 and t_3 the input voltage is constant so the slope is zero and thus no output voltage. Figures 2.24a and b are for theoretically perfect conditions. Figures 2.24c and d are sketches more nearly approaching an actual situation.

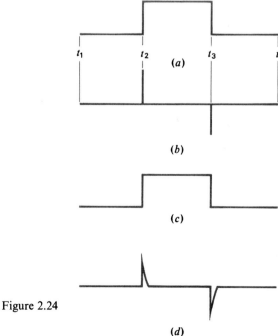

Figure 2.24

Exercise 2.12.   Make a sketch of each input waveform given in Figure 2.25 and then sketch the resulting differentiated output voltage waveform, assuming perfect differentiation.

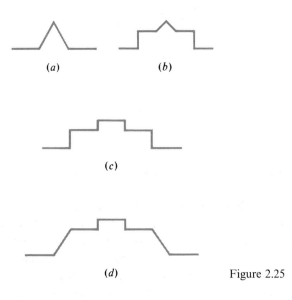

(a)   (b)

(c)

(d)   Figure 2.25

2.10 DIFFERENTIATING TRIGONOMETRIC FUNCTIONS

A. $y = \sin x$

Recall that the sine function is evaluated by summing what is known as the odd, infinite series (see the Precalculus Mathematics Review). Thus

$$y = \sin x = x - \frac{x^3}{3!} + \frac{x^5}{5!} - \frac{x^7}{7!} + \cdots$$

Differentiating this polynomial, we have:

$$y' = 1 - \frac{3x^2}{1 \cdot 2 \cdot 3} + \frac{5x^4}{1 \cdot 2 \cdot 3 \cdot 4 \cdot 5} - \frac{7x^6}{1 \cdot 2 \cdot 3 \cdot 4 \cdot 5 \cdot 6 \cdot 7} + \cdots$$

$$= 1 - \frac{x^2}{2!} + \frac{x^4}{4!} - \frac{x^6}{6!} + \cdots$$

which is the infinite series representing the cosine function. Therefore

If $y = k \sin x + C \Rightarrow y' = k \cos x$ (2.18)

(see Figure 2.26)

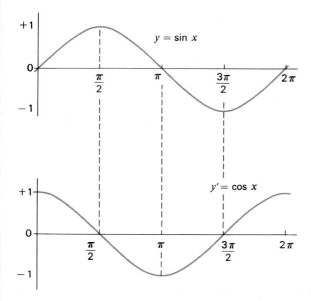

Figure 2.26

B. $y = \cos x$

Differentiating the infinite series that represents the cosine function shows the following to be true:

$$\text{If } y = k \cos x + C \Rightarrow y' = -k \sin x \qquad (2.19)$$

(see Figure 2.27)

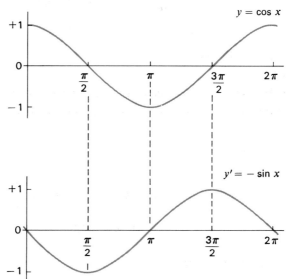

Figure 2.27

C. $y = \sin u$

where u is a function of x.

$$\text{If } y = k \sin u + C \Rightarrow y' = k \cos u \frac{du}{dx} *$$ (2.20)

Example 2.26.   Differentiate $y = 3 \sin (x^2 + 2x + 1)$.
Here $y = 3 \sin u$, where $u = x^2 + 2x + 1$ and $du/dx = 2x + 2$. Therefore

$$y' = 3 \cos (u) \frac{du}{dx}$$

$$= 3 \cos (x^2 + 2x + 1)(2x + 2)$$

$$= (6x + 6) \cos (x^2 + 2x + 1)$$

D. $y = \cos u$

where u is a function of x.

$$\text{If } y = k \cos u + C \Rightarrow y' = -k \sin u \frac{du}{dx} *$$ (2.21)

Example 2.27.   Differentiate $y = 2 \cos (x^3 + 2x^2 + x)$.
Here $y = 2 \cos u$ where $u = x^3 + 2x^2 + x$ and $du/dx = 3x^2 + 4x + 1$.
Therefore

$$y' = -2 \sin u \frac{du}{dx}$$

$$= -2 \sin (x^3 + 2x^2 + x)(3x^2 + 4x + 1)$$

$$= -2(3x^2 + 4x + 1) \sin (x^3 + 2x^2 + x)$$

E. $y = \tan u$

where u is a function of x.

Proof of this will be given in a later discussion when the derivative of a quotient is pursued. It is sufficient now to point out that:

$$\tan u = \frac{\sin u}{\cos u}$$

$$\text{If } y = k \tan u + C \Rightarrow y' = k \sec^2 u \frac{du}{dx} *$$ (2.22)

(see Figure 2.28)

*See Appendix for proof.

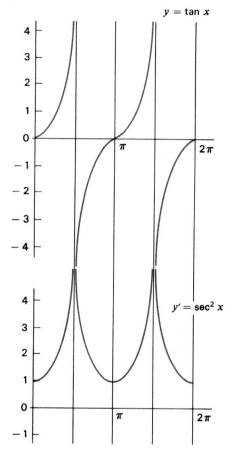

Figure 2.28

F. $y = \cot u$

where u is a function of x.

Here we use (2.22) and $\cot u = 1/\tan u$ for:

$$\text{If } y = k \cot u + C \Rightarrow y' = k \csc^2 u \, \frac{du}{dx} \qquad (2.23)$$

Exercise 2.13

1. With appropriate use of parentheses, rewrite the following trigonometric expressions so as to indicate that you know their exact true meaning!

   (a) $y = \sin^2 x$ (b) $y = \sin 2x$

   (c) $y = \sin x^2$ (d) $y = 2 \sin x$

   (e) $y = 2 \sin^2 x$ (f) $y = a \sin x^2$

   (g) $y = 2 \sin 2x$ (h) $y = 2 \sin^2 (2x^2)$

Calculate the first derivative (dy/dx) of the following trigonometric functions.

2. $y = \sin x^2$

3. $y = \sin 2x$

4. $y = \sin^2 x$

5. $y = \cos x^3$

6. $y = 3 \cos 3x$

7. $y = 3 \cos^3 x$

8. $y = 2 \tan x$

9. $y = 2 \tan 2x$

10. $y = 2 \tan^2 x$

11. $y = 2 \tan x^2$

12. $y = \cot x$

13. $y = \cot 2x$

14. $y = \cot^2 x$

15. $y = \cot x^2$

16. $y = 3 \cos x^4$

17. $y = 8 \cos (2x + 3)$

18. $y = 5 \cos (2/x)$

19. $y = 2 \cos \sqrt{x}$

20. $y = -9 \cos x^{¾}$

21. $y = \cos \sqrt{1 - x}$

22. $y = t \cos x^{1-t}$ (t is a constant)

23. $y = \sin \sqrt{1 - x}$

24. $y = \cos (x - 1/x)$

25. $y = \cos (\omega x + \pi/2)$($\omega$ is a constant)

26. $y = \sin (2x + 3)$

27. $y = \sin (2/x)$

28. $y = \sin \sqrt{x}$

29. $y = -6 \sin x^{¾}$

30. $y = \sin \theta^{1-t}$ (t is a constant)

2.11 THE DERIVATIVE OF A PRODUCT

Recall that we have defined the derivative of a sum as the sum of the derivatives and noted that this sounded rather redundant. We cannot make a similar simple statement about the derivative of a product.

The derivative of a product of two factors is the first factor multiplied by the derivative of the second factor plus the second factor multiplied by the derivative of the first factor.

$$\text{If } y = uv \Rightarrow y' = u\frac{dv}{dx} + v\frac{du}{dx} \text{ *} \tag{2.24}$$

where u and v are functions of x.

Example 2.28. Differentiate $y = x^2 \cos x$.

$y = x^2 \cos x$ is a $y = uv$ type where $u = x^2$ and $v = \cos x$.

If $u = x^2$ then $du/dx = 2x$ and $v = \cos x$, so $dv/dx = -\sin x$.

$$y = x^2 \cos x = uv \qquad \text{so} \qquad y' = u\frac{dv}{dx} + v\frac{du}{dx}$$

$$y' = x^2(-\sin x) + \cos x(2x)$$

$$= 2x \cos x - x^2 \sin x.$$

*See Appendix for proof.

Example 2.29. Calculate the first derivative of $y = (\sin x)(\cos x)$.

$y = (\sin x)(\cos x)$ is a $y = uv$ type where $u = \sin x$ and $v = \cos x$. If $u = \sin x$ then $du/dx = \cos x$ and $v = \cos\ x$, so $dv/dx = -\sin x$.

$$y' = u\frac{dv}{dx} + v\frac{du}{dx}$$

$$= (\sin x)(-\sin x) + (\cos x)(\cos x)$$

$$= \cos^2 x - \sin^2 x$$

Example 2.30. Calculate the instantaneous slope of the function $y = (x^3 + x^2 + 1)(x^2 + 1)$.

$y = (x^3 + x^2 + 1)(x^2 + 1)$ is a $y = uv$ type where $u = x^3 + x^2 + 1$ and $v = x^2 + 1$. If $u = x^3 + x^2 + 1$ then $du/dx = 3x^2 + 2x$ and $v = x^2 + 1$, so $dv/dx = 2x$.

$$y' = u\frac{dv}{dx} + v\frac{du}{dx}$$

$$= (x^3 + x^2 + 1)2x + (x^2 + 1)(3x^2 + 2x)$$

$$= 2x^4 + 2x^3 + 2x + 3x^4 + 2x^3 + 3x^2 + 2x$$

$$= 5x^4 + 4x^3 + 3x^2 + 4x$$

As a check on this result note that if $y = (x^3 + x^2 + 1)(x^2 + 1)$ then $y = x^5 + x^4 + x^3 + 2x^2 + 1$ and therefore $y' = 5x^4 + 4x^3 + 3x^2 + 4x$.

2.12 THE DERIVATIVE OF A QUOTIENT

If $y = \dfrac{u}{v} \Rightarrow y' = \dfrac{v\,du/dx - u\,dv/dx}{v^2}$* (2.25)

where u and v are functions of x.

Example 2.31. If $y = \sqrt{(3x^2 + 2)/(x^2 - x)}$, calculate y'.

$$\text{If } y = \sqrt{\frac{3x^2 + 2}{x^2 - x}} = \frac{(3x^2 + 2)^{\frac{1}{2}}}{(x^2 - x)^{\frac{1}{2}}} \qquad \text{then} \qquad y = \frac{u}{v}$$

where $u = (3x^2 + 2)^{\frac{1}{2}}$ and $v = (x^2 - x)^{\frac{1}{2}}$.

$$\text{If } u = (3x^2 + 2)^{\frac{1}{2}} \qquad \text{then} \qquad \frac{du}{dx} = \tfrac{1}{2}(3x^2 + 2)^{-\frac{1}{2}}(6x)$$

$$= \frac{3x}{(x^2 + 2)^{\frac{1}{2}}}$$

*See Appendix for proof.

and $v = (x^2 - x)^{1/2}$,

$$\text{so } \frac{dv}{dx} = \tfrac{1}{2}(x^2 - x)^{-1/2}(2x - 1)$$

$$= \frac{2x - 1}{2(x^2 - x)^{1/2}}$$

$$y' = \frac{(x^2 - x)^{1/2}}{(x^2 - x)} \cdot \frac{3x}{(3x^2 + 2)^{1/2}} - \frac{(3x^2 + 2)^{1/2}(2x - 1)}{2(x^2 - x)^{1/2}(x^2 - x)}$$

$$= \frac{3x(x^2 - x)^{1/2}}{(x^2 - x)(3x^2 - 2)^{1/2}} - \frac{(3x^2 + 2)^{1/2}(2x - 1)}{2(x^2 - x)^{3/2}}$$

$$= \frac{6x(x^2 - x)}{2(x^2 - x)^{3/2}(3x^2 + 2)^{1/2}} - \frac{(2x - 1)(3x^2 + 2)}{2(x^2 - x)^{3/2}(3x^2 + 2)^{1/2}}$$

$$= \frac{6x(x^2 - x) - (2x - 1)(3x^2 + 2)}{2(x^2 - x)^{3/2}(3x^2 + 2)^{1/2}}$$

$$= \frac{6x^3 - 6x^2 - (6x^3 - 3x^2 + 4x - 2)}{2(x^2 - x)^{3/2}(3x^2 + 2)^{1/2}}$$

$$= \frac{-3x^2 - 4x + 2}{2(x^2 - x)^{3/2}(3x^2 + 2)^{1/2}}$$

Example 2.32.   Calculate the instantaneous slope of $y = (\sin x)/x^2$.
  $y = (\sin x)/x^2$ is a $y = u/v$ type, where $u = \sin x$ and $v = x^2$. If $u = \sin x$ then $du/dx = \cos x$ and $v = x^2$, so $dv/dx = 2x$.

$$y' = \frac{x^2 \cos x - \sin x(2x)}{x^4} = \frac{x^2 \cos x - 2x \sin x}{x^4}$$

$$= \frac{x \cos x - 2 \sin x}{x^3}$$

Example 2.33.   Differentiate $y = \sin u/\cos u$.
  Note this is really $y = \tan u$, so it will be the proof for (2.22).
  $y = \sin u/\cos u$ is a $y = u/v$ type where $u = \sin u$ and $v = \cos u$. If $u = \sin u$ then $du/dx = \cos u \, du/dx$ and $v = \cos u$, so $dv/dx = -\sin u \, dv/dx$.

$$y' = \frac{\cos u \cos u \, du/dx - \sin u \, (-\sin u) \, du/dx}{\cos^2 u}$$

$$= \frac{\cos^2 u + \sin^2 u \, du/dx}{\cos^2 u} = \frac{du/dx}{\cos^2 u} = \frac{1}{\cos^2 u} \frac{du}{dx}$$

$$= \sec^2 u \frac{du}{dx}$$

Exercise 2.14. Differentiate the following functions.

1. $y = x^3\sqrt{2x + 1}$
2. $y = 2x^2(x^2 + 3)^3$
3. $y = x(x^2 + 1)$
4. $y = x^2(x + 1)^2$
5. $y = 2x^3(2x + 1)^3$
6. $y = (x + 1)^2(x^2 + 1)$
7. $y = x/(x^2 + 1)$
8. $y = \sqrt{2x - 3}/(x^2 + 1)^3$
9. $y = x^2/(1 - x)$
10. $y = (2x^2 + 1)/(x - 1)$
11. $y = (2x + 3)/(1 - x^2)$
12. $y = (5x + 2)^2/(2 - 3x)$

2.13 THE DERIVATIVE OF $y = e^x$

The number e, which is the base of natural logs and an important ingredient in problems concerned with natural growth or decay and radioactive decay, can be shown to equal the sum of the infinite series:

$$e = \lim_{m \to \infty} \left(1 + \frac{1}{m}\right)^m = 1 + 1 + \frac{1}{2!} + \frac{1}{3!} + \frac{1}{4!} + \cdots + \frac{1}{n!} + \cdots$$

$$\approx 2.71828 \qquad \text{(see Precalculus Mathematics Review)}$$

And

$$e^x = \lim_{m \to \infty} \left[\left(1 + \frac{1}{m}\right)^m\right]^x = 1 + x + \frac{x^2}{2!} + \frac{x^3}{3!} + \frac{x^4}{4!} + \frac{x^5}{5!} + \frac{x^6}{6!} + \cdots$$

so if $y = e^x$, then:

$$y' = 0 + 1 + \frac{2x}{2} + \frac{3x^2}{6} + \frac{4x^3}{24} + \frac{5x^4}{120} + \frac{6x^5}{720} + \cdots$$

$$= 1 + x + \frac{x^2}{2!} + \frac{x^3}{3!} + \frac{x^4}{4!} + \frac{x^5}{5!} + \frac{x^6}{6!} + \cdots$$

From this then:

$$\text{If } y = ke^x + C \Rightarrow y' = ke^x \qquad (2.26)$$

2.14 THE DERIVATIVE OF $y = e^u$

Here u is a function of x.

$$\text{If } y = ke^u + C \Rightarrow y' = ke^u \frac{du}{dx} \qquad ^* \qquad (2.27)$$

*See Appendix for proof.

Example 2.34. Calculate the instantaneous slope of $y = e^{1/x}$.

$y = e^{1/x}$ is a $y = e^u$. If $u = 1/x = x^{-1}$ then $du/dx = -x^{-2} = -1/x^2$.

$$y' = e^u \frac{du}{dx}$$

$$= (e^{1/x})(-1/x^2)$$

$$= \frac{-e^{1/x}}{x^2}$$

Example 2.35. Calculate the first derivative of $y = e^{5x^2}$

$y = e^{5x^2}$ is a $y = e^u$. If $u = 5x^2$ then $du/dx = 10x$.

$$y' = e^u \frac{du}{dx}$$

$$= e^{5x^2}(10x)$$

$$= 10xe^{5x^2}$$

2.15 THE DERIVATIVE OF $y = e^{-x}$

If $y = e^{-x}$ then it is of the type $y = ke^u$ where $u = -x$ and $du/dx = -1$, and $y' = -e^{-x}$.

$$\text{If } y = ke^{-x} \Rightarrow y' = -ke^{-x} \tag{2.28}$$

Recall that $e^x = 1 + x + \dfrac{x^2}{2!} + \dfrac{x^3}{3!} + \dfrac{x^4}{4!} + \dfrac{x^5}{5!} + \cdots$

so

$$e^{(jx)} = 1 + jx + \frac{j^2x^2}{2!} + \frac{j^3x^3}{3!} + \frac{j^4x^4}{4!} + \frac{j^5x^5}{5!} + \frac{j^6x^6}{6!} + \cdots$$

$$= 1 + jx - \frac{x^2}{2!} - \frac{jx^3}{3!} + \frac{x^4}{4!} + \frac{jx^5}{5!} - \frac{x^6}{6!} + \cdots$$

Here $j = \sqrt{-1}$, the standard operator in complex number and electronic vector notation.

If we now factor out all j terms in the preceding expansion, we have:

$$e^{(jx)} = \left(1 - \frac{x^2}{2!} + \frac{x^4}{4!} - \frac{x^6}{6!} + \cdots\right) + j\left(x - \frac{x^3}{3!} + \frac{x^5}{5!} + \cdots\right)$$

Note that this produces two infinite series sums. One is involved only with even numbers and the other only with odd numbers. If we let A represent the even series and B represent the odd series, we have

$$e^{(jx)} = A + jB$$

It can be shown that

$$\cos x = 1 - \frac{x^2}{2!} + \frac{x^4}{4!} - \frac{x^6}{6!} + \cdots$$

and

$$\sin x = x - \frac{x^3}{3!} + \frac{x^5}{5!} + \cdots$$

so $e^{(jx)} = \cos x + j \sin x$ which is known as Ehler's formula.

2.16 THE DERIVATIVE OF $y = \ln x$

Here "ln" means natural logarithm or base e. If $y = \ln x$ then $x = e^y$ and $dx/dy = 1/e^y$, but $e^y = x$, therefore $dy/dx = 1/x$.

$$\text{If } y = k \ln x + C \Rightarrow y' = \frac{k}{x} \tag{2.29}$$

$$\text{If } y = k \log x + C \Rightarrow y' = 0.4343 \frac{k}{x} \tag{2.30}$$

In (2.30) "log" means common logarithm or base ten. The constant 0.4343 in (2.30) converts natural logarithms to common logarithms.

2.17 THE DERIVATIVE OF $y = \ln u$

Here u is a function of x.

$$\text{If } y = k \ln u + C \Rightarrow y' = \frac{k}{u} \frac{du}{dx} \, ^* \tag{2.31}$$

Example 2.36. Differentiate $y = \ln(x^2 + 2)$.
$y = \ln(x^2 + 2)$ is a $y = \ln u$ type where $u = x^2 + 2$ and $du/dx = 2x$.

$$y' = \frac{k}{u} \frac{du}{dx}$$

$$= \frac{1}{x^2 + 2} 2x$$

$$= \frac{2x}{x^2 + 2}$$

*See Appendix for proof.

2.18 THE DERIVATIVE OF $y = ka^u$

If $y = ka^u$ with a a positive constant and u a function of x, we have:

If $y = ka^u + C \Rightarrow y' = ka^u \dfrac{du}{dx} \ln a$*   (2.32)

Example 2.37. Differentiate $y = 2^{\sqrt{x}}$.

$y = 2^{\sqrt{x}}$ is a $y = a^u$ type with $a = 2$, $u = \sqrt{x} = x^{\frac{1}{2}}$, so $du/dx = \frac{1}{2}\sqrt{x}$.

$$y' = a^u \frac{du}{dx} \ln u$$

$$= 2^{\sqrt{x}} \frac{1}{2\sqrt{x}} \ln 2 = \frac{2^{\sqrt{x}}}{2\sqrt{x}} \ln 2$$

$$= \frac{2^{\sqrt{x}}}{2^1 \sqrt{x}} \ln 2$$

$$= \frac{2^{\sqrt{x}-1}}{\sqrt{x}} \ln 2$$

Exercise 2.15. Calculate the first derivative of the following functions.

1. $y = e^{(x^2 + 3x + 5)}$
2. $y = (3e^{\sqrt{x}})^2$
3. $y = e^{\sqrt{x}}$
4. $y = e^{(2-x)/x}$
5. $y = e^{\sqrt{1-x}}$
6. $y = \sin(e^t)$
7. $y = e^{(x+8)}$
8. $y = \ln(x + 2)$
9. $y = 3 \log x$
10. $y = \ln(x^5)$
11. $y = \ln(x^6) - 3 \sin x + e^x$
12. $y = \ln(6x) - \ln(5/x^2)$
13. $y = 15 \log(x^{10})$
14. $y = \ln[1/(1 - x^2)]$
15. $y = \ln(x^2 + 3)^4$
16. $y = \ln\sqrt{x^2 - 1}$
17. $y = \ln(1/x)$
18. $y = \ln\sqrt[3]{4 - 3x}$
19. $y = \log(4 - x^2)$
20. $y = \log(4 - x)^2$
21. $y = \log[\sin(x + \pi)]$
22. $y = 3^{(x^2 + 2x)}/4$
23. $y = a^{\frac{1}{2}}$
24. $y = a^x$
25. $y = 5e^{(x+1)}$
26. $y = (x^2 + 2x + 3)(5e^{3x})$
27. $y = \sin x + \cos 2x$
28. $y = \sin x + \sin 2x$
29. $y = e^x \cos 2x$
30. $y = \frac{1}{4}\cos^2 x + \sin^2 x$
31. $y = (2/x^2) + \ln x$
32. $y = 3e^{-x} \sin x$

Exercise 2.16. Calculate the instantaneous slope of the following functions.

1. $y = \ln(\sin x)$
2. $y = \ln(\cos x)$
3. $y = \sin^3(5x)$
4. $y = \sqrt{\sin(4x^2)}$

*See Appendix for proof.

5. $y = \sin 3x \cos 3x$

6. $y = (x^2 + 3x)\ln x^2$

7. $y = \ln(x + \sqrt{x^2 - a^2}$

8. $y = x/(x^3 - 4)$

9. $y = (\sin x)/e^{2x}$

10. $y = 5\ln(e^{2x}) - e^2$

11. $y = (e^x + e^{-x})/(e^x - e^{-x})$

12. $y = \log(x^2 - 4x + 4)$

13. $y = \ln\{\tan[(u/4) + (x/2)]\}$

14. $y = \tan(x/2)$

15. $y = (x/2) + \sin(2x/4)$

16. $y = (\tan x) - x$

17. $y = (\tan^2 x)/2 + \ln(\cos x)$

18. $y = \cos x + x\sin x$

19. $y = (x\ln x) - x$

20. $y = -x/(9\sqrt{x^2 - 9})$

2.19 VECTORS—ANGULAR MOTION

By definition angular or rotary motion is motion about a point or axis. Motion about an axis is best served with radian measure. By definition a radian is a central angle subtended (or cut off) by an arc whose length equals the length of the radius. In Figure 2.29 we see an angle θ whose measure is exactly one radian.

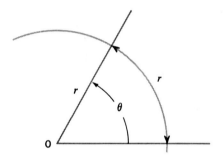

Figure 2.29

Since the circumference of any circle is $C = 2\pi r$, there must be 2π radians in each circumference or circle or revolution. Since one revolution equals 2π radians and one revolution equals 360 degrees, then

2π radians = 360 degrees

π radians = 180 degrees

$$1\text{ radian} = \frac{180}{\pi} \approx 57.29577 \text{ degrees}$$

$$1\text{ degree} = \frac{\pi}{180} \approx 0.01745 \text{ radians}$$

Therefore $\theta = \dfrac{s}{r}$ (2.33)

See Figure 2.30.

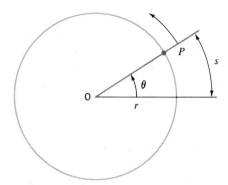

Figure 2.30

   In Figure 2.30 point P rotates about center 0 creating angle θ with a change in time. If angular velocity is represented by ω, we have:

$$\omega = \frac{d\theta}{dt} \tag{2.34}$$

If θ is in radians and t in seconds, then ω will be in radians per second. If θ is in degrees and t is in seconds, then ω will be in degrees per second.

   Any point P in motion about an axis or center travels through a distance. This distance is found using (2.33); $\theta = s/r$ or $s = \theta r$.

$$s = \theta r \tag{2.35}$$

If we now differentiate (2.35) we have $ds/dt = r\, d\theta/dt$, but $d\theta/dt = \omega$, and $ds/dt = v$, so

$$v = r\omega \tag{2.36}$$

   With (2.36) we have the link between angular and linear velocity. Differentiating (2.36) we have $dv/dt = r\, d\omega/dt$ or

$$a = r\alpha \tag{2.37}$$

where α represents angular acceleration.

   With (2.37) we have the link between linear acceleration and angular acceleration.

   When a point moves in a path that is equidistant from a fixed point, its direction at any given instant is along the tangent to the curved path. In Figure 2.31 point P is moving along the circular path or arc QP at constant angular velocity (ω). At any given instant P tends to move along the line PT which is tangent to arc QP at point P. The velocity of point P is represented by vector PT and its velocity v is $v = r\omega$ from (2.36). Note also in Figure 2.31 that the vector PT is broken up into its horizontal or x component (V_x) and vertical or y component (V_y). From this, V is the vector sum or V_x and V_y or

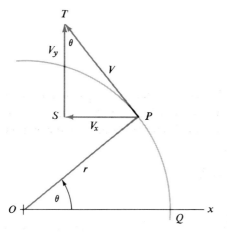

Figure 2.31

$$\mathbf{PT} = \mathbf{PS} \oplus \mathbf{ST}$$

($\oplus$ indicates vector addition).

Also $V_x = dx/dt$ and $V_y = dy/dt$, and since PT is perpendicular to OP and TS is perpendicular to OQ, angle PTS equals angle POQ or angle PTS equals θ. Therefore from the vector diagram, PST:

$$V_x = \frac{dx}{dt} = r\omega \sin \theta \tag{2.38}$$

$$V_y = \frac{dy}{dt} = r\omega \cos \theta \tag{2.39}$$

Vectors enter into a good many technical problems, so let us look at Figure 2.32 which pictures vector OP as the vector sum of vectors OQ and QP. In polar notation:

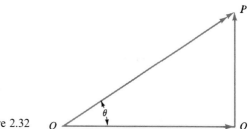

Figure 2.32

Vector $OP = |OP| \underline{/\theta}$

Vector $OQ = |OQ| \underline{/0^\circ}$

Vector $QP = |QP| \underline{/90^\circ}$

and $\mathbf{OP} = \mathbf{OQ} \oplus \mathbf{QP}$.

From trigonometry

$$\mathbf{OQ} = |OP| \cos \theta$$

$$\mathbf{QP} = |OP| \sin \theta$$

If $|OP| = 1$ then $\mathbf{OP} = \cos \theta + j \sin \theta$, which is trigonometric notation for a vector. Since $e^{jx} = \cos x + j \sin x$, we must conclude that e^{jx} is an exponential notation for a unit vector at x radians from zero. For a vector with magnitude ρ at θ degrees from zero, we have

$$\rho e^{j\theta} = \rho(\cos \theta + j \sin \theta)$$

$$= \rho \cos \theta + j\rho \sin \theta$$

Example 2.38. A radar antenna rotates in a counterclockwise direction at a constant angular velocity (ω) of two revolutions per minute. When a point on the antenna three feet from the axis of rotation reaches a position 30° north of east of the center, calculate the north and west components of the velocity of this point. Figure 2.33 pictures the situation.

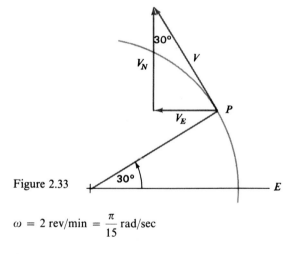

Figure 2.33

$$\omega = 2 \text{ rev/min} = \frac{\pi}{15} \text{ rad/sec}$$

and, from (2.38),

$$V_E = r\omega \sin 30° = 3\left(\frac{\pi}{15}\right)\left(\frac{1}{2}\right)$$

$$= \frac{\pi}{10} = 0.31416 \text{ ft/sec}$$

From (2.39),

$$V_N = r\omega \cos 30° = 3\left(\frac{\pi}{15}\right)(0.866)$$

$$= 0.54413 \text{ ft/sec}$$

Exercise 2.17

1. An automobile tire 30 inches in diameter rotates at 60 revolutions per minute. What is the linear speed of a point on the circumference?
2. If the tire in problem 1 is accelerated 15 revolutions per minute, what is the linear acceleration of a point on the circumference?
3. An armature 24 inches in diameter rotates at a speed of 100 revolutions per minute. What is the linear speed of a point on its circumference?
4. If the armature in problem 3 is accelerated at 10 revolutions per minute, what is the linear acceleration of the point?
5. If the armature in problem 3 turns in a clockwise direction, what are the horizontal and vertical components of the velocity of the point if the point is 50 degrees above the horizontal?
6. An airplane awaiting landing clearance is told to circle the tower at 5000 feet altitude in a counterclockwise direction with a ground radius of 20,000 feet. If the plane at constant velocity makes one complete revolution every 10 minutes, what is the southerly component of its velocity when it is 40° north of west?

2.20 REPEATED DIFFERENTIATION

If $y = 2x^3 + 3x^2 - 12x$, then the first derivative $dy/dx = y' = 6x^2 + 6x - 12$ and the second derivative $d(dy/dx)/dx = d^2y/dx^2 = y'' = 12x + 6$.

Note that the second derivative of a function is the first derivative of the first derivative. So to find the second derivative of a function differentiate the first derivative.

The third derivative $d(d^2y/dx^2)/dx = d^3y/dx^3 = y''' = 12$ and the fourth derivative $d^4y/dx^4 = y'''' = 0$.

The second derivative of $y = 2x^3 + 3x^2 - 12x$ is $y'' = 12x + 6$. The second derivative is the rate of change of slope of the original function.

Reviewing then:

If $y = 2x^3 + 3x^2 - 12x$

then $y' = 6x^2 + 6x$

and $y'' = 12x + 6$

and $y''' = 12$

$y'''' = 0$

Note that we started with a function of x and, by the process of differentiation, a new function of x was defined. Likewise by differentiating y', another function of x was defined, etc.

In Figure 2.34 y, y', y'', y''' have been plotted on separate but related axis systems. Every x-axis scale is identical and each is aligned vertically.

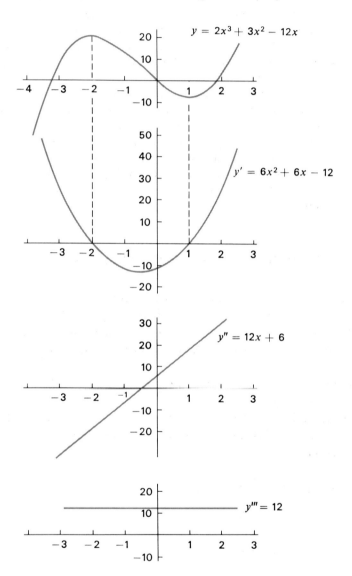

Figure 2.34

Let us focus our attention on the plot of y to the left of $x = -2$. Observation here shows the slope to be positive at any point to the left of $x = -2$. We also see that although the slope is positive to the left of $x = -2$, it is decreasing as we proceed along the curve from left to right approaching $x = -2$.

The plot of y', which is the instantaneous slope of y, to the left of $x = -2$ bears out our observation of the slope of y to the left of $x = -2$. Note that this plot is positive at all points to the left of $x = -2$ and that, as we move along the curve from left to right approaching $x = -2$, it is decreasing in value.

At $x = -2$, y is a maximum and the slope is observed to be zero. Note that at $x = -2$, y' equals zero, and further that y'' at $x = -2$ is negative.

At $x = -2$ we have a critical point because $y' = 0$, y is at a relative maximum, and y'' is negative.

From all of this comes a second method of testing or identifying a critical point. If a critical point occurs at x, substitute this value into the second derivative, and if the sign is negative, y is at a maximum.

As shown here, $x = -2$ is a critical point. Substituting $x = -2$ into the second derivative, $y'' = 12x + 6$, we have

$$y'' = 12(-2) + 6$$

$$= -24 + 6$$

$$= -18$$

Therefore y is a maximum when $x = -2$.

Looking once again to the plots of the functions in question, we note that the slope of y between $x = -2$ and $x = 1$ is negative. In this interval $(-2 < x < 1)$, the plot of y' is negative and the plot of y'' crosses the x axis at $x = -\frac{1}{2}$, indicating a critical point for y' because y'' is the first derivative of y'.

Note then that when y' crosses the x axis, its ordinal value is zero, y is at a minimum, and y'' is positive. From this we expand our testing of critical points. If the critical point occurs at x, substitute this value of into the second derivative y'', and if y'' is positive, y is at a minimum.

We should also note from Figure 2.34 that since y''' is the first derivative of y'', y''' should be the plot of the slope of y''. y''' is constant which is as it should be since y'' is a straight line and straight lines have constant slopes.

At this point we should begin to question what happens when a critical value of x is substituted into the second derivative and the result is zero. That is neither positive nor negative, therefore neither maximum or minimum.

If you guessed that this indicates an inflection point, you are not good at guessing even though the plot of $y = x^3$, $y' = 3x^2$, and $y'' = 6x$ in Figure 2.35 might tend to back up your guess.

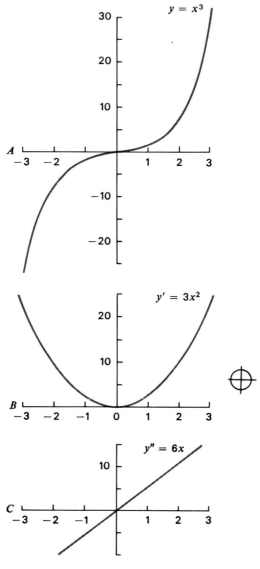

Figure 2.35

Suppose we now try the function $y = x^4$. From this $y' = 4x^3$ and $y'' = 12x^2$. Setting $y' = 0$ we find $x = 0$ is a critical point. Substituting $x = 0$ into $y'' = 12x^2$

produces zero, but a look at Figure 2.36 convinces us that this is not an inflection point but rather a minimum. Thus we see that when a critical value in y'' produces zero, our second derivative system of identifying critical points breaks down and we are forced to go back to substituting values close to and on either side of the critical point into the first derivative.

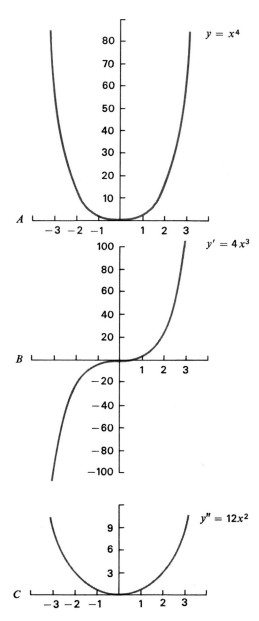

Figure 2.36

To summarize then, substitute a critical value into the second derivative, and if:

y'' is positive, y is at a minimum;

y'' is negative, y is at a maximum,

y'' is zero, go back to y' for identification.

Example 2.39. Locate and identify all critical points of $y = x^3$.

$$y = x^3 \qquad y' = 3x^2 \qquad y'' = 6x$$

Setting $y' = 0 = 3x^2$ produces $x = 0$ as a critical point. Substituting $x = 0$ into $y'' = 6x$ produces $y'' = 0$, and we must go back to the first derivative for identification.

$$x = -0.01 \Rightarrow y' \text{ is } +$$

$$x = 0.00 \Rightarrow y' \text{ is } 0$$

$$x = 0.01 \Rightarrow y' \text{ is } +$$

which shows that $x = 0$ is an inflection point.

Example 2.40. Locate and identify all critical points of $y = x^3 - 3x^2 - 24x - 7$.

If
$$y = x^3 - 3x^2 - 24x - 7$$

then
$$y' = 3x^2 - 6x - 24$$

and
$$y'' - 6x - 6$$

$$\text{Setting } y' = 0 = 3x^2 - 6x - 24$$

$$= 3(x^2 - 2x - 8)$$

$$= 3(x - 4)(x + 2)$$

thus producing the critical points $x = 4$ and $x = -2$. When $x = -2$, $y'' = 6(-2) - 6 = -18$ and a maximum exists. When $x = 4$, $y'' = 6(4) - 6 = +18$ and a minimum exists.

Exercise 2.18. For problems 1 through 15 locate and identify all critical points. For trigonometric functions keep $0 < x < 2\pi$.

1. $y = x^2$
2. $y = 3x^2 + 1$
3. $y = x^3 + 1$
4. $y = 3x^3 + 1$
5. $y = \sin x$
6. $y = \cos x$
7. $y = \frac{1}{3}x^3 + 3x^2 + 9x + 3$
8. $y = \frac{1}{3}x^3 - 4x^2 + 7x + 5$
9. $y = x^3 - 21x^2 + 39x + 2$
10. $y = \sin 2x$

11. $y = \cos 2x$

12. $y = \cos^2 x$

13. $y = 2 \sin x$

14. $y = x^3 - 6x^2 + 9x - 2$

15. $y = 5 - x - x^2$

16. Plot the graph of $y = x^2 - 2x$. Calculate y' and evaluate y' at $x = -1$, 0, 2, 3. What value of x represents a critical point? Identify this critical point. What is the sign of y'' at the critical point?

17. Divide 10 into two parts such that their product is a maximum.

An equation used in angular motion is involved with the second derivative. If angular acceleration is represented by α, we have

$$\alpha = \frac{d}{dt}\omega = \frac{d^2\theta}{dt^2} \tag{2.40}$$

If θ is in radians and t in seconds, then α will be in radians per second per second or rad/sec^2. If θ is in degrees and t is in seconds, then α will be in degrees per second per second or deg/sec^2.

2.21 DIFFERENTIATING IMPLICIT FUNCTIONS

An implicit function is one that may imply that y is a function of x but is not in a form which explicitly states what function y is of x.

Examples of implicit functions:

A. $y - x^2 = 0$

B. $x^2 + y^2 = 16$

C. $4x^2 + 9y^2 = 36$

D. $x^5 - x^2y^3 + y^5 = 0$

Examples A, B, and C can easily be algebraically converted to explicit functions.

A. $y - x^2 = 0 \Rightarrow y = x^2$

B. $x^2 + y^2 = 16 \Rightarrow y = \pm\sqrt{16 - x^2}$

C. $4x^2 + 9y^2 = 36 \Rightarrow y = \pm\dfrac{\sqrt{36 - 4x^2}}{3}$

To differentiate an implicit function we take the derivative of each term, with respect to x. If $y - x^2 = 0$ then differentiating y we get dy/dx, and differentiating $-x^2$ we get $-2x$ and the derivative of zero is zero, so

$$\frac{dy}{dx} - 2x = 0 \qquad \text{or} \qquad \frac{dy}{dx} = 2x$$

which is the derivative of the explicit function $y = x^2$.

Example 2.41. Differentiate the implicit function $x^2 + y^2 = 16$, and check by differentiating the corresponding explicit function $y = \pm\sqrt{16 - x^2}$.

In $x^2 + y^2 = 16$ the first term x^2 differentiates to $2x$. The next term y^2 is a u^n type with $u = y$, $n = 2$, and $du/dx = dy/dx$, so the derivative of y^2 is $2y(dy/dx)$. The last term, 16, has a derivative of zero. Putting this all together we have

$$2x + 2y\frac{dy}{dx} = 0 \qquad 2y\frac{dy}{dx} = -2x$$

from which $dy/dx = -2x/2y = -x/y$, the required derivative.

Checking this answer by differentiating the explicit function $y = \pm\sqrt{16 - x^2}$ $= (16 - x^2)^{\frac{1}{2}}$. Thus we have $y = \pm(16 - x^2)^{\frac{1}{2}}$ which is a u^n type, with $u = 16 - x^2$ and $du/dx = -2x$. Therefore

$$\frac{dy}{dx} = \tfrac{1}{2}(16 - x^2)^{-\frac{1}{2}}(-2x) = \frac{-x}{\pm(16 - x^2)^{\frac{1}{2}}}$$

$$= -x/\pm\sqrt{16 - x^2}$$

and since $y = \pm\sqrt{16 - x^2}$

$$\frac{dy}{dx} = \frac{-x}{y}$$

Example 2.42. Differentiate the implicit function $x^5 - x^2y^3 + y^5 = 0$.

Differentiating term by term, we have:

First term x^5 whose derivative is $5x^4$.

Second term $-x^2y^3$ which is a uv type with $u = -x^2$ and $du/dx = -2x$. $v = y^3$ and $dv/dx = 3y^2\, dy/dx$, so the derivative is $-x^2(3y^2)dy/dx + y^3(-2x)$, which simplifies to $-3x^2y^2dy/dx - 2xy^3$.

The third term y^5 has $5y^4\, dy/dx$ as its derivative. Putting this all together, we have:

$$5x^4 - 3x^2y^2\frac{dy}{dx} - 2xy^3 + 5y^4\frac{dy}{dx} = 0$$

or

$$5y^4\frac{dy}{dx} - 3x^2y^2\frac{dy}{dx} + 5x^4 - 2xy^3 = 0$$

and

$$(5y^4 - 3x^2y^2)\frac{dy}{dx} = 2xy^3 - 5x^4$$

therefore

$$\frac{dy}{dx} = \frac{2xy^3 - 5x^4}{5y^4 - 3x^2y^2}$$

Since the given expression cannot be easily changed into an explicit function, we see the reason for differentiating implicitly term by term.

Example 2.43. Calculate the first derivative of $x^2y + 2y - 3 = 0$.

Here the first term is x^2y, which is a uv type with $u = x^2$ and $du/dx = 2x$; $v = y$ and $dv/dx = dy/dx$. Therefore the first term differentiates to

$$x^2 \frac{dy}{dx} + y2x \qquad \text{or} \qquad x^2 \frac{dy}{dx} + 2xy$$

The second term is $2y$ which differentiates to $2\,dy/dx$. The third term -3 differentiates to zero and the derivative of the right side is zero. Putting all of this together, we have:

$$x^2 \frac{dy}{dx} + 2xy + 2\frac{dy}{dx} = 0$$

or

$$x^2 \frac{dy}{dx} + 2\frac{dy}{dx} = -2xy$$

or

$$(x^2 + 2)\frac{dy}{dx} = -2xy$$

therefore

$$\frac{dy}{dx} = \frac{-2xy}{x^2 + 2}$$

Exercise 2.19. Differentiate each of the following functions.

1. $y^2 = 2x$
2. $(x^2/a^2) + (y^2/b^2) = 1$
3. $xy = a$
4. $(x^2/a^2) - (y^2/b^2) = 1$
5. $[(x^2 + 1)^3 - 6]/7$
6. $[(2/x)^3 + 5]^7$
7. $5x^2 + 3y^2 = 25$
8. $x^2 - y^2 = 10$
9. $y^2 = 15x$
10. $xy - y - 3x = 8$
11. $x^3 + 3y^2 = y$
12. $x^2 + y^3 - 3x^3 = 0$

2.22 DIFFERENTIALS

Thus far we have considered the derivative y' or dy/dx, as a complete entity which is obtained by taking the limit of $\Delta y/\Delta x$ as Δx approaches zero. As we conclude our study of the derivative we look forward to integral calculus and here we will consider dy and dx portions of the derivative as separate entities.

If y is a function of x, $[y = f(x)]$, then the differential dy is defined as

$$dy = \frac{dy}{dx}(dx)$$

where dy is the differential of the dependent variable and dx is the differential of the independent variable. And dy/dx is the derivative of the function.

Example 2.44. Calculate the derivative and the differential of $y = 5x^3 + 3x^2 + x + 1$.

$$y' = \frac{dy}{dx} = 15x^2 + 6x + 1 = \text{the derivative}$$

$$dy = (15x^2 + 6x + 1)\,dx = \text{the differential of } y$$

Example 2.45. Calculate the derivative and the differential of $y = x^2 + C$.

$$y' = \frac{dy}{dx} = 2x = \text{the derivative}$$

$$dy = (2x)\,dx = \text{the differential of } y$$

Exercise 2.20. Calculate the differentials of the following functions.

1. $y = 3x^5 + 7$
2. $y = \frac{1}{2}x^2 + 2$
3. $y = 5x + 5$
4. $y = -3x$
5. $y = 4x^{1/2} + 1$
6. $y = x^2 + \sqrt{2x} + 3$
7. $y = -\frac{1}{4}x^4 + 4$
8. $y = -\frac{1}{8}x^{-8} + 4$
9. $y = 5 \sin \pi$
10. $y = 3 \cos 2x$
11. $y = e^x \sin x$
12. $y = 6\sqrt{x}$
13. $y = \sqrt{6x}$
14. $y = {}^1x + (x/4)$
15. $y = \sin x + \sin 2x$
16. $y = e^x$

2.23 APPLICATIONS

2.23.1 *Electronics*

Example 2.46. Figure 2.37 pictures a dc generator with internal resistance R ohms. Prove maximum power output occurs when the load resistance r equals the internal resistance R. Then calculate the equation for maximum generator output.

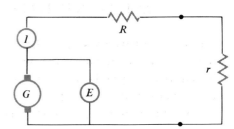

Figure 2.37

Output current

$$i = \frac{E}{R + r}$$

and load power

$$p = i^2 r = \left(\frac{E}{R + r}\right)^2 r = \frac{E^2 r}{R^2 + 2Rr + r^2}$$

Differentiating,

$$\frac{dp}{dr} = \frac{(R^2 + 2Rr + r^2)E^2 - E^2 r(2R + 2r)}{(R^2 + 2Rr + r^2)^2}$$

$$= \frac{E^2 R^2 + 2E^2 Rr + E^2 r^2 - 2E^2 Rr - 2E^2 r^2}{(R^2 + 2Rr + r^2)^2}$$

$$= \frac{E^2 R^2 - E^2 r^2}{(R^2 + 2Rr + r^2)^2} = \frac{E^2(R^2 - r^2)}{(R^2 + 2Rr + r^2)^2}$$

Setting the derivative equal to zero:

$$\frac{E^2(R^2 - r^2)}{(R^2 + 2Rr + r^2)^2} = 0$$

$$E^2(R^2 - r^2) = 0$$

$$R^2 - r^2 = 0$$

$$r^2 = R^2$$

$$r = \pm R$$

From a practical physical standpoint only a positive load resistance is possible, so $r = R$ is a critical value. Going to the second derivative for identification:

$$\frac{d^2 p}{dr^2} = -2E^2 r$$

Therefore, when $r = R$, power is at a maximum.

For maximum generator output when $r = R$:

$$p_{max} = \frac{E^2 R}{R^2 + 2R^2 + R^2} = \frac{E^2 R}{4R^2} = \frac{E^2}{4R}$$

Example 2.47. The mutual inductance between two coils is 4 henrys and the current at coil 1 is $i = 2t^2 - t^3$ amp. Calculate the time the induced emf e_2 will have its greatest negative value, e_2, i_1 when e_2 is at a minimum.

$$e_2 = -M\frac{di}{dt} = -4(4t - 3t^2) = -16t + 12t^2 \text{ volts}$$

Differentiating, $de_2/dt = -16 + 24t$ volts per second.

Setting this equal to zero:

$$-16 + 24t = 0$$

$$8(3t - 2) = 0$$

$$3t - 2 = 0$$

$$3t = 2$$

$$t = \tfrac{2}{3} \text{ second}$$

Calculating the second derivative for identification purposes:

$$\frac{d^2e_2}{dr^2} = 24$$

which indicates a minimum.

$$e_{2\,min} = 12(\tfrac{2}{3})^2 - 16(\tfrac{2}{3}) = -\tfrac{16}{3} \text{ volts}$$

Finally $i_1 = 2t^2 - t^3$

$$= 2(\tfrac{2}{3})^2 - (\tfrac{2}{3})^3 = \tfrac{16}{27} \text{ amp when } t = \tfrac{2}{3}$$

Example 2.48. Figure 2.38 shows a series RL circuit in parallel with a capacitance C. If the angular frequency $\omega = 2\pi f$, then the impedance of the circuit is:

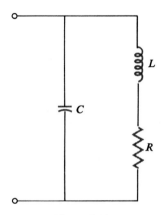

Figure 2.38

$$Z = \frac{\sqrt{R^2 + \omega^2 L}}{\sqrt{\omega^2 C^2 R^2 + (\omega^2 LC - 1)^2}} \text{ ohms}$$

When L and R are constant, what capacitance will make Z a maximum?

$$Z = (R^2 + \omega^2 L)^{1\!/\!2}[\omega^2 C^2 R^2 + (\omega^2 LC - 1)^2]^{-1\!/\!2}$$

And differentiating,

$$\frac{dz}{dc} = -(R^2 + \omega^2 L^2)^{1\!/\!2}[\omega^2 C^2 R^2 + (\omega^2 LC - 1)^2]^{-3\!/\!2}$$

$$(\omega^2 R^2 C + \omega^4 L^2 C - \omega L)$$

Equating the derivative to zero and dividing by

$$-\omega^2(R^2 + \omega^2 L^2)^{1\!/\!2}[\omega^2 C^2 R^2 + (\omega^2 LC - 1)^2]^{-3\!/\!2}$$

we have
$$R^2 C + \omega^2 L^2 C - L = 0$$

and
$$C = \frac{1}{R^2 + \omega^2 L^2} \text{ farads}$$

This is a critical value and, although it is possible to test for maximum or minimum, it is quite lengthy and we should know that the impedance in a circuit of this nature has a pronounced maximum with no minimum or inflection.

Example 2.49. Figure 2.39*a* illustrates a circuit with an inductive reactance X_L and resistance R in series. Figure 2.39*b* shows the impedance phase angle α in the vector diagram. Figure 2.39*c* shows the sinusoidal waves for *e* and *i*. Find di/dt.

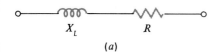

(a)

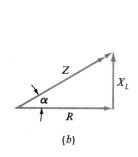

(b)

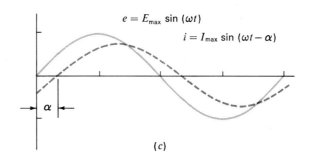

(c)

Figure 2.39

Since
$$i = I_{max} \sin (\omega t - \alpha)$$

$$\frac{di}{dt} = I_{max} \left[\cos (\omega t - \alpha) \right] \omega$$

$$= \omega(I_{max}) \cos (\omega t - \alpha)$$

2.23.2 *Beams*

Total or maximum deflection in a beam is of extreme importance in the design of machines and structures. A sample problem will illustrate what is involved.

Figure 2.40 pictures a simple beam with a uniformly distributed load. Here R_1 and R_2 are the end reactions, l is the free span, x is the distance to any point from the left end, y is the deflection at any point, and w is the load per unit length. Thus the total load $W = wl$.

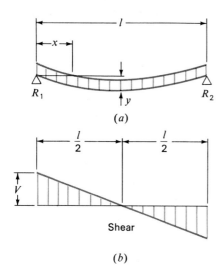

(a)

(b)

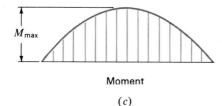

Moment

(c)   Figure 2.40

Since this is a simple, uniformly loaded beam

$$R_1 = R_2 = \frac{wl}{2}$$

and the deflection

$$y = \frac{wx}{24EI}(l^3 - 2lx^2 + x^3)$$

or

$$y = \frac{wl^3}{24EI}(x) - \frac{2wl}{24EI}(x)^3 + \frac{w}{24EI}(x)^4$$

and

$$\frac{dy}{dx} = \frac{wl^3}{24EI} - \frac{6wl}{24EI}(x)^2 + \frac{4w}{24EI}(x)^3$$

Equating this first derivative to zero and multiplying through by $24EI/w$, we have:

$$4x^3 - 6l + l^3 = 0$$

from which $x = l/2$. Thus $l/2$ is a critical point. Substituting $x = l/2$ into the deflection formula, we have

$$y_{max} = \frac{wl/2}{24EI}\left[l^3 - 2l\left(\frac{l}{2}\right)^2 + \left(\frac{l}{3}\right)^3\right]$$

$$= \frac{wl}{48EI}\left(\frac{8l^3}{8} - \frac{4l^3}{8} + \frac{l^3}{8}\right)$$

$$= \frac{wl}{48EI}\left(\frac{5l^3}{8}\right) = \frac{5wl^4}{384EI}$$

From all of this then total deflection (y_{max}) can be calculated and it will occur at $l/2$ or midspan. In the foregoing formula E is the modulus of elasticity, a constant for the material used, and I is the moment of inertia, a constant for the cross-sectional shape of the beam. Moment of inertia will be considered later in a separate section.

In Figure 2.40b a shear diagram for this beam is plotted. The shear V at any point x is

$$V_x = w\left(\frac{l}{2} - x\right)$$

Thus we see the shear will be zero when $x = l/2$ and $wl/2$ or maximum when $x = 0$, and $-wl/2$ or minimum when $x = l$.

Figure 2.40c shows the moment diagram for this beam. The moment at any point x is

$$M_x = \frac{wx}{2}(l - x)$$

To determine maximum moment we differentiate the equation for M_x. Since

$$M_x = \frac{wl}{2}(x) - \frac{w}{2}(x^2)$$

and $\quad \dfrac{d(M_x)}{dx} = \dfrac{wl}{2} - wx$

equating to zero and dividing through by w yields $(l/s) - x = 0$, so $x = l/2$. Thus $x = l/2$ is a critical point. Substituting $x = l/2$ into the equation for M_x, we have

$$M_{max} = \frac{w(l/2)}{2}\left(l - \frac{l}{2}\right)$$

$$= \frac{wl}{4}\left(\frac{2l}{2} - \frac{l}{2}\right) = \frac{wl}{4}\left(\frac{l}{2}\right)$$

$$= \frac{wl^2}{8}$$

Example 2.50. For the simple beam, uniformly loaded, as pictured in Figure 2.41a, calculate maximum deflection y, total shear V, R_1, and R_2. Plot a shear diagram, a moment diagram, and calculate maximum moment. Let $E = 28 \cdot 10^6$, $I = 40$, $w = 25$ pounds per foot, and $l = 20$ feet.

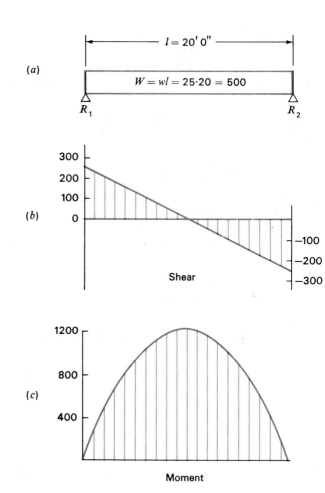

(a)

$l = 20'\,0"$

$W = wl = 25 \cdot 20 = 500$

R_1 R_2

(b)

Shear

(c)

Moment

Figure 2.41

$$R_1 = R_2 = \frac{wl}{2} = \frac{(25)(20)}{2} = 250 \text{ lb}$$

$$V_{max} = w\left(\frac{l}{2} - 0\right) = 25(10) = 250$$

$$V_{min} = w\left(\frac{l}{2} - l\right) = 25(-10) = -250$$

The shear diagram is pictured in Figure 2.41*b*.

$$y_{max} = \frac{5wl^4}{384EI} = \frac{5(25)(20)^4}{384(28)10^6(40)} = 0.00093 \text{ in.}$$

$$M_{max} = \frac{wl^2}{8} = \frac{25(20)20}{8} = 1250 \text{ lb-ft}$$

To plot the moment curve shown in Figure 2.41*c*, we make a chart of values.

x	$M = \dfrac{25x}{2}(20 - x)$
0	0
2	450
4	800
6	1050
8	1200
10	1250
12	1200
14	1050
16	800
18	450
20	0

Figure 2.42*a* pictures a cantilever beam with a uniformly distributed load of *w* pounds per unit length. For this beam $R = V = wl$; shear at any point *x*: $V_x = -wx$; moment at any point *x*: $M_x = -wx^2/2$. Deflection *y* is defined as

$$y = \frac{w}{24EI}(x^4 - 4l^3x + 3l^4)$$

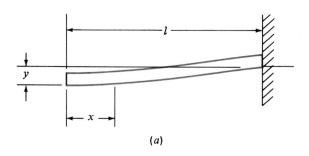

(*a*)

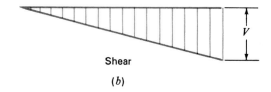

Shear

(*b*)

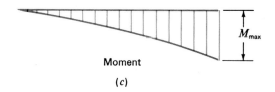

Moment

(*c*)

Figure 2.42

Example 2.51. For the beam in Figure 2.42*a*, calculate equations for M_{max}, y_{max}, and plot the shear and moment diagrams.

The shear diagram is plotted by calculating shear values as shown below. For the diagram itself see Figure 2.42*b*.

x	0	$l/8$	$l/4$	$l/2$	l
$V_x = -wx$	0	$-wl/8$	$-wl/4$	$-wl/2$	$-wl$

The moment diagram is plotted by calculating moment values as shown below. See Figure 2.42*c* for the moment diagram.

x	0	$l/8$	$l/4$	$l/2$	l
$M_x = -wx^2/2$	0	$-wl^2/128$	$-wl^2/32$	$-wl^2/8$	$-wl^2/2$

Since
$$y = \frac{w}{24EI}(x^4 - 4l^3 + 3l^4)$$

$$= \frac{w}{24EI}(x^4) - \frac{4wl^3}{24EI}(x) + \frac{3wl^4}{24EI}$$

and
$$y' = \frac{4w}{24EI}(x^3) - \frac{4wl^3}{24EI}$$

setting the first derivative to zero, we have

$$\frac{4w}{24EI}(x^3) - \frac{4wl^3}{24EI} = 0$$

and $4wx^3 = 4wl^3$, so $x^3 = l^3$, and $x = l$. Thus $x = l$ is a critical point. A look at Figure 2.42a shows that when $x = l$ the deflection will be zero, so when $x = l$ we have a minimum. Substituting l into the equation for y, we have

$$y_{min} = \frac{w}{24EI}(l^4 - 4l^4 + 3l^4)$$

$$= \frac{w}{24EI}(0) = 0$$

Figure 2.42a indicates that maximum deflection will occur at the extreme tip of the beam, when $x = 0$. When $x = 0$,

$$y_{max} = \frac{w}{24EI}[0 - 4l^3(0) + 3l^4]$$

$$= \frac{3wl^4}{24EI}$$

$$= \frac{wl^4}{8EI}$$

To check into this maximum deflection when $x = 0$, let us calculate the second derivative, y''.

If
$$y' = \frac{4w}{24EI}(x^3) - \frac{4wl^3}{24EI}$$

then
$$y'' = \frac{12w}{24EI}(x^2) = \frac{wx^2}{2EI}$$

Equating y'' to zero, we have $wx^2/2EI = 0$, and $x = 0$.

Here the second derivative test fails because y'' will be zero when $x = 0$. We cannot test the first derivative at $x = 0$ because no points to the left of $x = 0$ have any physical meaning. We therefore must either observe from the physical situation that deflection will be maximum when $x = 0$, or we must plot the deflection curve and make an observation there. The following chart is used to plot the deflection curve shown in Figure 2.43.

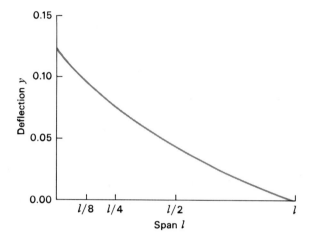

Figure 2.43

x	y
l	0.000
$l/2$	0.0442 (wl^4/EI)
$l/4$	0.0834 (wl^4/EI)
$l/8$	0.1040 (wl^4/EI)
0	0.1250 (wl^4/EI)

Checking for maximum moment we differentiate the equation for $M = -(w/2)x^2$.

$$\frac{dM}{dx} = -\frac{2w}{2}x = -wx$$

Equating dM/dx to zero we have $-wx = 0$, and $x = 0$ is a critical point. From Figure 2.42c the moment is zero when $x = 0$, which is a maximum. When $x = l$, moment is at a minimum. Once again the practical physical

situation tells us that no one would be concerned about zero moment, so for
maximum moment, even though it is negative, we conclude:

$$M_{max} = -\frac{wl^2}{2}$$

Exercise 2.21

1. During a given interval the current in a resistor of R ohms is $i = t^3/3 - t$
   amp. At what time t will the current flowing through the resistor be at a
   minimum?
2. After what time will the power in the resistor in problem 1 be at a maximum?
3. Calculate the maximum current in a 10-microfarad capacitor if the applied
   voltage varies according to: $e = 250t^2 - 200t^3$.
4. If the charge in a circuit varies according to $q = 4t^4 - t^3$ coulombs, when
   will the current be at a maximum?
5. What would be the maximum induced voltage if a 10-henry inductor is
   put into the circuit in problem 4?
6. Given the fixed-end beam with uniformly distributed load as pictured in
   Figure 2.44, and given $R_1 = R_2 = V = wl/2$, $V_x = w[(l/2) - x]$, $M_x = (w/12)(6lx - l^2 - 6x^2)$, and $y = (wx^2/24EI)(l - x)^2$, plot the shear and
   moment diagrams and prove that $M_{max} = wl^2/12$ and occurs at the ends.
   Also prove that maximum deflection $y = (wl^4)/38EI$ and that it occurs
   at the center.

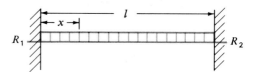

Figure 2.44

7. Given the cantilever beam with load increasing uniformly to the fixed end
   as pictured in Figure 2.45, and given $R = V = W$, $V_x = Wx^2/l^2$, $M_x = Wx^3/3l^2$, and $y = (W/60EIl^2)(x^5 - 5l^4x + 4l^5)$, plot shear and moment
   diagrams and prove that $M_{max} = Wl/3$ and occurs at the fixed end. Also
   prove that maximum deflection $y = Wl^3/15EI$ and occurs at the free end.

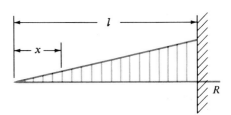

Figure 2.45

TABLE OF DERIVATIVES

If $y = kx^n + C \Rightarrow y' = nkx^{n-1}$

If $y = u + v \Rightarrow y' = du/dx + dv/dx$

If $y = ku^n + C \Rightarrow y' = nku^{n-1}\, du/dx$

If $y = k \sin x + C \Rightarrow y' = k \cos x$

If $y = k \cos x + C \Rightarrow y' = -k \sin x$

If $y = k \sin u + C \Rightarrow y' = k \cos u\, du/dx$

If $y = k \cos u + C \Rightarrow y' = -k \sin u\, du/dx$

If $y = k \tan u + C \Rightarrow y' = k \sec^2 u\, du/dx$

If $y = k \cot u + C \Rightarrow y' = k \csc^2 u\, du/dx$

If $y = uv \Rightarrow u\, dv/dx + v\, du/dx$

If $y = u/v \Rightarrow y' = \dfrac{v\, du/dx - u\, dv/dx}{v^2}$

If $y = ke^x + C \Rightarrow y' = ke^x$

If $y = ke^u + C \Rightarrow y' = ke^u\, du/dx$

If $y = ke^{-x} + C \Rightarrow y' = -ke^{-x}$

If $y = k \ln x + C \Rightarrow y' = k/x$

If $y = k \log x + C \Rightarrow y' = 0.4343k/x$

If $y = k \ln u + C \Rightarrow y' = k/u\, du/dx$

If $y = ka^u + C \Rightarrow y' = ka^u\, (du/dx) \ln a$

REVIEW PROBLEMS

1. Explain in your own words what the average slope of a curve is.

2. Explain in your own words the instantaneous slope of a curve.

3. Outline the delta method for calculating the average slope of a curve.

4. What is the difference between the instantaneous slope of a curve and the first derivative of the equation of that curve?

5. Name the first derivative of the first derivative of a function.

6. Explain how to calculate the instantaneous slope from the average slope.

7. $\lim\limits_{x \to 3} \dfrac{25}{27 - x^3} = ?$

8. $\lim\limits_{x \to 1} \dfrac{5}{1 + x} = ?$

9. $\lim\limits_{x \to 0} x + \dfrac{4}{x} = ?$

10. Locate and identify all critical points of $y = 2x^2$.

11. Locate and identify all critical points of $y = x/(x + 3)$.

12. Locate and identify all critical points of $y = 6\sqrt{x}$.

13. What do all critical points have in common?

14. If $y = 2 \sin x$, what is the instantaneous slope at $x = \pi/2$? At $x = \pi$? At $x = 2\pi$?

15. If $y = (\sin 2x)/x$, what is the instantaneous slope at $x = \pi/2$?

16. Given the function $y = -x^3 + 3x^2 + 24x + 7$, calculate y', y'', and y'''. Plot y, y', y'', and y''' as done in Figure 2.34.

17. In problem 16, what is the slope of y at $x = 1, 2, 3, -2$?

18. Differentiate the implicit function $3xy - y^2 + 3x^3 = 7$.

19. Differentiate the implicit function $y^3 + 5xy - x^2 = y$.

20. Explain the difference between a derivative and the instantaneous slope and a differential.

3 Integral Calculus

In this unit we shall endeavor to find the area under a curve by mathematical methods. This process is called *integration.* Integration is the inverse operation of differentiation. Thus finding the function from whence a given derivative came is really defining integration. Recall that differentiation is a precise mathematical process. Integration for the most part will be a process of remembering what we know about differentiation. Integration is sometimes referred to as the "anti-derivative."

As has been previously stated we shall be concerned here only with real variables. The functions we use shall be single valued and continuous.

3.1 THE INDEFINITE INTEGRAL

From example 2.4, Section 2.5, recall that if $y = 5x^3 \Rightarrow dy/dx = y' = 15x^2$. For this new inverse operation (antiderivative), we say that if $y' = 15x^2 \Rightarrow y = 5x^3 + C$. Note that since an additive constant in the original function disappears after differentiation, we have no idea about this constant when integrating, so we must recognize that it might exist by including it as the C.

In mathematical symbolism, then, if $y' = dy/dx = 15x^2$, or $dy = 15x^2\,dx$, then $\int dy = y$, and $\int 15x^2\,dx = 5x^3 + C$.

Since, as we have already said, we are not sure about this constant, we say the process is *indefinite* and thus the symbol $\int$ is called the *indefinite integral sign.*

3.2 THE INTEGRAL OF $kx^n\,dx$

Instead of trying to analyze each and every integration problem, we shall set up rules for certain types, much as we did in differentiating. We see then from $dy/dx = 15x^2$ that $dy = kx^n\,dx$ is a type. If $dy = kx^n\,dx$ is the type, then $\int dy = \int kx^n\,dx$, and $y = kx^{n+1}/(n+1) + C$, where $n \neq -1$. From this then:

$$\int kx^n\,dx = \frac{kx^{n+1}}{n+1} + C \tag{3.1}$$

where $n \neq -1$.

Example 3.1. Integrate $3x^4 \, dx$.

$$\int 3x^4 \, dx = 3 \int x^4 \, dx = \frac{3x^5}{5} + C$$

Note from the above that the multiplicative constant may be moved across the integral sign with no effect on the result. Note further that we may check our answer by differentiating $y = \frac{3}{5}x^5 + C$. If

$$y = \tfrac{3}{5}x^5 + C \Rightarrow \frac{dy}{dx} = 3x^4$$

Example 3.2. Integrate $15x^{-4}$.

$$\int 15x^{-4} \, dx = 15 \int x^{-4} \, dx = \frac{15x^{-3}}{-3} + C$$

$$= -5x^{-3} + C$$

$$= \frac{-5}{x^3} + C$$

Checking: If $y = -(5/x^3) + C = -5x^{-3} + C$, then

$$\frac{dy}{dx} = y' = 15x^{-4}$$

We mentioned above that a multiplicative constant could be moved across the integral sign, but now we must add that this constant must multiply *every* term just as when a constant is factored from a polynomial. Thus:

$$\int (5x^3 + 15x^2 + 10x) \, dx = \int 5(x^3 + 3x^2 + 2x) \, dx$$

$$= 5 \int (x^3 + 3x^2 + 2x) \, dx$$

and

$$\int (12x^4 + 18x^3) \, dx = \int 6(2x^4 + 3x^3) \, dx$$

$$= 6 \int (2x^4 + 3x^3) \, dx$$

It should further be noted that the multiplicative constant *may* be moved across the integral sign, *but* it is not mandatory!

$$\int 5x^3 \, dx = \frac{5x^4}{4} + C$$

and $\qquad 5 \int x^3 \, dx = 5\frac{x^4}{4} + C = \frac{5x^4}{4} + C$

Exercise 3.1. Calculate the indefinite integral of each of the following. Check each by differentiating your answer.

1. $x^2\, dx$
2. $5x^{2/3}\, dx$
3. $3x^2\, dx$
4. $2x^{5/3}\, dx$
5. $2x^{-1/2}\, dx$
6. $\frac{1}{8}x^{-8/5}\, dx$
7. dx
8. dy
9. $-10\, dx$
10. $4\sqrt[3]{x^2}\, dx$
11. $2x\, dx$
12. $10\, dx$
13. $x^{1/3}\, dx$
14. $-dx$
15. $x\, dx$
16. $-x\, dx$
17. $3x^{-1/3}\, dx$
18. $\frac{1}{3}\sqrt{x}\, dx$
19. $-(2/3)\sqrt[3]{x^2}\, dx$
20. $(5/x^5)\, dx$

Since we have shown previously that the derivative of a sum is the sum of the derivatives, it must follow that the integral of a sum is the sum of the integrals. That is,

$$\int (3x^2 + 2x + 5)\, dx = \int 3x^2\, dx + \int 2x\, dx + \int 5\, dx$$

$$= \tfrac{3}{3}x^3 + C_1 + \tfrac{2}{2}x^2 + C_2 + 5x + C_3$$

$$= x^3 + x^2 + 5x + C$$

where $C = C_1 + C_2 + C_3$.

Checking: If $y = x^3 + x^2 + 5x + C \Rightarrow y' = 3x^2 + 2x + 5$. From this then:

$$\int (kx^n \pm Kx^m)\, dx = \int kx^n\, dx \pm \int Kx^m\, dx + C \qquad (3.2)$$

3.3 THE CONSTANT OF INTEGRATION

The constant of integration shows up as a result of the use of the indefinite integral and has the effect of raising or lowering the graph of the function but does not affect its shape.

Example 3.3. Calculate $\int 2x\, dx$. Assume some values for C and plot.

$$\int 2x\, dx = 2\int x\, dx$$

$$= \tfrac{2}{2}x^2 + C$$

$$= x^2 + C$$

Thus $y = x^2 + C$ and by assuming some values for C we obtain the plots shown in Figure 3.1. $y_0 = x^2 + 0$; $y_1 = x^2 + 1$; $y_2 = x^2 + 5$; $y_3 = x^2 - 3$.

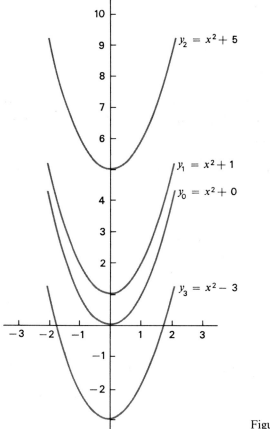

$y_2 = x^2 + 5$

$y_1 = x^2 + 1$

$y_0 = x^2 + 0$

$y_3 = x^2 - 3$

Figure 3.1

From the plots in Figure 3.1 we see that the shapes are identical in every instance and the only effect the constant of integration has is to move the curve up or down. The slope of all of the curves would be identical for any given value of x.

For the most part then the constant of integration will be of little importance to us except that whenever we take the indefinite integral we *must* indicate the constant or we run the risk of forgetting that it exists. Do not lose sight of the fact that even when $C = 0$ it exists with a value of zero.

There are times when the constant of integration is important to us. To evaluate the constant of integration some additional information must be given.

Example 3.4.   Determine y, if $dy/dx = 2x$ and $x = 2$ when $y = 5$.

$$\int dy = \int 2x \, dx$$

$$y = x^2 + C$$

When $x = 2$, $y = 5$, so $5 = (2)^2 + C$

$$5 = 4 + C$$

$$1 = C$$

Thus the required $y = x^2 + 1$.

Finally, although we will not prove it, we must state that the process of integration is unique, that is, only $\int 2x\, dx$ produces $x^2 + C$ and the results of integrating $2x\, dx$ can vary only by at most the constant C.

> **Exercise 3.2.** In each case determine the exact function y, including the value of the constant of integration.
>
> 1. $dy/dx = 3x^2$ and $y = 0$ when $x = 1$.
> 2. $dy/dx = 5$ and $y = 5$ when $x = -1$.
> 3. $dy/dx = x^{1/3}$ and $y = 12$ when $x = 8$.
> 4. $dy/dx = 3x^{-1/2}$ and $y = 0$ when $x = 4$.
> 5. $dy/dx = 2x$ and $y = 4$ when $x = 2$.
> 6. $dy/dx = 5x^4 + 3x^2$ and $y = 2$ when $x = 1$.
> 7. $dy/dx = 2x^{-1/3}$ and $y = 14$ when $x = 8$.
> 8. $dy/dx = 3x^{-1/4}$ and $y = 34$ when $x = 16$.
> 9. Why do you think (3.1) stipulates that n may not equal -1?

3.4 THE INTEGRAL OF $ku^n\, du$

Most everyone at this point could easily predict the rule for the integral of $ku^n\, du$, but very few find the rule easy to apply.

$$\int ku^n\, du = \frac{ku^{n+1}}{n+1} \mid C, \qquad n \neq -1 \tag{3.3}$$

Let us understand (3.3) before we try an example. According to (3.3), if u is a function of x and this function of x is raised to a power n, and du is the *exact* derivative of u, then and only then the integral equals the function u raised to the $n + 1$ power with all divided by $n + 1$. Naturally the constant of integration shows up and n may not equal -1. All will agree that this seems straightforward and relatively simple, and it is if each requirement is *exactly* and *completely* met. Let us try an example with some comments.

> **Example 3.5.** Suppose we start with a function $y = [(x^3/3) + (x^2/2) + x]^3$. Now let us find the derivative of this function. It is of the type $y = u^n$, so
>
> $$\frac{dy}{dx} = 3\left(\frac{x^3}{3} + \frac{x^2}{2} + x\right)^2 (x^2 + x + 1)$$
>
> where $u = (x^3/3) + (x^2/2) + x$, and $du/dx = x^2 + x + 1$.

Since integration is the inverse of differentiation or the "antiderivative," let us now integrate.

$$y = 3 \int \left(\frac{x^3}{3} + \frac{x^2}{2} + x \right)^2 (x^2 + x + 1)\, dx$$

Here we find $n = 2$, $u = (x^3/3) + (x^2/2) + x$, $du = (x^2 + x + 1)$. So

$$y = \frac{3\left(\dfrac{x^3}{3} + \dfrac{x^2}{2} + x \right)^3}{3} + C$$

$$= \left(\frac{x^3}{3} + \frac{x^2}{2} + x \right)^3 + C$$

This still seems quite straightforward with little opportunity for trouble, but perhaps this was because we knew the answer. Let us now change the problem slightly and observe the process again.

Example 3.6.   Integrate

$$y = \int \left(\frac{x^3}{3} + \frac{x^2}{2} + x \right)^2 (6x^2 + 6x + 6)\, dx$$

Here $u = (x^3/3) + (x^2/2) + x$, and $du = (x^2 + x + 1)\, dx$. Obviously $6x^2 + 6x + 6 = 6(x^2 + x + 1)$ is not du/dx; however, only the multiple of 6 is the difference, so if we divide by 6 we will have du exactly, but we have no right to divide by 6 unless we compensate by multiplying by 6. This then yields:

$$y = 6 \int \left(\frac{x^3}{3} + \frac{x^2}{2} + x \right)^2 \frac{6}{6}(x^2 + x + 1)\, dx$$

$$= 6 \int \left(\frac{x^3}{3} + \frac{x^2}{2} + x \right)^2 (x^2 + x + 1)$$

$$\frac{6\left(\dfrac{x^3}{3} + \dfrac{x^2}{2} + x \right)^3}{3} + C$$

$$= 2\left(\frac{x^3}{3} + \frac{x^2}{2} + x \right)^3 + C$$

Since we did not know the answer in advance we differentiate to check.

$$y = 2\left(\frac{x^3}{3} + \frac{x^2}{2} + x \right)^3 + C$$

so
$$y' = 3 \cdot 2\left(\frac{x^3}{3} + \frac{x^2}{2} + x \right)^2 (x^2 + x + 1)$$

and
$$dy = 6\left(\frac{x^3}{3} + \frac{x^2}{2} + x\right)^2 (x^2 + x + 1)\, dx$$

$$= \left(\frac{x^3}{3} + \frac{x^2}{2} + x\right)^2 (6x^2 + 6x + 6)\, dx$$

Obviously our integration was correct.

Let us now go back to our original problem, trying a solution without knowing the answer.

Example 3.7.   Integrate

$$\left(\frac{x^3}{3} + \frac{x^2}{2} + x\right)^2 3(x^2 + x + 1)\, dx$$

Not knowing the answer here we must assume the multiple 3 goes with the *du*. Closer observation shows this multiple makes the *du* three times too large. To get rid of the multiple 3 we divide by 3 and compensate by multiplying by 3, thus arriving at the correct solution.

$$y = 3 \int \left(\frac{x^3}{3} + \frac{x^2}{2} + x\right)^2 \frac{3}{3}(x^2 + x + 1)\, dx$$

$$= 3 \int \left(\frac{x^3}{3} + \frac{x^2}{2} + x\right)^2 (x^2 + x + 1)\, dx$$

The concepts involved in integrating

$$\left(\frac{x^3}{3} + \frac{x^2}{2} + x\right)^2 3(x^2 + x + 1)\, dx$$

are sometimes easier to understand if the problem is attacked in this manner:

Let
$$u = \frac{x^3}{3} + \frac{x^2}{2} + x$$

then $du = (x^2 + x + 1)\, dx$ and our problem can now be written

$$3 \int u^2\, du$$

which produces
$$3\frac{u^3}{3} = u^3 + C$$

But when we substitute the value of *u* we get:

$$3 \int u^2\, du = u^3 + C = \left(\frac{x^3}{3} + \frac{x^2}{2} + x\right)^3 + C$$

Example 3.8.   Calculate *y* if:

$$\frac{dy}{dx} = \frac{x + 1}{\sqrt{x^2 + 2x}}$$

$$y = \int \frac{(x + 1)}{(x^2 + 2x)^{\frac{1}{2}}} dx$$

$$= \int (x^2 + 2x)^{-\frac{1}{2}} (x + 1) dx$$

Here $u = x^2 + 2x$, and $du/dx = 2x + 2 = 2(x + 1)$, therefore

$$y = \frac{1}{2} \int (x^2 + 2x)^{-\frac{1}{2}} 2(x + 1) dx$$

$$= \frac{1}{2} \int (x^2 + 2x)^{-\frac{1}{2}} (2x + 2) dx$$

$$= \frac{\frac{1}{2}(x^2 + 2x)^{\frac{1}{2}}}{\frac{1}{2}} + C$$

$$= (x^2 + 2x)^{\frac{1}{2}} + C$$

$$y = \sqrt{x^2 + 2x} + C$$

Check:

$$y' = \frac{1}{2}(x^2 + 2x)^{-\frac{1}{2}}(2x + 2)$$

$$= (x^2 + 2x)^{-\frac{1}{2}} \frac{1}{2}(2)(x + 1)$$

$$= \frac{x + 1}{(x^2 + 2x)^{\frac{1}{2}}}$$

$$= \frac{x + 1}{\sqrt{x^2 + 2x}}$$

Exercise 3.3.   Integrate the following. Check by differentiation.

1. dx/x^6

2. $5x^4(2 - x^5)^5 \, dx$

3. $x\sqrt{2x^2 + 1} \, dx$

4. $(x \, dx)/(x^2 + 100)^2$

5. $(x^3 \, dx)/\sqrt{200x^4 + 2}$

6. $(\phi^2 \, d\phi)/\sqrt{\pi - \phi^3}$

7. $(3 - x)^4 \, dx$

8. $(4 - x)^{\frac{1}{2}} \, dx$

9. $x^3(3 - x^4)^5 \, dx$

10. $(y + 1)/(y^2 + 2y)^{\frac{1}{2}} \, dy$

11. $15x(4x^2 - 9)^{\frac{3}{2}} \, dx$

12. $(3 - 5y)^{-6} \, dy$

13. $(4\phi - 1)^{\frac{1}{2}} \, d\phi$

14. $(x^3 \, dx)/(2 - x^4)^6$

15. $(x - 3)(x^2 - 6x - 7)^{\frac{1}{2}} \, dx$

16. $(x^2 - 3)(x^2 - 6x - 7)^{\frac{1}{2}} \, dx$

3.5 THE AREA UNDER A CURVED LINE

We have already found that if we desire to find the area under a curve we can plot the graph of the function in question and then count square units. It is obvious that this is not satisfactory and that a precise mathematical method should be sought. Let us look at Figure 3.2 where $y = \frac{1}{2}x$, is plotted. Suppose we wish to calculate the area under $y = \frac{1}{2}x$ between $x = 1$ and $x = 5$. This area is obviously 6, but let us proceed using the ideas of calculus.

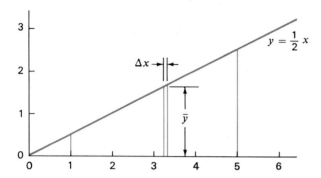

Figure 3.2

We set up a thin elemental strip Δx wide, $\bar{y}$ long, and calculate the area of this strip:

$$A = \bar{y}(\Delta x)$$

from which $A/\Delta x = \bar{y}$, and if we now take the limit of this expression as Δx approaches zero, we have $dA/dx = y$ or $dA = y\,dx$.

From this we assert a basic principle of calculus: *The ordinate of a graph equals the rate of change of the area under the graph.* We still do not have an equation for calculating the area under a graph, but we do have an equation for the rate of change of the area. If we now take this equation and apply our knowledge of integration, we have $dA = y\,dx$ and $\int dA = \int y\,dx$, therefore $A = \int y\,dx$.

We now have an equation involving area. In our problem from Figure 3.2, then:

Example 3.9

$$A = \int y\,dx$$

$$= \frac{1}{2}\int x\,dx$$

$$= \frac{x^2}{4} + C$$

All that remains now is to evaluate the constant of integration and we will have the equation that will produce the area we seek. There are two approaches to evaluating the constant of integration. We shall illustrate both.

Looking to Figure 3.2 we see that when $x = 0$, no area is involved, so $A = 0$ and $0 = (0/4) + C$, therefore $C = 0$ and $A = (x^2/4) + 0 = (x^2/4)$. Now that we have evaluated C when $x = 0$, we can calculate the area between $x = 0$

and $x = 5$, then the area between $x = 0$ and $x = 1$, and then take the difference of these area for the required area between $x = 1$ and $x = 5$.

$$C = 0,\ x = 0,\ \underset{0 \to 5}{A} = \frac{5^2}{4} + 0$$

$$= \tfrac{25}{4} = 6.25$$

$$\underset{0 \to 1}{A} = \frac{1^2}{4} + 0$$

$$= \tfrac{1}{4} = 0.25$$

$$\underset{1 \to 5}{A} = \underset{0 \to 5}{A} - \underset{0 \to 1}{A} = 6.25 - 0.25 = 6.00$$

Another approach is to observe that when $x = 1$ none of the area with which we are concerned has been touched, so $A = 0$. When $x = 1$, $0 = (1^2/4) + C$, therefore $C = -\tfrac{1}{4}$, and

$$\underset{1 \to 5}{A} = (5^2/4) - \tfrac{1}{4}$$

$$= \tfrac{25}{4} - \tfrac{1}{4}$$

$$= \tfrac{24}{4} = 6.00$$

Note that in each instance C is evaluated at the left limit of the area in question, and this C is used in the equation for the area using the x of the right limit of the area.

Example 3.10.   Calculate the area under $x = \tfrac{1}{8}y^2$, between $x = 1$ and $x = 9$. The plot of the graph of $x = \tfrac{1}{8}y^2$ is given in Figure 3.3.

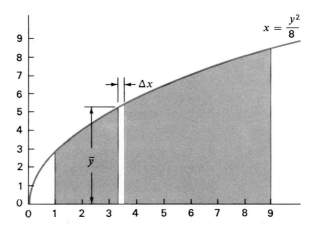

Figure 3.3

Here $A = \int y\,dx$ and $y = \sqrt{8x}$, so $A = \int \sqrt{8x}\,dx$.

$$A = 2\int \sqrt{2x}\,dx$$

$$= 2\int (2x)^{\frac{1}{2}}\,dx$$

$$= 2\sqrt{2}\int x^{\frac{1}{2}}\,dx$$

$$= \frac{2\sqrt{2}\,x^{\frac{3}{2}}}{3/2} + C$$

$$= \frac{4\sqrt{2}\,x^{\frac{3}{2}}}{3} + C$$

Now we evaluate the constant of integration. When $x = 1$, $A = 0$, so

$$0 = \frac{4\sqrt{2}\,(1)^{\frac{3}{2}}}{3} + C$$

therefore $C = \dfrac{-4\sqrt{2}}{3}$ and

$$A_{1\to9} = \frac{4\sqrt{2}\,(9)^{\frac{3}{2}}}{3} - \frac{4\sqrt{2}}{3}$$

$$= \frac{4\sqrt{2}\,(27)}{3} - \frac{4\sqrt{2}}{3} = \frac{108\sqrt{2}}{3} - \frac{4\sqrt{2}}{3}$$

$$= \frac{104\sqrt{2}}{3} = 34.66\sqrt{2} = 48.66$$

A second method would be to evaluate C when $x = 0$ and $A = 0$; then

$$0 = \frac{4\sqrt{2}\,(0)^{\frac{3}{2}}}{3} + C$$

therefore $C = 0$, and

$$A_{0\to9} = \frac{4\sqrt{2}\,(9)^{\frac{3}{2}}}{3} + 0 = \frac{4\sqrt{2}\,(27)}{3}$$

$$= \frac{108\sqrt{2}}{3}$$

$$A_{0\to1} = \frac{4\sqrt{2}\,(1)^{\frac{3}{2}}}{3} + 0 = \frac{4\sqrt{2}}{3}$$

$$A_{1\to9} = \frac{108\sqrt{2}}{3} - \frac{4\sqrt{2}}{3} = \frac{104\sqrt{2}}{3} = 48.66$$

Example 3.11. Calculate the area under $x = y^2 - 2$ between $x = 2$ and $x = 14$.

If $x = y^2 - 2$, then $y = \sqrt{x + 2}$ and

$$A = \int y\,dx$$

$$= \int \sqrt{x + 2}\,dx = \int (x + 2)^{\frac{1}{2}}\,dx$$

$$= \frac{(x + 2)^{\frac{3}{2}}}{3/2} + C$$

$$= \tfrac{2}{3}(x + 2)^{\frac{3}{2}} + C$$

Now we evaluate the constant C. When $A = 0$, $x = 0$, so $0 = \tfrac{2}{3}(0 + 2)^{\frac{3}{2}} + C$ and

$$C = -\frac{2(2)^{\frac{3}{2}}}{3}$$

therefore

$$A = \frac{2(14 + 2)^{\frac{3}{2}}}{3} - \frac{2(2)^{\frac{3}{2}}}{3}$$

$$A = \frac{2(16)^{\frac{3}{2}}}{3} - \frac{2(2)^{\frac{3}{2}}}{3} = \frac{2(64)}{3} - \frac{2(2)^{\frac{3}{2}}}{3}$$

$$= \frac{128 - 2.828}{3} = 41.724$$

And

$$A_{0 \to 2} = \frac{2(2 + 2)^{\frac{3}{2}}}{3} - \frac{2(2)^{\frac{3}{2}}}{3}$$

$$= \frac{2(4)^{\frac{3}{2}}}{3} - \frac{2(2)^{\frac{3}{2}}}{3} = \frac{2(8)}{3} - \frac{2(2)^{\frac{3}{2}}}{3}$$

$$= \frac{16 - 2.828}{3} = 4.391$$

$$A_{2 \to 14} = A_{0 \to 14} - A_{0 \to 2}$$

$$= 41.724 - 4.391 = 37.333$$

Another method: When $x = 2$, $A = 0$, so

$$0 = \tfrac{2}{3}(2 + 2)^{\frac{3}{2}} + C$$

$$= \tfrac{2}{3}(8) + C$$

from which $C = -\frac{16}{3}$. Then

$$A_{2 \to 14} = \frac{2}{3}(14 + 2)^{\frac{3}{2}} - \frac{16}{3}$$

$$= \frac{2}{3}(16)^{\frac{3}{2}} - \frac{16}{3}$$

$$= \frac{128}{3} - \frac{16}{3}$$

$$= \frac{112}{3} = 37.333$$

Figure 3.4 should act as a summary of the methods of evaluating the constant of integration so as to calculate the area under a curve. In Figure 3.4a, C is evaluated at $x = 1$ and the area between $x = 1$ and $x = 5$ is calculated using $x = 5$ and $C = 0$. Figures 3.4b, c, and d summarize the method that calculates the area between $x = 0$ and $x = 5$, and then the area between $x = 0$ and $x = 1$ and the difference taken for the required area.

Exercise 3.4.   Calculate the area under the following curves between the limits given.

1. $y = x^2 + 4$ between $x = 0$ and $x = 1$.
2. $y = x^2 + 3x - 5$ between $x = 1$ and $x = 2$.
3. $y = \sqrt{x}$ between $x = 1$ and $x = 4$.
4. $y = (2x + 1)^2$ between $x = -2$ and $x = 1$.
5. $y = x^{-3}$ between $x = 1$ and $x = 10$.
6. $y = x^3$ between $x = 1$ and $x = 3$.
7. $y = x^2 + 10x$ between $x = 0$ and $x = 2$.
8. $y = x^2/4$ between $x = 4$ and $x = 10$.
9. $y = 6x^{\frac{1}{2}}$ between $x = 4$ and $x = 9$.
10. $y = -x^2 + 9$ between $x = -3$ and $x = 3$.
11. $y = x^2 - 4$ between $x = -2$ and $x = 2$.
12. $y = 16/x^3$ between $x = 1$ and $x = 4$.
13. $y = 8/x^2$ between $x = -1$ and $x = 2$.
14. $y = (x + 9)^{\frac{1}{2}}$ between $x = 0$ and $x = 16$.
15. $y = 100 - x^2$ between $x = 4$ and $x = 6$.
16. $y = \frac{1}{2}x + 2$ between $x = -4$ and $x = 4$.

3.6 THE DEFINITE INTEGRAL

Calculating the area under a curve between given values of x using the indefinite integral requires integration and then the evaluation of the constant of integration. As is so often true in mathematics, after repeated observation of an operation, a simplified method of handling this was developed. This new method makes use of what is known as the *definite integral*. Suppose we desire to calculate the area under $y = x^2$ between $x = 1$ and $x = 4$. Using the definite integral, we would have

$$A_{1 \to 4} = \int_{1}^{4} x^2 \, dx$$

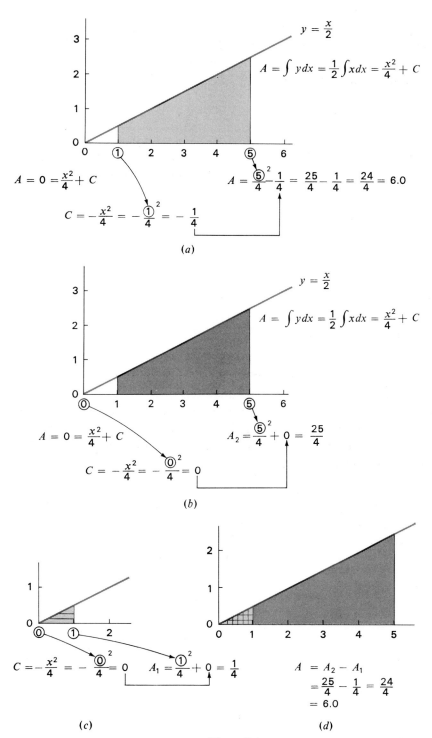

Figure 3.4

The numbers given with the integral sign make it a definite integral sign, and the numbers are called the *limits of integration*. The 1 or lower limit is the value of x at the left of the area wanted and the 4 or upper limit is the value of x at the right of the area wanted. Evaluating a definite integral gives

$$A \underset{1 \to 4}{=} \int_1^4 x^2 \, dx = \frac{x^3}{3} \Big]_1^4$$

The bracket along with the limits indicates that first the 4 should be substituted for the x and then 1 is substituted for x and their difference taken.

$$\frac{x^3}{3} \Big]_1^4 = \frac{4^3}{3} - \frac{1^3}{3} = \frac{64}{3} - \frac{1}{3}$$

$$= \frac{63}{3} = 31$$

From all of this then, for the definite integral, we have:

$$\int_a^b f(x) \, dx = g(x) + C \Big]_a^b = g[b] - g[a] \tag{3.4}$$

From (3.4) we see that when we integrate a function of x, using the definite integral we obtain another function of x, $g(x)$, plus some constant. The upper limit of integration is then substituted into the new function $g(x)$ and from this is subtracted the value obtained by substituting the lower limit into the new function $g(x)$. Since the constant of integration is the same in both substitutions, it disappears in the subtraction operation.

Example 3.12.   Calculate the area under $y = \frac{1}{2}x$ between $x = 1$ and $x = 5$. This is the same example as presented in Section 3.5 where the definite integral was not used.

$$A = \int_1^5 y \, dx = \int_1^5 \tfrac{1}{2} x \, dx$$

$$= \frac{1}{2} \int_1^5 x \, dx$$

$$= \frac{1}{2} \frac{x^2}{2} \Big]_1^5 = \frac{x^2}{4} \Big]_1^5$$

$$= \frac{5^2}{4} - \frac{1^2}{4} = \frac{25}{4} - \frac{1}{4}$$

$$= \tfrac{24}{4} = 6.0$$

Example 3.13. Solve Example 3.10 using the definite integral.
Here $x = \frac{1}{8}y^2$ and the limits are $x = 1$ and $x = 9$.

$$A = \int_1^9 y\,dx$$
$$\underset{1 \to 9}{}$$

$$= 2\sqrt{2} \int_1^9 x^{1/2}\,dx$$

$$= \frac{2\sqrt{2}\,x^{3/2}}{3/2}\Bigg]_1^9 = \frac{4\sqrt{2}\,x^{3/2}}{3}\Bigg]_1^9$$

$$= \frac{4\sqrt{2}\,(9)^{3/2}}{3} - \frac{4\sqrt{2}\,(1)^{3/2}}{3}$$

$$= \frac{4\sqrt{2}\,(27)}{3} - \frac{4\sqrt{2}}{3} = \frac{108\sqrt{2}}{3} - \frac{4\sqrt{2}}{3}$$

$$= \frac{104\sqrt{2}}{3} = 48.66$$

Example 3.14. Solve Example 3.11 using the definite integral.
Here $x = y^2 - 2$ and the limits are $x = 2$ and $x = 14$.

$$A = \int_2^{14} y\,dx = \int_2^{14} (x + 2)^{1/2}\,dx$$
$$\underset{2 \to 14}{}$$

$$= \tfrac{2}{3}(x + 2)^{3/2}\Bigg]_2^{14}$$

$$= \tfrac{2}{3}(14 + 2)^{3/2} - \tfrac{2}{3}(2 + 2)^{3/2}$$

$$= \tfrac{128}{3} - \tfrac{16}{3} = \tfrac{112}{3}$$

$$= 37.333$$

Exercise 3.5. Calculate all the areas asked for in Exercise 3.4 using the definite integral.

3.7 THE FUNDAMENTAL THEOREM OF INTEGRAL CALCULUS

The fundamental theorem of integral calculus equates the definite integral to the area under a curve. Suppose we are given a function $y = f(x)$ (see Figure

3.5), and we desire to calculate the area under the graph of that function between $x = a$ and $x = b$.

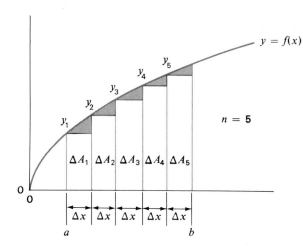

$n = 5$

Figure 3.5

We begin by dividing the line segment $\overline{ab}$ into five equal parts Δx long. It should be understood that it is not necessary to make all these parts equal to obtain the same correct results. We now divide the required area into five strips whose combined area will be less than the area in question by the area of the shaded portions.

The area of the first strip (ΔA_1) is calculated using the width of the strip (Δx) and the length of the strip (y_1). Since $y = f(x)$, $y_1 = f[a]$ and

$$y_2 = f[a + \Delta x]$$
$$y_3 = f[a + 2(\Delta x)]$$
$$y_4 = f[a + 3(\Delta x)]$$
$$y_5 = f[a + 4(\Delta x)]$$

Likewise the strip areas are:

$$\Delta A_1 = y_1(\Delta x)$$
$$\Delta A_2 = y_2(\Delta x)$$
$$\Delta A_3 = y_3(\Delta x)$$
$$\Delta A_4 = y_4(\Delta x)$$
$$\Delta A_5 = y_5(\Delta x)$$

The sum of all these areas will approximate the area we seek, as shown by

$$A \underset{a \to b}{\approx} \Delta A_1 + \Delta A_2 + \Delta A_3 + \Delta A_4 + \Delta A_5$$

$$\approx y_1(\Delta x) + y_2(\Delta x) + y_3(\Delta x) + y_4(\Delta x) + y_5(\Delta x)$$

$$\approx \sum_{i=1}^{5} y_i(\Delta x) \quad \text{(see Precalculus Mathematics Review)}$$

Note that we say the area from a to b is approximately equal to the sum of the $y_i(\Delta x)$ as i ranges from 1 to 5. As we have said, this area varies from the required area by the shaded portion of Figure 3.5.

Now suppose we divide the line segment $\overline{ab}$ into ten parts as shown in Figure 3.6. We now have ten rectangles and the sum of their areas is less than the required area by the amount of the shaded portions. Note, however, that as we increased the number of rectangles the shaded area was reduced. Now

$$A \underset{a \to b}{\approx} \sum_{i=1}^{10} y_i(\Delta x)$$

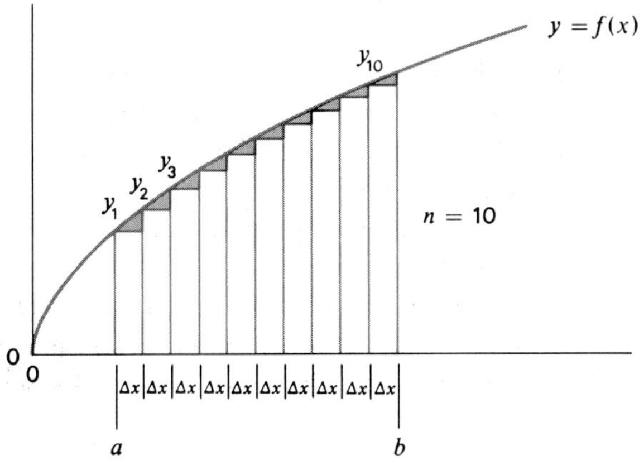

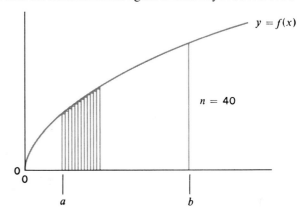

Figure 3.6

Following this line of attack we divide the line segment $\overline{ab}$ into forty parts as shown in Figure 3.7 and note that the shaded area is again drastically reduced. Now

Figure 3.7

$$A \approx \sum_{i=1}^{40} y_i(\Delta x)$$
$$_{a \to b}$$

If we should let Δx approach zero, we would in effect be letting n become infinitely large. Under these conditions there would be no shaded area, and the sum of the areas of the rectangles would equal exactly the required area. To achieve all this we take the limit of the sum of these rectangles as Δx approaches zero.

$$A = \lim_{\substack{a \to b \\ \Delta x \to 0}} \sum_{i=1}^{n} y_i(\Delta x)$$

But from discussions on area under a curve and the definite integral, we know:

$$A = \int_{a}^{b} y \, dx$$
$$_{a \to b}$$

Therefore:

$$A = \lim_{\substack{a \to b \\ \Delta x \to 0}} \sum_{i=1}^{n} y_i(\Delta x) = \int_{a}^{b} y \, dx \tag{3.5}$$

It should now be noted that the integral sign is nothing more than a "lazy letter S" coming from the first letter of the word *sum*.

Thus (3.5) is the fundamental theorem of the integral calculus. Let us note now that a is the lower limit of the definite integral and b is the upper limit. Note further that $\overline{ab}$ represents a line segment on the x axis and that n is the number of parts into which the line segment $\overline{ab}$ is divided.

To calculate the area under a curve using the definite integral, a picture should be sketched. Should we desire to calculate the area under $y = x^2$ between $x = 0$ and $x = 2$, we first make a sketch of the situation (see Figure 3.8).

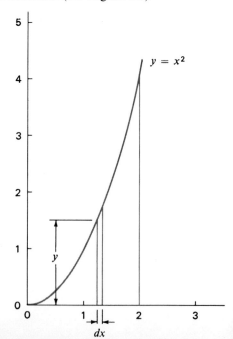

Figure 3.8

Then

$$A \atop 0 \to 2 = \int_0^2 y\,dx$$

but $y = x^2$, so

$$A = \int_0^2 x^2\,dx = \left.\frac{x^3}{3}\right]_0^2$$

$$= \frac{(2)(2)(2)}{3} - \frac{(0)(0)(0)}{3}$$

$$= \tfrac{8}{3}$$

We could also make a sketch as shown in Figure 3.9. Remembering that $y(dx)$ is the area of a small elemental strip, then $y(dx)$ is really dA, the area of this small elemental strip. We could write then:

$$A \atop c \to d = \int_c^d dA$$

and from Figure 3.9:

$$A \atop 0 \to 4 = \int_0^4 h\,dy$$

where $h(dy)$ is dA, and $h = 2 - x$, but $y = x^2$, so $x = y^{1/2}$, and $h = 2 - y^{1/2}$,

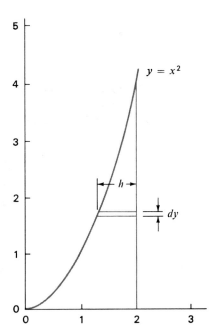

Figure 3.9

therefore

$$A_{0 \to 4} = \int_0^4 (2 - y^{1/2})\, dy$$

$$= 2y - \frac{2y^{3/2}}{3} \Bigg]_0^4$$

$$= 2(4) - \frac{2(4)^{3/2}}{3}$$

$$= 8 - \frac{16}{3} = \frac{24}{3} - \frac{16}{3}$$

$$= \frac{8}{3}$$

From all this along with Figure 3.10, we say:

$$A_{a \to b} = \int_a^b y\, dx = \int_c^d x\, dy \qquad (3.6)$$

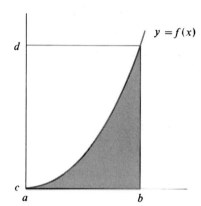

Figure 3.10

Example 3.15.   Calculate the area under $y = \frac{1}{4}x^2$, between $x = 2$ and $x = 4$, in two ways.

Method 1 (see Figure 3.11):

$$A_{2 \to 4} = \int_2^4 y\, dx$$

$$= \frac{1}{4} \int_2^4 x^2\, dx = \frac{x^3}{12} \Bigg]_2^4$$

$$= \frac{(4)(4)(4)}{12} - \frac{(2)(2)(2)}{12} = \frac{64}{12} - \frac{8}{12}$$

$$= \frac{56}{12} = \frac{14}{3}$$

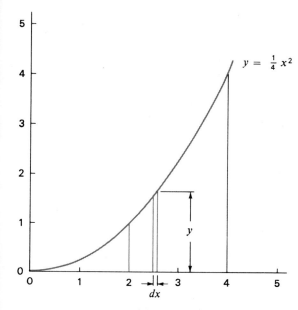

Figure 3.11

Method 2 (see Figure 3.12):

$$A_{1 \to 4} = \int_1^4 h\,dy$$

but $h = 4 - x$, and $x = \sqrt{4y} = 2\sqrt{y} = 2y^{\frac{1}{2}}$, so

$$A_{1 \to 4} = \int_1^4 (4 - 2y^{\frac{1}{2}})\,dy$$

Figure 3.12

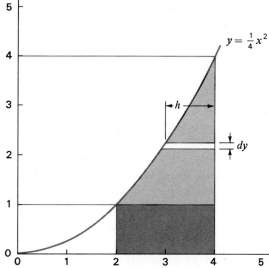

$$= 4y - \left.\frac{4y^{3/2}}{3}\right]_1^4$$

$$= 4 \cdot 4 - \frac{4(4)^{3/2}}{3} - 4 \cdot 1 - \frac{4(1)^{3/2}}{3}$$

$$= (16 - \tfrac{32}{3}) - (4 - \tfrac{4}{3})$$

$$= (\tfrac{48}{3} - \tfrac{32}{3}) - (\tfrac{12}{3} - \tfrac{4}{3})$$

$$= \tfrac{16}{3} - \tfrac{8}{3}$$

$$= \tfrac{8}{3}$$

and
$$A_{0 \to 1} = 1(2) = 2 = \tfrac{6}{3}$$

therefore
$$A_{0 \to 4} = A_{0 \to 1} + A_{1 \to 4}$$

$$= \tfrac{8}{3} + \tfrac{6}{3}$$

$$= \tfrac{14}{3}$$

Note that using this method we could not integrate from $y = 0$ to $y = 4$ because if we did we would get the area under the curve between $x = 0$ and $x = 2$ in addition to the required area.

Exercise 3.6. For each function and limits given, make an appropriate sketch and calculate the area using dx; then make another sketch using dy and recalculate the same area.

1. $y = x$ between $x = 0$ and $x = 4$.
2. $y = x^2/2$ between $x = 1$ and $x = 4$.
3. $y = x^2 + 2$ between $x = 1$ and $x = 4$.
4. $y = x^2 - 2$ between $x = 2$ and $x = 3$.
5. $x = y^2$ between $x = 0$ and $x = 2$.
6. $y = (x + 1)^2$ between $x = -1$ and $x = 2$.
7. $y = (x - 1)^2$ between $x = 1$ and $x = 3$.

3.8 AVERAGE ORDINATE

Many situations present themselves in which the area under a curve is not the primary goal, but rather is a step toward that goal. For instance, the average ordinate over a given interval on the x axis may be the goal.

Suppose we are given a function of x and an interval on the x axis and are asked for the average ordinate. We analyze it this way: Call the interval on the x axis L and calculate the area under the curve between the given limits (L units apart). Now we are asked to find the width of a rectangle L units long that will have the same area as that under the curve.

Example 3.16.   Find the average ordinate under $y = x^2$, between $x = 1$ and $x = 4$. See Figure 3.13.

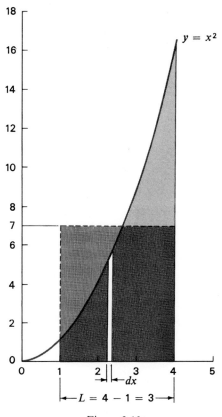

Figure 3.13

$$A_{1 \to 4} = \int_1^4 y\,dx$$

$$= \int_1^4 x^2\,dx = \left. \frac{x^3}{3} \right]_1^4$$

$$= \frac{4 \cdot 4 \cdot 4}{3} - \frac{1 \cdot 1 \cdot 1}{3} = \frac{64}{3} - \frac{1}{3}$$

$$= 21$$

$L = 4 - 1 = 3$, and average ordinate $= A/L = \frac{21}{3} = 7$. Figure 3.13 shows both the problem and the resulting rectangle having the same area as the area under the curve. The width of the rectangle is 7, so the average ordinate is 7.

Exercise 3.7.   Calculate the average ordinate for each problem in Exercise 3.6.

3.9 THE DOUBLE INTEGRAL

An intuitive approach to the multiple or double integral in evaluating an area under a curve will now be attempted. Formal proof will not appear.

Suppose we desire to calculate the area shown in Figure 3.14. We set up an elemental strip dy wide and h long and write:

$$A_{0 \to 8} = \int_0^8 h\,dy = \int_0^8 x\,dy$$

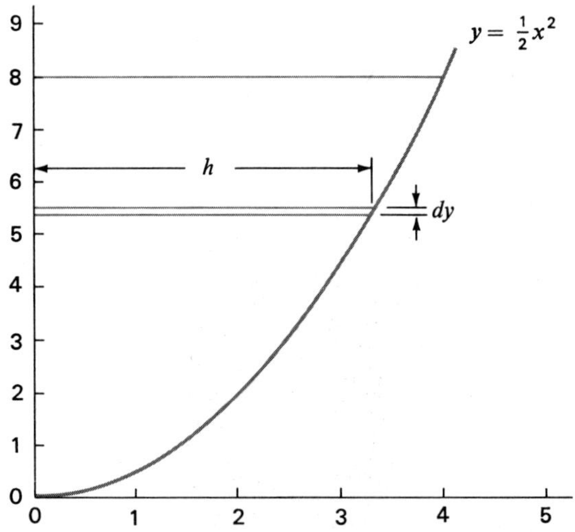

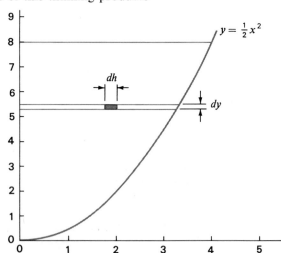

Figure 3.14

Looking at Figure 3.15 we see that, instead of taking an elemental strip h long and dy wide, we set up an elemental area dh long and dy wide—the thinking being that first we will integrate dh between 0 and x, and then integrate that result from 0 to 8. The result of this thinking produces

Figure 3.15

$$A = \int_{0 \to 8}^{8} \int_0^x dh\, dy = \int_0^8 \left\{ \int_0^x dh \right\} dy = \int_0^8 \left\{ h \Big]_0^x \right\} dy = \int_0^8 x\, dy$$

Note that the result using Figure 3.15 is the same as that obtained using Figure 3.14, leading us to the rule for double integration:

$$\int_{y=a}^{y=b} \int_{h=c}^{h=x} f(h)\, dh\, dy = \int_a^b \left\{ \int_c^x f(h)\, dh \right\} dy$$

$$= \int_a^b \left\{ g(h) \Big]_c^x \right\} dy \qquad (3.7)$$

$$= \int_a^b \{ g[x] - g[c] \}\, dy$$

Example 3.17.   Evaluate $\displaystyle\int_0^4 \int_0^x h^2\, dh\, dy$, if $h = x$ and $y = x^3$.

$$\int_0^4 \int_0^x h^2\, dh\, dy = \int_0^4 \frac{h^3}{3} \Big]_0^x dy$$

$$= \int_0^4 \frac{x^3}{3}\, dy$$

$$= \frac{1}{3} \int_0^4 y\, dy$$

$$= \frac{1}{3} \frac{y^2}{2} \Big]_0^4$$

$$= \tfrac{16}{6} - \tfrac{0}{6}$$

$$= \tfrac{8}{3}$$

Example 3.18.   Evaluate $\displaystyle\int_0^2 \int_1^x s\, ds\, dy$ if $s = x$ and $y = x$.

$$\int_0^2 \int_1^x s\, ds\, dy = \int_0^2 \frac{s^2}{2} \Big]_1^x dy$$

$$= \frac{1}{2} \int_0^2 (x^2 - 1)\, dy$$

$$= \frac{1}{2} \left(\frac{y^3}{3} - y \right) \Big]_0^2$$

$$= \frac{1 \cdot 2 \cdot 2 \cdot 2}{2 \cdot 3} - \frac{2}{2} = \frac{8}{6} - \frac{6}{6} = \frac{1}{3}$$

3.10 ADDITIONAL INTEGRATION TYPES

Recall that (3.1) and (3.3) specify that in $\int kx^n \, dx$ and $\int ku^n \, du$, n may not be negative 1. Since we know that the exponent negative 1 exists, we must then have a separate rule for this type or situation.

From (2.31) we know that if $y = \ln u$, then $dy/dx = k/u \, du/dx = ku^{-1} \, du/dx$, and we conclude

$$\int ku^{-1} \, du = k \ln u + C \tag{3.8}$$

The integration types for the trigonometric functions come from our knowledge of differentiating these functions, so

$$\int k \sin u \, du = -k \cos u + C \tag{3.9}$$

$$\int k \cos u \, du = k \sin u + C \tag{3.10}$$

$$\int k \tan u \, du = k \ln (\sec u) + C \tag{3.11}$$

$$\int ke^u \, du = ke^u + C \tag{3.12}$$

Example 3.19.   Integrate $(x^2 + 1)^{-1} \, 2x \, dx$.

$$\int \frac{2x \, dx}{(x^2 + 1)} = \ln (x^2 + 1) + C$$

Example 3.20.   Integrate $(2x^3 - 3)^{-1} \, 3x^2 \, dx$.

$$\int \frac{3x^2 \, dx}{(2x^3 - 3)} = \frac{1}{2} \int \frac{2 \cdot 3x^2 \, dx}{2x^3 - 3}$$

$$= \tfrac{1}{2} \ln (2x^3 - 3) + C$$

In this example $u = 2x^3 - 3$ and $du = 6x^2 \, dx$.

Example 3.21.   Calculate the average ordinate under $y = \sin x$ between $x = 0$ and $x = \pi$.

$$A = \int_0^\pi \sin x \, dx = -\cos x \Big]_0^\pi$$

$$= (-\cos \pi) - (-\cos 0)$$

$$= -(-1) - (-1)$$

$$= 1 + 1 = 2$$

Average ordinate $= A/\Delta x = 2/\pi = 0.6366$.

Example 3.22. Calculate the average ordinate under $y = \cos 2x$ between $x = \pi/2$ and $x = \pi$.

$$A \underset{\pi/2 \to \pi}{=} \int_{\pi/2}^{\pi} \cos 2x \, dx$$

Here $u = 2x$ and $du = 2 \, dx$, so

$$A = \frac{1}{2} \int_{\pi/2}^{\pi} \cos (2x) \, 2 \, dx$$

$$= \frac{1}{2} \sin 2x \Bigg]_{\pi/2}^{\pi}$$

$$= \frac{1}{2} \sin 2\pi - \frac{1}{2} \sin \pi$$

$$= \frac{1}{2}(0) - \frac{1}{2}(1) = -\frac{1}{2}$$

$$= -0.500$$

$$\text{Average ordinate} = \frac{-0.5}{\pi - (\pi/2)} = \frac{-0.5}{1.5708} = -0.3183$$

Exercise 3.8. Calculate the area and average ordinate under the following functions between the given limits.

1. $y = \sin 2x$ between $x = \pi/4$ and $x = 3\pi/4$.
2. $y = 1/\sin x$ between $x = 0$ and $x = \pi$.
3. $y = 3 \cos x$ between $x = \pi/2$ and $x = \pi$.
4. $y = 2e^x$ between $x = 0$ and $x = 1$.

Integrate the following.

5. $\int 4 \cos 2x \, dx$.
6. $\int x \cos x^2 \, dx$.
7. $\int \cos (4 - x) \, dx$.
8. $\int (\sin x)/(\cos^2 x) \, dx$.
9. $\int e^{1-4x} \, dx$.
10. $\int e^{\pi x} \, dx$.
11. $\int dx/e^x$.
12. $\int 6x^2 \, e^{x^3} \, dx$.
13. $\int e^{3x+1} \, dx$.
14. $\int x \, e^{x^2} \, dx$.
15. $\int_0^1 \int_0^x h^3 \, dh \, dy$ if $h = x$ and $y = x^2$.
16. $\int_1^2 \int_1^x s^2 \, ds \, dy$ if $s = x$ and $y = x$.
17. $\int_2^{10} \int_0^x R^4 \, dR \, dy$ if $R = x$ and $y = x^{1/5}$.
18. $\int_{\pi}^{3\pi/2} \int_{\pi/2}^x \sin h \, dh \, dy$ if $h = x$ and $y = x$.
19. $\int_{\pi}^{3\pi/2} \int_{\pi/2}^x \sin h \, dh \, dy$ if $h = x$ and $y = 2x$.

3.11 ACCELERATION

We have defined speed or velocity as the time rate of change of distance traveled, and now that velocity is defined we begin to think about time rate of change of velocity. Time rate of change of velocity is called *acceleration* and average acceleration is defined as the change in velocity divided by the change in time, or

$$a_{av} = \frac{\Delta v}{\Delta t} \tag{3.13}$$

Thus if a particle has a velocity of 100 fps at time $t = 2$ seconds and a velocity of 900 fps at time $t = 4$ seconds, then

$$\Delta v = 900 - 100 = 800 \text{ fps}$$

$$\Delta t = 4 - 2 = 2 \text{ sec}$$

So $a_{av} = \Delta v/\Delta t = 800/2 = 400$ fps per second.

Equation (3.13) represents an arithmetic situation and is presented here only as an entree to the calculus idea of instantaneous acceleration. Our limit concepts allow us to write

$$a = \lim_{\Delta t \to 0} \frac{\Delta v}{\Delta t} = \frac{dv}{dt} \tag{3.14}$$

Thus we say

$$a = \frac{dv}{dt} = \frac{d}{dt} v$$

but $v = ds/dt$, so

$$a = \frac{d}{dt} v = \frac{d}{dt} \frac{ds}{dt}$$

therefore:

$$a = \frac{d^2s}{dt^2} \tag{3.15}$$

From (3.15) we see that instantaneous acceleration can be found by taking the second derivative of the distance formula.

> **Example 3.23.**   Calculate the acceleration of an object in free fall.
> Here $s = 16t^2$ feet and $v = 32t$ fps, so $a = 32$ ft/sec/sec.
> From our knowledge that integration is the inverse of differentiation and $a = dv/dt$, $dv = a\,dt$, and $\int dv = \int a\,dt$,
>
> $$v = \int a\,dt \tag{3.16}$$

Further, if $v = ds/dt$, then $ds = v\,dt$ and $\int ds = \int v\,dt$, so

$$s = \int v\,dt \qquad\qquad (3.17)$$

Example 3.24. A stone is dropped from a rooftop in free fall. Calculate a formula for the distance in terms of time. What distance is traversed in two seconds?

Since $a = 32$, and

$$v = \int a\,dt$$

$$= \int 32\,dt$$

$$= 32t + C$$

when time $t = 0$, and $v = 0$, we have $0 = 32(0) + C$ or $C = 0$. Thus $v = 32t$ and since

$$s = \int v\,dt$$

$$= \int 32t\,dt$$

$$= \frac{32t^2}{2} + C$$

$$= 16t^2 + C$$

when time $t = 0$, and $s = 0$, we have $0 = 16(0) + C$ or $C = 0$. Thus $s = 16t^2$ and

$$s = 16(2)^2$$

$$= 16(4)$$

$$= 64 \text{ feet}$$

Example 3.25. A stone is thrown down from a rooftop with an initial velocity of 20 fps. Calculate a formula for distance traveled and the distance traveled in three seconds.

Here $a = 32$ fps and $v = \int a\,dt$, so $v = \int 32\,dt = 32t + C$. If $v = 20$ when $t = 0$, then $20 = 32(0) + C$, and $C = 20$. Likewise $v = 32t + 20$. Also

$$s = \int v\,dt$$

$$= \int (32t + 20)\,dt$$

$$= \frac{32t^2}{2} + 20t + C$$

$$= 16t^2 + 20t + C$$

If $s = 0$ when $t = 0$, then $0 = 16(0)^2 + C$ and $C = 0$. Therefore $s = 16t^2 + 20t$, and when $t = 3$,

$$s = 16(3)^2 + 20(3)$$
$$= 16(9) + 60$$
$$= 144 + 60$$
$$= 204 \text{ feet}$$

Example 3.26.   A stone is thrown upward from a rooftop with an initial velocity of 30 fps. Calculate formulas for velocity and distance traveled.

Here $a = 32$ fps, so $v = \int s\,dt = \int 32\,dt = 32t + C$. When $t = 0$, $v = -30$, so $-30 = 32(0) + C$, and $C = -30$.

Note since we have arbitrarily taken velocity toward the center of the earth as positive, that velocity away from the center of the earth must be negative.

Now $v = 32t - 30$ and since

$$s = \int v\,dt$$
$$= \int (32t - 30)\,dt$$
$$= 16t^2 - 30t + C$$

when $t = 0$, $s = 0$, so $0 = 16(0)^2 - 30(0) + C$ and $C = 0$. Thus

$$s = 16t^2 - 30t$$

Example 3.27.   A ball is dropped from a height h_1. Write the equation for its velocity and altitude in terms of time.

Since $a = 32$ fps, $v = \int a\,dt = \int 32\,dt = 32t + C$. And $v = 0$ when $t = 0$, so $0 = 32(0) + C$ and $C = 0$. Thus $v = 32t$ and

$$s = \int v\,dt$$
$$= \int 32t\,dt$$
$$= 16t^2 + C$$

when $s = h_1$, $t = 0$, so $h_1 = 16(0)^2 + C$, $C = h_1$, and

$$s = 16t^2 + h_1$$

Example 3.28.   A ball is thrown downward with a velocity of 100 fps from a height of 200 feet. Write the equations for its velocity and altitude as a function of time.

$a = 32$ fps, so $v = \int 32\,dt = 32t + C$. And when $v = 100$, $t = 0$, so $100 = 32(0) + C$, and $C = 100$. Thus $v = 32t + 100$.

Since $s = \int v\,dt$

$$= \int (32t + 100)\,dt$$

$$= 16t^2 + 100t + C$$

when $t = 0$, $s = -200$, so $-200 = 16(0)^2 + 100(0) + C$ and $C = -200$. Therefore

$$s = 16t^2 + 100t - 200$$

Example 3.29. With what velocity will the ball in Example 3.28 hit the ground?
When the ball strikes the ground s will be zero, so $0 = 16t^2 + 100t - 200$ or $4t^2 + 25t - 50 = 0$. Thus

$$t = \frac{-25 \pm \sqrt{(25)^2 - 4(4)(-50)}}{2(4)}$$

$$= \frac{-25 \pm \sqrt{625 + 800}}{8}$$

$$= \frac{-25 \pm \sqrt{1425}}{8} = \frac{-25 \pm 37.74}{8}$$

$$= 1.59 \text{ or } -7.84$$

Discarding the negative time as extraneous, we proceed:

$$v = 32t + 100$$

$$= 32(1.59) + 100$$

$$= 50.88 + 100$$

$$= 150.88 \text{ fps}$$

Example 3.30. A ball is thrown straight up from a point 300 feet above the ground with an initial velocity of 50 fps. Calculate equations for acceleration, velocity, and altitude.
First $a = 32$, so once again $v = \int 32\,dt$. And when $t = 0$, $v = -50$, so $-50 = 32(0) + C$, and $C = -50$. Therefore $v = 32t - 50$. Also

$$s = \int v\,dt$$

$$= \int (32t - 50)\,dt$$

$$= 16t^2 - 50t + C$$

But $s = 300$ when $t = 0$, so $300 = 16(0)^2 - 50(0) + C$ and $C = 300$. Therefore

$$s = 16t^2 - 50t + 300$$

Exercise 3.9

1. A rock is dropped from a height of 400 feet. Calculate equations for velocity and distance (altitude) in terms of time.
2. A rock is thrown downward from a height of 400 feet with an initial velocity of 50 fps. Calculate equations for velocity and distance in terms of time.
3. A rock is thrown upward from a height of 400 feet with an initial velocity of 50 fps. Calculate equations for velocity and distance in terms of time.
4. Using Figure 3.16:
   (a) Graphically calculate the average acceleration between 10 and 20 seconds.
   (b) Graphically calculate the instantaneous acceleration at $t = 10$ seconds; at $t = 20$ seconds; at $t = 30$ seconds; at $t = 40$ seconds; at $t = 60$ seconds.
   (c) Graphically calculate maximum speed. At what time was maximum speed reached?
   (d) When was acceleration a maximum?
   (e) When was acceleration a minimum?

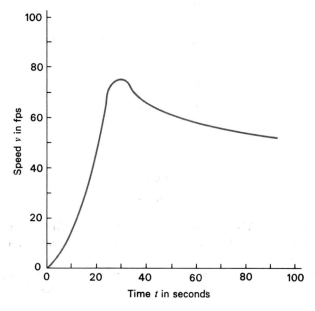

Figure 3.16

3.12 VOLUMES

Our approach to volumes will be quite similar to the one used for the area under a curve. Recall that in the area problem we summed n elemental strips Δx wide and y_i long for the area sought.

Let us analyze the problem of finding the volume of a right square pyramid and a right circular cone. See Figures 3.17*a* and *b*.

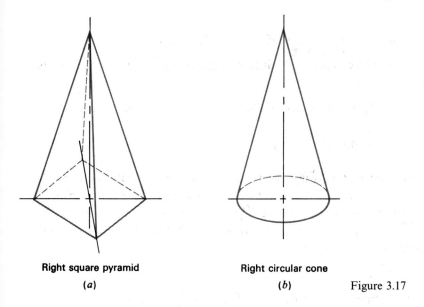

Right square pyramid

(a)

Right circular cone

(b)

Figure 3.17

For the pyramid, let us assume it is made up of a series of squares Δx thick, as pictured in Figure 3.18a. If we let the volume of the first square be V_1, the next V_2, the next V_3, and so forth, and assume n such square volumes,

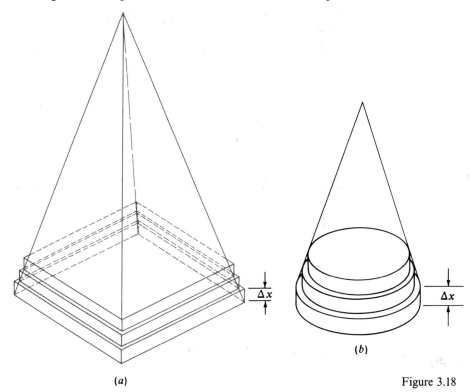

(a)

(b)

Figure 3.18

then:

$$V \approx V_1 + V_2 + V_3 + V_4 + \cdots + V_{n-1} + V_n$$

And each elemental volume is obtained by multiplying the area of the square by the thickness (Δx), so

$$V \approx A_1(\Delta x) + A_2(\Delta x) + A_3(\Delta x) + \cdots + A_{n-1}(\Delta x) + A_n(\Delta x)$$

$$\approx \sum_{i=1}^{n} A_i(\Delta x)$$

The same kind of thinking with regard to the right circular cone produces Figure 3.18b, where we see the cone made up of a stack of discs, Δx thick. Here each elemental volume is V_i, obtained by multiplying the area of each disc by the thickness Δx. The appropriate volume desired is obtained by summing all these elemental volumes, so once again:

$$V \approx A_i(\Delta x)$$

Applying our limit theory ideas to the foregoing, we obtain:

$$V = \lim_{\substack{a \to b \\ x \to 0}} \sum_{i=1}^{n} A_i(\Delta x) = \int_{a}^{b} A \, dx \tag{3.18}$$

Example 3.31. Calculate the volume of a right square pyramid whose base is 5 by 5 and height is 10.

Figure 3.19 shows this typical problem set up on an x, y, z axis system

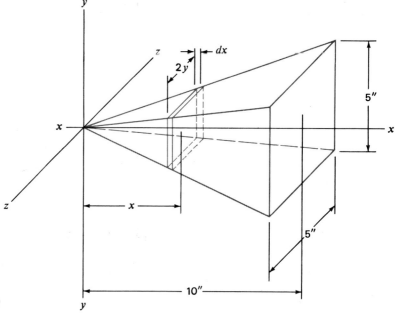

Figure 3.19

with one elemental square volume dx thick. Here

$$V \atop {0 \to 10} = \int_0^{10} A\, dx$$

In this problem the area of the elemental square will be $A = (2y)(2y) = 4y^2$, so

$$V = \int_0^{10} 4y^2\, dx$$

Since we cannot integrate $4y^2$ with respect to x, we must find some relationship between x and y from the physical setup of the pyramid. Figure 3.20 shows a side view of the pyramid which is an isosceles triangle, ABC. Now if we introduce our elemental square volume we produce triangle ADE which is similar to triangle ABC, therefore:

$$\frac{10}{5} = \frac{x}{2y} \qquad \text{or} \qquad 20y = 5x$$

and

$$y = \frac{x}{4} \qquad \text{or} \qquad y^2 = \frac{x^2}{16}$$

Therefore $4y^2 = 4x^2/16 = x^2/4$, and

$$V = \frac{1}{4} \int_0^{10} x^2\, dx = \frac{1}{4} \cdot \frac{x^3}{3} \Big]_0^{10} = \frac{10^3}{12} = \frac{1000}{12}$$

$$= 83.3333$$

Since we know the volume of a right square pyramid is $\frac{1}{3}$ the base times the altitude, we can check the preceding results.

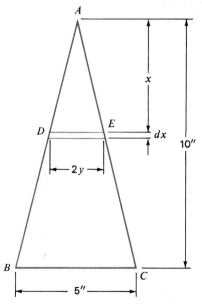

Figure 3.20

$$V = \tfrac{1}{3}(5)(5)10 = \tfrac{250}{3} = 83.3333$$

which shows our calculations to be correct.

Example 3.32.   Calculate the volume of a right circular cone with altitude 6 and radius of the base equal to 2.

See Figure 3.21 for a typical sketch of a volume problem. Here

$$V = \int_{0 \to 6}^{6} A\, dx \quad \text{and} \quad A = \pi y^2$$

so

$$V = \int_{0}^{6} \pi y^2\, dx$$

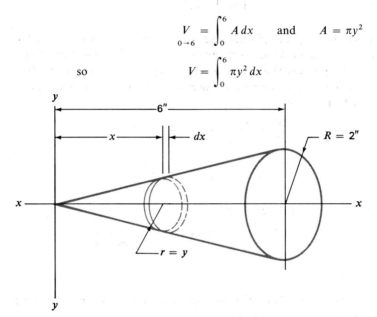

Figure 3.21

Now we must find a relationship between x and y. Figure 3.22 shows a side view of the cone. Once again the elemental volume cuts off a triangle that is

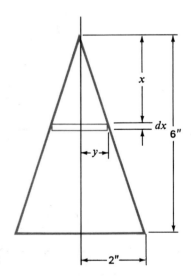

Figure 3.22

similar to the original triangle. Therefore

$$\frac{x}{y} = \frac{6}{2} \qquad \text{and} \qquad 6y = 2x$$

so
$$y = \frac{x}{3} \qquad \text{and} \qquad y^2 = \frac{x^2}{9}$$

Therefore $V = \dfrac{\pi}{9} \displaystyle\int_0^6 x^2 \, dx$

$$= \frac{\pi}{9} \cdot \frac{x^3}{3}\bigg]_0^6 = \frac{\pi \cdot 6 \cdot 6 \cdot 6}{9 \cdot 3} = 8\pi \text{ cubic units}$$

We can check our answer with the formula for the volume of a right circular cone, which is $V = \frac{1}{3}BA$, so

$$V = \tfrac{1}{3}\pi \cdot 2 \cdot 2 \cdot 6 = \frac{24\pi}{3} = 8\pi \text{ cubic units}$$

With success like this let us try our hand at something a little more complicated.

Example 3.33. Calculate the volume of a hemisphere whose radius is 10 inches.

This problem lends itself to several different approaches, but for our first attempt let us stay with our stack of elemental discs yielding a picture similar to Figure 3.23 and

$$V_{0 \to 10} = \int_0^{10} A \, dy$$

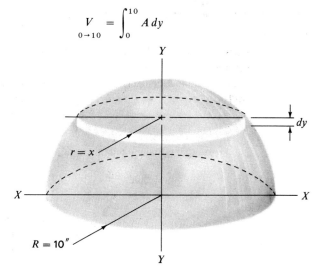

Figure 3.23

Here A represents the area of the elemental disc whose radius is x. Therefore $A = \pi x^2$, and

$$V = \pi \int_0^{10} x^2 \, dy$$

Now we must once again find a relationship between x and y. A side view of our hemisphere is shown in Figure 3.24, along with the elemental disc. All of this produces a right triangle one leg of which is x, the other y, and hypotenuse 10. From this then: $x^2 + y^2 = 100$ and $x^2 = 100 - y^2$, therefore

$$V = \pi \int_0^{10} (100 - y^2)\, dy$$

$$= 100\pi y - \frac{\pi y^3}{3} \Big]_0^{10}$$

$$= 100\pi 10 - \frac{\pi \cdot 10 \cdot 10 \cdot 10}{3}$$

$$= 1000\pi - \frac{1000\pi}{3}$$

$$= \frac{3000\pi}{3} - \frac{1000\pi}{3} = \frac{2000\pi}{3} \text{ cu in.}$$

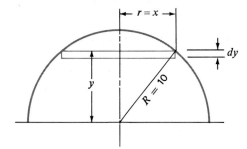

Figure 3.24

Example 3.34.   Calculate the volume asked for in Example 3.33 using another method.

In this analysis let us envision not a stack of discs, but rather a nest of thin-walled cylinders as pictured in Figure 3.25. Here:

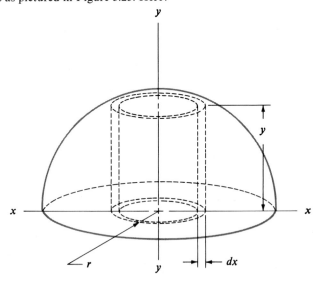

Figure 3.25

$$V = \int_{0 \to 10} \int_0^{10} A\,dx$$

A is the area of the cylinder, which is the circumference times the height, or $A = 2\pi ry = 2\pi xy$ and $V = 2\pi \int_0^{10} xy\,dx$. For the relationship between x and y we look to Figure 3.26, which is a side view of the hemisphere showing a

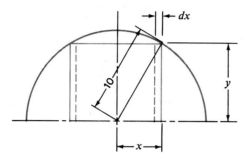

Figure 3.26

right triangle with legs x and y and hypotenuse 10. From this then $y = \sqrt{100 - x^2}$ and

$$V = 2\pi \int_0^{10} x(100 - x^2)^{1/2}\,dx$$

$$= 2\pi \int_0^{10} (100 - x^2)^{1/2}\,x\,dx$$

$$= -\frac{2\pi}{2} \int_0^{10} (100 - x^2)^{1/2}\,(-2x)\,dx$$

$$= -\pi \int_0^{10} (100 - x^2)^{1/2}\,(-2x)\,dx$$

$$= \left. \frac{-\pi(100 - x^2)^{3/2}}{3/2} \right]_0^{10} = \left. \frac{-2\pi(100 - x^2)^{3/2}}{3} \right]_0^{10}$$

$$= \frac{-2\pi(100 - 100)^{3/2}}{3} - \frac{-2\pi(100 - 0)^{3/2}}{3}$$

$$= \frac{2000\pi}{3}\ \text{cu in.}$$

Example 3.35. Calculate the volume asked for in Example 3.33 with still another method.

In this analysis instead of a stack of discs or a nest of cylinders, let us envision a nest of hemispherical shells as pictured in Figure 3.27.

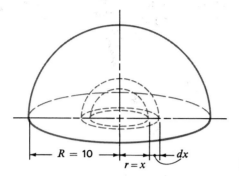

Figure 3.27

$$V_{0 \to 10} = \int_0^{10} A\,dx$$

A is the surface area of a hemisphere. Since the surface area of a sphere is $4\pi r^2$, then that of a hemisphere is $2\pi r^2$, but since $r = x$, $A = 2\pi x^2$, and

$$V = 2\pi \int_0^{10} x^2\,dx$$

$$= \frac{2\pi x^3}{3}\Big]_0^{10} = \frac{2\pi 10^3}{3} - \frac{2\pi 0^3}{3}$$

$$= \frac{2000\pi}{3}\ \text{cu in.}$$

Example 3.36. Calculate the volume of water remaining in a cylindrical vessel 6 inches in diameter and 6 inches tall when the vessel is tipped until the water line just coincides with a diameter of the base.

Figure 3.28 illustrates this situation. Figures 3.29a and b show the two triangles abc and bcd. Here the elemental volume will be the area of triangle bcd multiplied by the thickness dx. These triangles will be stacked from −3 to +3, but since this will involve two equal volumes, we could take the stacks from 0 to +3 and double the result. Therefore

$$V_{-3 \to +3} = 2\int_0^3 \tfrac{1}{2} h y\,dx$$

All the triangles stacked against triangle bcd will be similar to the triangle at $x = 0$ where $h = 6$ and $y = 3$. From this then $h = 2y$ and

$$V = 2\int_0^3 \tfrac{1}{2} 2yy\,dx$$

$$= 2\int_0^3 y^2\,dx$$

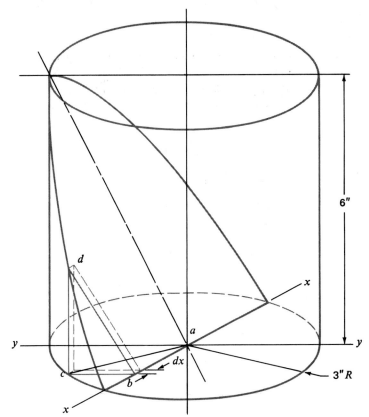

6"

y ——————————— y

3" R

Figure 3.28

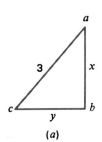

Figure 3.29   (a)   (b)

From triangle abc: $x^2 + y^2 = 9$ and $y^2 = 9 - x^2$, so

$$V = 2 \int_0^3 (9 - x^2)\,dx$$

$$= 2\left(9x - \frac{x^3}{3}\right)\Big]_0^3$$

$$= 18x - \frac{2x^3}{3}$$

$$= 18 \cdot 3 - \frac{2 \cdot 3 \cdot 3 \cdot 3}{3}$$

$$= 54 - 18$$

$$= 36 \text{ cu in.}$$

Example 3.37.   Calculate the volume common to two 4-inch diameter cylinders that intersect at right angles.

Figure 3.30 illustrates the problem. Note that the dark shaded area is the area with which we will be concerned. Note further that this area is a square. Therefore

$$V_{-2 \to +2} = 2 \int_0^2 (2w)^2 \, dx$$

but $x^2 + w^2 = 2^2$, so $w^2 = 4 - x^2$, and

$$V = 2 \int_0^2 4(4 - x^2) \, dx$$

$$= 8 \int_0^2 (4 - x^2) \, dx$$

$$= 8 \cdot 4x - \frac{8x^3}{3} \Bigg]_0^2$$

$$= 8 \cdot 4 \cdot 2 - \frac{8 \cdot 2 \cdot 2 \cdot 2}{3}$$

$$= 64 - \tfrac{64}{3} = \tfrac{128}{3}$$

$$= 42.666 \text{ cu in.}$$

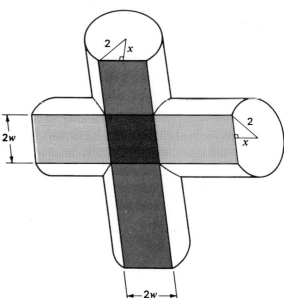

Figure 3.30

Exercise 3.10

1. Using integration calculate the volumes of spheres with radii of 6, 12, 18, and 20 inches.

2. Using integration calculate the volumes of both parts of a sphere with radius 18 when a plane is passed 12 inches from the center. Repeat for a sphere with 20-inch radius.
3. Find the volume common to two 4-inch radii cylinders intersecting at right angles.
4. Calculate the volume of the wedge cut from the 24-inch diameter cylindrical solid illustrated in Figure 3.31.

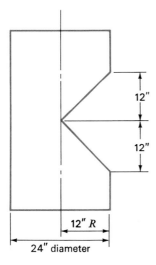

Figure 3.31

5. Find the volume removed from a 12-inch radius sphere when a 3-inch radius hole is bored through the center.
6. Calculate the number of cubic feet of liquid in a 6-foot diameter tank 10 feet long if it is laid horizontal and filled to within 4 feet of the top.

3.13 VOLUMES OF REVOLUTION

Whenever an area is revolved about a line, a *solid of revolution* results, and a cross-sectional area perpendicular to the axis of revolution is either a *disc* or a *ring*. If the cross section is a disc of radius r, then $V = \int \pi r^2 \, dx$. If the cross section is a ring with outside radius R and inside radius r, then

$$V = \int (\pi R^2 - \pi r^2) \, dx$$

$$= \pi \int (R^2 - r^2) \, dx$$

Example 3.38. Calculate the volume generated by revolving area A about the x axis, when area A is bounded by $y = x/2$, $x = 0$, $x = 4$, and $y = 0$.

Figure 3.32 illustrates the problem. Here

$$V = \int_0^4 \pi r^2 \, dx = \pi \int_0^4 r^2 \, dx$$

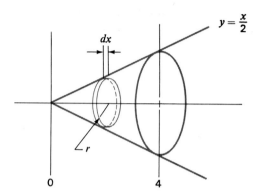

$$y = \frac{x}{2}$$

dx

r

0   4   Figure 3.32

However, $r = y$, so

$$V = \pi \int_0^4 y^2 \, dx$$

and from $y = x/2$, $y^2 = x^2/4$, therefore

$$V = \frac{\pi}{4} \int_0^4 x^2 \, dx$$

$$= \frac{\pi}{4} \left. \frac{x^3}{3} \right]_0^4 = \frac{\pi \cdot 4 \cdot 4 \cdot 4}{4 \cdot 3}$$

$$= \frac{16\pi}{3} \text{ cu in.}$$

Example 3.39.   Calculate the volume generated by revolving area A about the x axis when area A is bounded by $y = x/2$, $y = 1$, $x = 2$, and $x = 4$.
From Figure 3.33

$$V = \pi \int_2^4 (R^2 - r^2) \, dx$$

where $R = y$ and $r = 1$, so

$$V = \pi \int_2^4 (y^2 - 1) \, dx$$

but $y^2 = x^2/4$ from $y = x/2$, therefore

$$V = \pi \int_2^4 \left(\frac{x^2}{4} - 1 \right) dx$$

$$= \frac{\pi x^3}{4 \cdot 3} - \pi x \Big]_2^4$$

$$= \left[\left(\frac{\pi \cdot 4 \cdot 4 \cdot 4}{4 \cdot 3} \right) - \pi 4 \right] - \left[\left(\frac{\pi \cdot 2 \cdot 2 \cdot 2}{4 \cdot 3} \right) - \pi 2 \right]$$

$$= \left(\frac{16\pi}{3} - 4\pi \right) - \left(\frac{2\pi}{3} - 2\pi \right)$$

$$= \left(\frac{16\pi}{3} - \frac{12\pi}{3} \right) - \left(\frac{2\pi}{3} - \frac{6\pi}{3} \right)$$

$$= \frac{4\pi}{3} - \left(-\frac{4\pi}{3} \right)$$

$$= \frac{8\pi}{3} \text{ cu in.}$$

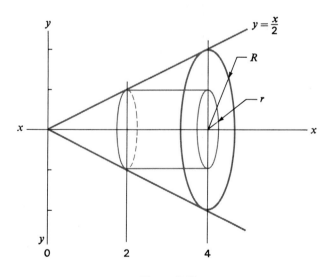

Figure 3.33

Example 3.40. Calculate the volume generated by revolving area A about the x axis and then about the y axis where area A is bounded by $y = x^2$, $y = 0$, $x = 0$, and $x = 3$.

For revolution around the x axis see Figure 3.34. Here

$$V = \int_0^3 A\,dx$$

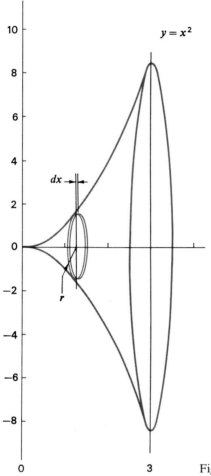

$$y = x^2$$

$$dx$$

$$r$$

0   3   Figure 3.34

$A = \pi r^2$, and $r = y = x^2$, so $r^2 = x^4$. Therefore

$$V = \pi \int_0^3 x^4\,dx$$

$$= \frac{\pi x^5}{5}\bigg]_0^3 = \frac{\pi \cdot 3 \cdot 3 \cdot 3 \cdot 3 \cdot 3}{5} = \frac{243\pi}{5} \text{ cu in.}$$

For revolution around the y axis see Figure 3.35. Here

$$V = \int_0^9 \pi r^2 \, dy$$

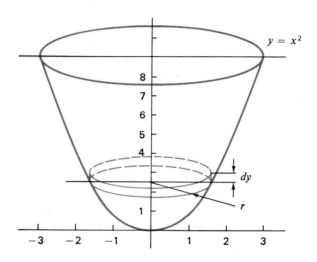

Figure 3.35

where $r = x = \sqrt{y} = y^{1/2}$ and $r^2 = y$; therefore

$$V = \pi \int_0^9 y \, dy$$

$$= \frac{\pi y^2}{2} \bigg]_0^9 = \frac{\pi \cdot 9 \cdot 9}{2}$$

$$= \frac{81\pi}{2} \text{ cu in.}$$

Example 3.41.   Calculate the volume generated by revolving area A about the x axis and then about the y axis where area A is bounded by $y = x^2/2$, $x = 2$, $x = 4$, and $y = 2$.

For revolution about the x axis see Figure 3.36. Here

$$V = \pi \int_2^4 (R^2 - r^2)\, dx$$

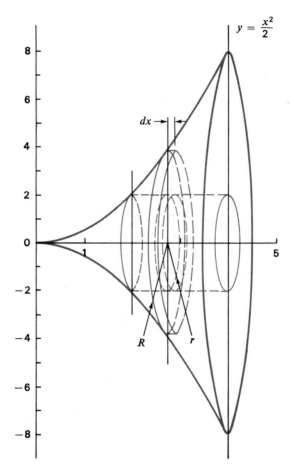

Figure 3.36

where $y = x^2/2$, $R^2 = x^4/4$, and $r = 2$, so $r^2 = 4$. Therefore

$$V = \pi \int_2^4 \left(\frac{x^4}{4} - 4 \right) dx$$

$$= \frac{\pi x^5}{4 \cdot 5} - 4\pi x \bigg]_2^4$$

$$= \left(\frac{\pi \cdot 4 \cdot 4 \cdot 4 \cdot 4 \cdot 4}{4 \cdot 5} - 4\pi 4 \right) - \left(\frac{\pi \cdot 2 \cdot 2 \cdot 2 \cdot 2 \cdot 2}{4 \cdot 5} - 4\pi 2 \right)$$

$$= \left(\frac{256\pi}{5} - 16\pi \right) - \left(\frac{8\pi}{5} - 8\pi \right)$$

$$= \frac{176\pi}{5} + \frac{32\pi}{5}$$

$$= \frac{208\pi}{5} \text{ cu in.}$$

For revolution about the *y* axis see Figure 3.37. Here

$$V = \pi \int_2^8 r^2 \, dy$$

where $r = x = \sqrt{2y}$, so $r^2 = 2y$ and

$$V = 2\pi \int_2^8 y \, dy$$

$$= \frac{2\pi y^2}{2} \Big]_2^8$$

$$= \pi \cdot 8 \cdot 8 - \pi \cdot 2 \cdot 2 = 64\pi - 4\pi$$

$$= 60\pi \text{ cu in.}$$

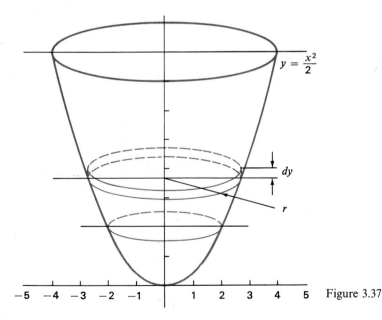

$$y = \frac{x^2}{2}$$

dy

r

−5   −4   −3   −2   −1   1   2   3   4   5   Figure 3.37

Example 3.42. Calculate the volume generated by revolving area *A* about the *x* axis if area *A* is bounded by $y = x$, $y = 1$, $x = 0$, and $y = 4$.

Figure 3.38 shows the area *abcd* with which we are concerned. Note that if we integrate from $x = 0$ to $x = 4$ with respect to x, the area *abe* will be included.

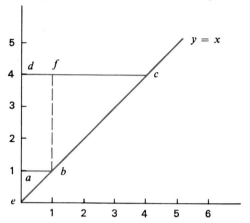

Figure 3.38

One method of overcoming this would be to calculate the volume generated by area *ecd*. Next calculate the volume generated by area *abe* and finally subtract the latter from the former. Or we could calculate the volume generated by area *bcf* and then the volume generated by area *abfd* and take their sum. Figure 3.39 shows the volume we seek.

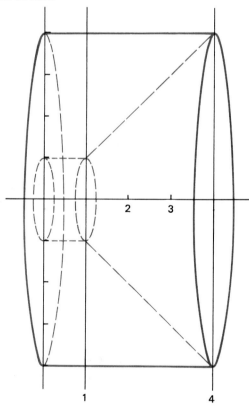

Figure 3.39

The former method is tried first.

$$V_{ecd} = \pi \int_0^4 (16 - y^2)\, dx$$

$$= \pi \int_0^4 (16 - x^2)\, dx$$

$$= 16\pi x - \left. \frac{x^3 \pi}{3} \right]_0^4$$

$$= 16(4\pi) - \frac{4 \cdot 4 \cdot 4 \cdot \pi}{3} = 64\pi - \frac{64\pi}{3}$$

$$= \frac{192\pi}{3} - \frac{64\pi}{3} = \frac{128\pi}{3}$$

$$V_{abe} = \pi \int_0^1 (1 - y^2)\, dx$$

$$= \pi \int_0^1 (1 - x^2)\, dx$$

$$= nx - \left. \frac{nx^3}{3} \right]_0^1$$

$$= \pi - \frac{\pi}{3} = \frac{3\pi}{3} - \frac{\pi}{3}$$

$$= \frac{2\pi}{3}$$

$$V_{abcd} = \frac{128\pi}{3} - \frac{2\pi}{3}$$

$$= \frac{126\pi}{3}$$

By the second or addition method:

$$V_{bcf} = \pi \int_1^4 (16 - x^2)\, dx$$

$$= \pi 16x - \left. \frac{\pi x^3}{3} \right]_1^4$$

$$= \left(16 \cdot 4\pi - \frac{4 \cdot 4 \cdot 4\pi}{3} \right) - \left(16 \cdot 1 - \frac{1 \cdot 1 \cdot 1\pi}{3} \right)$$

$$= \left(\frac{192\pi}{3} - \frac{64\pi}{3} \right) - \left(\frac{48\pi}{3} - \frac{\pi}{3} \right)$$

$$= \frac{128\pi}{3} - \frac{47\pi}{3} = \frac{81\pi}{3}$$

$$V_{abfd} = \pi(16 - 1)1 = 15\pi = \frac{45\pi}{3}$$

$$V_{abcd} = \frac{81\pi}{3} + \frac{45\pi}{3} = \frac{126\pi}{3}$$

Example 3.43.   Revolve the area in Example 3.42 about the *y* axis and calculate the volume.

See Figure 3.40. Here

$$V = \pi \int_{1}^{4} r^2 \, dy$$

$$= \pi \int_{1}^{4} x^2 \, dy$$

$$= \pi \int_{1}^{4} y^2 \, dy = \frac{\pi y^3}{3}\Bigg]_{1}^{4}$$

$$= \frac{4 \cdot 4 \cdot 4\pi}{3} - \frac{1 \cdot 1 \cdot 1\pi}{3}$$

$$= \frac{64\pi}{3} - \frac{\pi}{3} = \frac{63\pi}{3} = 21\pi$$

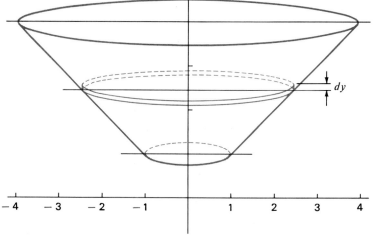

Figure 3.40   −4   −3   −2   −1   1   2   3   4

Exercise 3.11

1. Derive the formula for the volume of a right circular cone by revolving any line $y = mx$ about the *x* axis between $x = 0$ and $x = a$.
2. Calculate the volume generated by revolving area *A* about the *x* axis if area *A* is bounded by $y = x$, $y = x^2/2$, $x = 0$, and $x = 2$.

3. Calculate the volume generated by revolving area A from problem 2 about the y axis.
4. Calculate the volume generated by revolving area A about the x axis if area A is bounded by $y = 2x^2$, $y = 0$, $x = 0$, and $x = 1$.
5. Calculate the volume generated by revolving area A from problem 4 about the y axis.
6. Calculate the volume generated by revolving area A about the x axis if area A is bounded by $y = x^2/3$, $y = 1$, $x = 0$, and $x = 4$.
7. Calculate the volume generated by revolving area A from problem 6 about the y axis.
8. Calculate the volume generated by revolving area A about the x axis if area A is bounded by $x = y^2$, $x = 4$, $y = 0$, and $x = 0$.
9. Calculate the volume generated by revolving area A from problem 9 about the y axis.

3.14 ELECTRONICS

3.14.1 Total Charge by Integration

From (2.6) the current flowing in any circuit is $i = dq/dt$ from which $dq = i\,dt$. Integrating both sides we have $\int dq = \int i\,dt$, or

$$q = \int i\,dt \tag{3.19}$$

Here q is total charge in coulombs, i is current in amperes, and t is time.

Thus from (3.19) the total charge in a given circuit is found by integrating the formula for the current flowing with respect to time.

Recall from Section 2.9.7 that the charge in a capacitor is $q = Ce$, therefore $Ce = \int i\,dt$, and

$$e = \frac{1}{C}\int i\,dt \tag{3.20}$$

Example 3.44. Calculate the voltage across a 1-microfarad capacitor charged to 10 volts at $t = 0.05$ second. If at $t = 0$ the current flowing is $i = t^2$, then

$$e = \frac{1}{C}\int i\,dt$$
$$= \frac{1}{10^{-6}}\int t^2\,dt$$
$$= \frac{1}{10^{-6}}\frac{t^3}{3} + C$$
$$= \frac{10^6}{3}t^3 + C$$

When $t = 0$, $e = 10$, so $C = 10$; therefore, when $t = 0.05$,

$$e = \frac{10^6}{3}(0.05)^3 + 10$$

$$= \frac{10^6}{3}(.000125) + 10$$

$$= 41.66 + 10 = 51.66 \text{ volts}$$

3.14.2 Required Flux for a Given Emf

From (2.7) we have $e = -N\, d\phi/dt$, so $e\, dt = -N\, d\phi$, or $-N\, d\phi = e\, dt$ or $d\phi = -(1/N)e\, dt$. By integrating both sides we have:

$$\phi = -\frac{1}{N}\int e\, dt \tag{3.21}$$

where ϕ is in webers.

3.14.3 Required Current for a Given Emf

From (2.10) $e = -L\, di/dt$, so $-L\, di = e\, dt$ or $di = -(1/L)e\, dt$, and by integrating both sides:

$$i = -\frac{1}{L}\int e\, dt \tag{3.22}$$

where i is in amperes.

Likewise from (2.11) $e_2 = -M\, di_1/dt$, so $-M\, di_1 = e_2\, dt$ or $di_1 = -(1/M)e_2\, dt$, and by integration

$$i_1 = -\frac{1}{M}\int e_2\, dt \tag{3.23}$$

Example 3.45.   Calculate the formula for the current in an inductance circuit if the induced voltage varies according to $e = 9t^2 - 2t$ and the current in the 10-henry coil is 2.0 amp, at $t = 0$.

From (3.21) $$i = -\frac{1}{L}\int e\, dt$$

$$= -\frac{1}{10}\int (9t^2 - 2t)\, dt$$

$$= -\frac{1}{10}\left(\frac{9t^3}{3} - \frac{2t^2}{2} + C_1\right)$$

$$= -\frac{3t^3}{10} + \frac{t^2}{10} + C$$

But $i = 2.2$ when $t = 0$, so $2.2 = 0 + 0 + C$, from which $C = 2.2$; therefore

$$i = -\frac{3t^3}{10} + \frac{t^2}{10} + 2.2$$

3.14.4 Work from Power

From (2.8) $p = dw/dt$, so $p\,dt = dw$, and by integration

$$w = \int p\,dt \qquad\qquad (3.24)$$

Here work (w) is in joules and p can be expressed in one of several ways:

$$p = ei \qquad \text{or} \qquad p = i^2 r \qquad \text{or} \qquad p = \frac{e^2}{r}$$

Exercise 3.12

1. How many coulombs are transmitted in 2 seconds in a circuit where the current is $i = 3t^3$?
2. What is the charge after 0.2 second in a circuit if the current varies as $i = 2t$ and the capacitor charge is 0.01 coulomb?
3. Calculate the time in seconds it takes a 75-microfarad capacitor voltage to build to 220 volts if the initial charge is 90 volts and the current supplied so as to boost the charge varies as $i = 3t^3$.
4. Calculate a formula for current in a 10-henry inductor if the induced voltage varies as $e = t^{1/2} - 3$.
5. Calculate the formula for primary current in a transformer, where the mutual inductance is 5 henrys, which will induce a secondary voltage that varies as $e_2 = t^2 - 3t$.
6. Calculate the energy used in a circuit where $p = 1200t^2 + 400t$ and t varies from zero to 3 seconds.
7. Calculate the energy used in a circuit if the current varies according to $i = 3t^2$ and resistance varies according to $r = t^{-1/2}$ between $t = 0$ and $t = 3$ seconds.

3.14.5 Integrating Circuits

Recall that we discussed two circuits whose output was proportional to the derivative of the input voltage. Figure 3.41 is a circuit whose output voltage is proportional to the integral of the input current, that is,

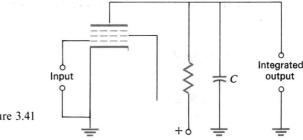

Figure 3.41

$$e = \frac{1}{C} \int i \, dt \qquad (3.25)$$

Figure 3.42 illustrates an RL integrating circuit. Here $e = L \, di/dt$, so $L \, di = e \, dt$ and $di = (1/L)e \, dt$; then integrating produces

$$i = \frac{1}{L} \int e \, dt \qquad (3.26)$$

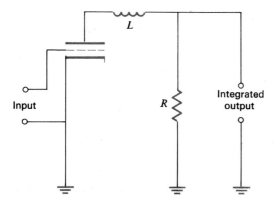

Figure 3.42

where i is the current in the inductor and e is the voltage applied to the inductor. Here then the voltage output E will be: $E = Ri$, so by substitution

$$E = \frac{R}{L} \int e \, dt \qquad (3.27)$$

Here the output voltage is proportional to the integral of the input voltage.

> **Exercise 3.13.**   Make a sketch of each input waveform in Exercise 3.12, and under each sketch the wave resulting from integration using a capacitive integrator circuit.

3.15 INTEGRATION BY PARTS

Recall from Section 2.11 that if $y = uv$, then $dy/dx = u \, dv/dx + v \, du/dx$ where u and v are functions of x. And since integration is the inverse of differentiation, we have

$$\int dy = \int u \, dv + \int v \, du$$

or $$uv = \int u \, dv + \int v \, du$$

and

$$\int u \, dv = uv - \int v \, du \tag{3.28}$$

Equation (3.28) allows us to manipulate certain difficult integrals into forms that can be integrated.

Example 3.46. Integrate ln x dx.

Here no method so far will do, so we try integration by parts. That is, we must equate ln x to $u \, dv$: $\ln x = u \, dv$.

We can do this if $u = \ln x$ and $dv = 1$, then $du = (1/x) \, dx$ and $v = x$, and from (3.28)

$$\int \ln x = x \ln x - \int x \frac{1}{x} \, dx$$

$$= x \ln x - x + C$$

If we had decided at the start to let $u = 1$ and $dv = \ln x$, which would be possible, we would arrive at a stalemate. If $dv = \ln x$, then to find v we would have to integrate ln x, which is the given problem.

Example 3.47. Evaluate $\int xe^x \, dx$.

Here again no method seems to apply, so we try integration by parts.

Let $u = x$ and $dv = e^x \, dx$, from which $du = dx$ and $v = \int e^x \, dx = e^x$. From (3.27) then

$$\int xe^x \, dx = xe^x - \int e^x \, dx$$

and

$$\int xe^x \, dx = xe^x - e^x + C$$

Example 3.48. Evaluate $\int_0^\pi x \sin x \, dx$.

Using integration by parts we let $u = x$ and $dv = \sin x \, dx$, from which $du = dx$ and $v = -\cos x$. Then

$$\int_0^\pi x \sin x \, dx = -x \cos x \Big]_0^\pi - \int_0^\pi - \cos x \, dx$$

$$= -\pi \cos \pi + 0 \cos 0 + \sin \pi - \sin 0$$

$$= \pi$$

If we had chosen at the start to let $u = \sin x$ and $dv = x \, dx$, from which $du = \cos x \, dx$ and $v = x^2/2$, we would have

$$\int_0^\pi x \sin x \, dx = \frac{x^2}{2} \sin x \Big]_0^\pi - \frac{1}{2} \int_0^\pi x^2 \cos x \, dx$$

This is just as difficult as the given problem, so obviously the first choice was the best.

Example 3.49. Evaluate

$$\int \frac{x^3}{\sqrt{1 + x^2}} \, dx$$

Here let $u = x^2$ and

$$dv = \frac{x}{\sqrt{1 + x^2}} \, dx$$

$$= x(1 + x^2)^{-\frac{1}{2}} \, dx$$

Then $du = 2x \, dx$ and

$$v = \int x(1 + x^2)^{-\frac{1}{2}} \, dx = \sqrt{1 + x^2}$$

Using (3.28)

$$\int \frac{x^3}{\sqrt{1 + x^2}} \, dx = x^2 \sqrt{1 + x^2} - \int 2x \sqrt{1 + x^2} \, dx$$

$$= x^2 \sqrt{1 + x^2} - \tfrac{2}{3}(1 + x^2)^{\frac{3}{2}} + C$$

$$= \frac{x^2 - 2}{3} \sqrt{1 + x^2} + C$$

At the start it may have seemed natural to let $u = x^3$ and $dv = 1/\sqrt{1 + x^2} \, dx$, from which $du = 3x^2 \, dx$ and $v = \int (dx)/\sqrt{1 + x^2}$. Obviously v would be no easier than the original problem.

Integration by parts is a fine method but does require experience in choosing u and dv. You must solve many problems to become proficient in your choice of u and dv.

Exercise 3.14.   Integrate the following.

1. $\int e^x \cos x \, dx$
2. $\int e^x \sin x \, dx$
3. $\int x^2 \sin x \, dx$
4. $\int x^3 \sqrt{x^2 - 2} \, dx$
5. $\int x^2 \ln x \, dx$
6. $\int \sqrt{x} \ln x \, dx$
7. $\int x \cos x \, dx$
8. $\int x e^x \, dx$
9. $\int \sec^5 x \, dx$
10. $\int x^2 e^x \, dx$
11. $\int (x \, dx)/\sqrt{2x + 1}$
12. $\int e^{2x} \sin 3x \, dx$
13. $\int e^{-x} \cos x \, dx$
14. $\int x^3 \sqrt{1 - x^2} \, dx$
15. $\int \ln (x^2 + 1) \, dx$
16. $\int x^3/e^{x^2} \, dx$

3.16 INTEGRATION BY DIVISION (PARTIAL FRACTIONS)

Suppose we are asked to integrate a quotient such as $(2x^4 + 3x^3 - x^2 + x - 1)/(x^3 - x)$. It soon becomes evident that by regular or special methods to date this will be difficult. Let us then explore an additional method.

If $2x^4 + 3x^3 - x^2 + x - 1$ is divided by $x^3 - x$, the quotient becomes:

$$2x + 3 + \frac{x^2 + 4x - 1}{x3 - x}$$

or $\quad f(x) = \dfrac{F(x)}{G(x)} = Q(x) + \dfrac{R(x)}{G(x)}$ \hfill (3.29)

In (3.29) $f(x)$ is known as a rational function with $Q(x)$ the quotient and $R(x)$ the remainder. Both $Q(x)$ and $R(x)$ are polynomials and $R(x)$ is of degree less than the degree of $G(x)$. Should $F(x)$ be of degree less than $G(x)$, then $Q(x)$ will be zero and $R(x) = F(x)$.

From all of this then:

$$\int \frac{2x^4 + 3x^3 - x^2 + x - 1}{x^3 - x}\, dx = \int 2x\, dx + \int 3\, dx$$

$$+ \int \frac{x^2 + 4x - 1}{x^3 - x}\, dx$$

We now turn our attention to $(x^2 + 4x - 1)/(x^3 - x)$ as we discuss partial fractions.

Most proper fractions can be written as the sum of other fractions, called *partial fractions*, whose denominators are of lower degree than the denominator of the given fraction. For example, the fraction $(3x - 5)/(x^2 - 3x + 2)$ can be written as the sum of two partial fractions:

$$\frac{3x - 5}{x^2 - 3x + 2} = \frac{3x - 5}{(x - 1)(x - 2)} = \frac{2}{x - 1} + \frac{1}{x - 2}$$

The formation of partial fractions from a given proper fraction is controlled by the factors of the given denominator. Several possibilities present themselves.

> *Given denominator has linear factors, none of which is repeated.*
> *If a linear factor* ax + b *occurs once as a factor of the given*
> *denominator, then to this factor associate the partial fraction*
> A/(ax + b), *where A is a constant not equal to zero.*   (3.30)

Examples:

$$\frac{x + 4}{2x^2 + 15x + 7} = \frac{x + 4}{(x + 7)(2x + 1)} = \frac{A}{x + 7} + \frac{B}{2x + 1}$$

$$\frac{x^2 + 4x - 1}{x^3 - x} = \frac{x^2 + 4x - 1}{x(x + 1)(x - 1)} = \frac{A}{x} + \frac{B}{x - 1} + \frac{C}{x + 1}$$

> *Given denominator has linear factors, some of which are*
> *repeated. If a linear factor* ax + b *occurs* p *times in the given*   (3.31)
> *denominator, then to these factors associate* p *partial fractions.*

$$\frac{A_1}{ax + b} + \frac{A_2}{(ax + b)^2} + \frac{A_3}{(ax + b)^3} + \cdots + \frac{A_p}{(ax + b)^p}$$

where $A_1, A_2, A_3, \ldots A_p$ are constants and $A_p \neq 0$.

Examples:

$$\frac{3x - 1}{(x + 4)^2} = \frac{3x - 1}{(x + 4)(x + 4)} = \frac{A}{x + 4} + \frac{B}{(x + 4)^2}$$

$$\frac{5x^2 - 2}{x^3(x + 1)^2} = \frac{5x^2 - 2}{x^3(x + 1)(x + 1)} = \frac{A}{x^3} + \frac{B}{x^2} + \frac{C}{x}$$

$$+ \frac{D}{(x + 1)^2} + \frac{E}{x + 1}$$

> *Given denominator has quadratic factors, none of which is repeated. If a quadratic factor* $ax^2 + bx + c$ *occurs as a factor of the given denominator, then to this factor associate the partial fraction* $(Ax + B)/(ax^2 + bx + c)$, *where A and B are constants both of which are not zero.* $ax^2 + bx + c$ *cannot be factored into two real linear factors with integral coefficients.*   (3.32)

Examples:

$$\frac{x^2 - 3}{x^3 + 4x - 2x^2 - 8} = \frac{x^2 - 3}{(x - 2)(x^2 + 4)} = \frac{A}{x - 2} + \frac{Bx + C}{x^2 + 4}$$

$$\frac{2x^3 - 6}{x(2x^2 + 3x + 8)(x^2 + x + 1)} = \frac{A}{x} + \frac{Bx + C}{2x^2 + 3x + 8} + \frac{Dx + E}{x^2 + x + 1}$$

> *Given denominator has quadratic factors, some of which are repeated. If a quadratic factor* $ax^2 + bx + c$ *occurs p times as a factor of the given denominator, then associate p partial fractions.*   (3.33)

Examples:

$$\frac{A_1x + B_1}{ax^2 + bx + c} + \frac{A_2x + B_2}{(ax^2 + bx + c)^2} + \cdots + \frac{A_px + B_p}{(ax^2 + bx + c)^p}$$

with $A_1, B_1, A_2, B_2, \ldots, A_p, B_p$ constants and A_p, B_p not both equal to zero.

$$\frac{x^2 - 4x + 1}{(x^2 + 1)^2(x^2 + x + 1)} = \frac{Ax + B}{(x^2 + 1)^2} + \frac{Cx + D}{(x^2 + 1)} + \frac{Ex + F}{x^2 + x + 1}$$

Example 3.50. Resolve $(x + 2)/(2x^2 - 7x - 15)$ into partial fractions.

$$\frac{x + 2}{2x^2 - 7x - 15} = \frac{A}{2x + 3} + \frac{B}{x - 5} = \frac{A(x - 5) + B(2x + 3)}{(2x + 3)(x - 5)}$$

From this then

$$x + 2 = A(x - 5) + B(2x + 3)$$

$$= Ax - 5A + 2Bx + 3B$$

$$= Ax + 2Bx - 5A + 3B$$

$$= (A + 2B)x + (-5A + 3B)$$

Equating the coefficients of x and the constants,

$$A + 2B = 1$$

$$-5A + 3B = 2$$

and solving these simultaneous equations:

$$5A + 10B = 5$$

$$\underline{-5A + 3B = 2}$$

$$13B = 7 \qquad \text{or} \qquad B = \tfrac{7}{13}$$

and

$$3A + 6B = 3$$

$$\underline{-10A + 6B = 4}$$

$$13A = -1 \qquad \text{or} \qquad A = -\tfrac{1}{13}$$

therefore:

$$\frac{x + 2}{2x^2 - 7x - 15} = \frac{-1/13}{2x + 3} + \frac{7/13}{x - 5} = \frac{-1}{13(2x + 3)} + \frac{7}{13(x - 5)}$$

Example 3.51. Integrate the expression given at the beginning of this section. Using (3.29) and our current discussion, we have:

$$\frac{x^2 + 4x - 1}{x(x + 1)(x - 1)} = \frac{A}{x} + \frac{B}{x - 1} + \frac{C}{x + 1}$$

$$= \frac{A(x - 1)(x + 1)}{x(x + 1)(x - 1)} + \frac{B(x)(x + 1)}{x(x + 1)(x - 1)} + \frac{C(x)(x - 1)}{x(x + 1)(x - 1)}$$

$$= \frac{A(x^2 - 1) + B(x^2 + x) + C(x^2 - x)}{x(x + 1)(x - 1)}$$

$$= \frac{Ax^2 - A + Bx^2 + Bx + Cx^2 - Cx}{x(x + 1)(x - 1)}$$

$$= \frac{Ax^2 + Bx^2 + Cx^2 + Bx - Cx - A}{x(x + 1)(x - 1)}$$

So $x^2 + 4x - 1 = (A + B + C)x^2 + (B - C)x - A$ and

$$A + B + C = 1$$

$$B - C = 4$$

$$-A = -1$$

Therefore $A = 1$ and

$$B + C = 0$$

$$\underline{B - C = 4}$$

$$2B \quad = 4 \qquad \text{or} \qquad B = 2 \text{ and } C = -2$$

$$\frac{x^2 + 4x - 1}{x(x + 1)(x - 1)} = \frac{1}{x} + \frac{2}{x - 1} - \frac{2}{x + 1}$$

Our integration problem then becomes:

$$\int \frac{2x^4 + 3x^3 - x^2 - 1}{x^3 - x} dx =$$

$$\int 2x \, dx + \int 3 \, dx + \int \frac{x^2 + 4x - 1}{x^3 - x} dx =$$

$$2 \int x \, dx + 3 \int dx + \int \frac{dx}{x} + 2 \int \frac{dx}{x - 1} - 2 \int \frac{dx}{x + 1}$$

Exercise 3.15

1. Resolve $(x + 2)/(2x^2 - 7x - 15)$ into partial fractions.
2. Resolve $(2x^2 + 10x - 3)/(x + 1)(x + 3)(x - 3)$ into partial fractions.
3. Resolve $(2x^2 + 7x + 23)/(x - 1)(x + 3)^2$ into partial fractions.
4. Find A, B, and C if:

$$\frac{2x^2 + 7x + 23}{(x - 1)(x + 3)^2} = \frac{A}{x - 1} + \frac{B}{(x + 3)^2} + \frac{C}{x + 3}$$

5. Resolve $(x^2 - 4x - 15)/(x + 2)^3$ into partial fractions.
6. Find A, B, and C if:

$$\frac{7x^2 - 25x + 6}{(x^2 - 2x - 1)(3x - 2)} = \frac{Ax + B}{x^2 - 2x - 1} + \frac{C}{3x - 2}$$

7. Resolve $(4x^2 - 28)/(x^4 + x^2 - 6)$ into partial fractions.

3.17 ADDITIONAL INTEGRATION METHODS

Since integration is not a precise mathematical process many expressions will not integrate by any method thus far discussed. For these there are many approaches. We shall explore five of these methods.

Integral Tables

Many formulas for integration have been developed over the years and have been printed in standard tables of integration. These tables appear in mathematical, engineering, and electronic handbooks. Every technical student should own at least one handbook that applies to his field of endeavor.

Before trying to use a table of integrals, the student should spend some time in familiarizing himself with the tables. The various types of expressions to be integrated are classified into groups by type. The following precautions should be carefully exercised.

1. If exact limits are given these must be observed.
2. At no time may a denominator evaluate to zero.
3. Even roots of negative numbers must be avoided.
4. Make sure what base is intended when logarithmic expressions are presented.

Many times your problem will not fit any type listed, but by mathematical manipulation it might be changed into a listed type.

> *Example 3.52.* Calculate the average ordinate under $y = \sin^2 x$ between $x = 0$ and $x = \pi$. Finally calculate the effective ordinate.
>
> First we must find the area under the curve.
>
> $$A \underset{0 \to \pi}{=} \int_0^\pi \sin^2 x\, dx = \int_0^\pi (\sin x)^2\, dx$$
>
> and since this will not integrate by ordinary methods, we go to the integral tables. Here we find:
>
> $$\int \sin^2 x\, dx = \tfrac{1}{2}x - \tfrac{1}{4}\sin 2x$$
>
> so
>
> $$A \underset{0 \to \pi}{=} \int_0^\pi \sin^2 x\, dx = \tfrac{1}{2}x - \tfrac{1}{4}\sin 2x \Big]_0^\pi$$
>
> $$= \left(\frac{\pi}{2} - \frac{1}{4}\sin 2\pi\right) - \left(\frac{0}{2} - \frac{0}{4}\sin 0\right)$$
>
> $$= \frac{\pi}{2}$$
>
> It should be noted that we did not have to use the integral tables. We could have used trigonometric identities:
>
> $$\cos 2x = 1 - 2\sin^2 x$$
>
> $$-2\sin^2 x = \cos 2x - 1$$
>
> $$2\sin^2 x = 1 - \cos 2x$$
>
> $$\sin^2 x = \tfrac{1}{2} - \tfrac{1}{2}\cos 2x$$

Therefore:

$$\int_0^\pi \sin^2 x \, dx = \frac{1}{2} \int_0^\pi dx - \frac{1}{2} \int_0^\pi \cos 2x \, dx$$

$$= \frac{1}{2} x - \frac{1}{4} \sin 2x \Big]_0^\pi$$

$$= \frac{\pi}{2}$$

By two methods we have found the area under $y = \sin^2 x$ between $x = 0$ and $x = \pi$ to be $\pi/2$. The average ordinate then is found by dividing the area by the change in x.

$$\text{Average ordinate} = \frac{\pi}{2} \div \frac{\pi}{1} = \frac{\pi}{2} \cdot \frac{1}{\pi} = \frac{1}{2}$$

The average ordinate is important to us in finding the effective ordinate. Effective ordinate under $y = \sin^2 x$ is, by definition:

$$y_{\text{eff}} = \sqrt{(\text{av ord}) \sin^2 x}$$

$$= \sqrt{(1/2)}$$

$$= \frac{1}{\sqrt{2}} = \frac{\sqrt{2}}{2} = 0.707$$

Example 3.53.   Integrate $(4x \, dx)/(5x + 3)$.

From a table of integrals we find:

$$\int \frac{x \, dx}{a + bx} = \frac{1}{b^2} [a + bx - a \ln (a + bx)]$$

With a minor change our problem fits this type, thus we have

$$\int \frac{4x \, dx}{5x + 3} = 4 \int \frac{x \, dx}{3 + 5x}$$

where $a = 3$ and $b = 5$, from which

$$4 \int \frac{x \, dx}{3 + 5x} = \frac{1}{25} [3 + 5x - 3 \ln (3 + 5x)]$$

Example 3.54.   Integrate $8 \sin^4 x \, dx$ between $x = 0$ and $x = \pi/2$.

From a table:

$$\int \sin^4 x \, dx = \frac{3x}{8} - \frac{\sin 2x}{4} + \frac{\sin 4x}{32}$$

Therefore

$$8 \int_0^{\pi/2} \sin^4 x \, dx = 3x - 2 \sin 2x + \left. \frac{\sin 4x}{4} \right]_0^{\pi/2}$$

$$= \frac{3\pi}{2} - 2 \sin \pi + \frac{\sin 2\pi}{4}$$

$$= 4.7124 - 2(0) + \frac{0}{4}$$

$$= 4.7124$$

Example 3.55. Integrate $\sqrt{9 - x^2} \, dx$ between $x = 0$ and $x = 1$.
From a table:

$$\int \sqrt{a^2 - x^2} \, dx = \frac{1}{2} \left(x \sqrt{a^2 - x^2} + a^2 \sin^{-1} \frac{x}{a} \right)$$

In our problem, $a = 3$ and $a^2 = 9$, therefore

$$\int_0^1 \sqrt{9 - x^2} \, dx = \frac{1}{2} \left(x \sqrt{9 - x^2} + 9 \sin^{-1} \frac{x}{3} \right) \Big]_0^1$$

$$= \frac{1}{2} (1 \sqrt{9 - 1} + 9 \cdot 0.34034) - \frac{1}{2} (0 \sqrt{9 - 0} + 9(0))$$

$$= \frac{1}{2} (\sqrt{8} + 3.063) - 0$$

$$= \frac{\sqrt{8}}{2} + 1.532$$

$$= \frac{2\sqrt{2}}{2} + 1.532$$

$$= 1.414 + 1.532$$

$$= 2.946$$

Binomial Expansion

Since $(x + 1)^2 = x^2 + 2x + 1$, to integrate $(x + 1)^2$ we should be able to integrate $x^2 + 2x + 1$. Let us see if this is true.

$$\int_0^1 (x + 1)^2 \, dx = \left. \frac{(x + 1)^3}{3} \right]_0^1$$

$$= \frac{(1 + 1)^3}{3} - \frac{(0 + 1)^3}{3}$$

$$= \frac{2^3}{3} - \frac{1}{3} = \frac{8}{3} - \frac{1}{3} = \frac{7}{3}$$

And $$\int_0^1 (x + 1)^2 \, dx = \int_0^1 (x^2 + 2x + 1) \, dx$$

$$= \left. \frac{x^3}{3} + \frac{2x^2}{2} + x \right]_0^1 = \frac{1}{3} + 1 + 1$$

$$= \frac{1}{3} + \frac{3}{3} + \frac{3}{3} = \frac{7}{3}$$

This then shows us what we could do, though with this particular problem we probably would not, for there is no apparent need. However, if we are asked to integrate some $(1 + x)^n$ which turns out to be difficult and the expansion of $(1 + x)^n$ is a convergent series, expanding to integrate is advised. Convergency means that each succeeding term of the expansion is smaller than its predecessor or the sum of the series approaches a limit.

Example 3.56.   Evaluate

$$\int_0^1 \left(1 + \frac{1}{2x^2} \right)^{\frac{1}{2}} dx$$

Here $u = 1 + \frac{1}{2}x^{-2}$ and $du = -x^{-1} \, dx = -dx/x$ and no mathematical manipulation will produce the required du. We then can either look to a table of integrals or try expansion. Let us try the expansion which will produce an infinite number of terms. Convergency will allow us to drop all terms that become very small.

$$\left(1 + \frac{1}{2x^2} \right)^{\frac{1}{2}} = 1 \cdot 1^{\frac{1}{2}} + \frac{1}{2} 1^{-\frac{1}{2}} \left(\frac{1}{2x^2} \right) + \frac{-1}{8} 1^{-\frac{3}{2}} \left(\frac{1}{2x^2} \right)^2$$

$$+ \frac{1}{16} 1^{-\frac{5}{2}} \left(\frac{1}{2x^2} \right)^3 + \frac{-5}{128} 1^{-\frac{7}{2}} \left(\frac{1}{2x^2} \right)^4 + \cdots$$

$$= 1 + \frac{1}{4x^2} - \frac{1}{32x^4} + \frac{1}{128x^6} - \frac{5}{2048x^8} + \cdots$$

Therefore:

$$\int_0^1 \left(1 + \frac{1}{4}x^{-2} - \frac{1}{32}x^{-4} + \frac{1}{128}x^{-6} - \frac{5}{2048}x^{-8} + \cdots\right)dx$$

$$= x - \frac{1}{4x} + \frac{1}{96x^3} - \frac{1}{640x^5} - \frac{5}{14336x^7} - \cdots\Bigg]_0^1$$

$$= 1 - \frac{1}{4} + \frac{1}{96} - \frac{1}{640} + \frac{5}{14336} + \cdots$$

$$= 0.759204$$

It should be noted that the answer thus obtained is not exact because all the terms after the fifth were dropped. The last term used was 5/14336, which is 0.000348, so the next term would have to be very small with the succeeding terms even smaller. If the series is convergent and the value of the terms falls off rapidly after a certain point, then this method is recommended.

Graphical Methods

The graphical method has already been mentioned in Unit 1 and, although it is not an ideal method, it is still a usable method when others fail. To integrate with limits some function of x using the graphical method, a large exact plot of the function between the limits of integration must be made. The area under the curve is then broken up into rectangles, squares, and triangles, or approximate triangles and their individual areas calculated and summed.

Computer Methods

Modern high-speed computers are ideally suited to successive multiplication with a running total being kept of these products. This is nothing more than calculating the area under a curve by adding all the areas of small elemental strips under the curve very much as was done in Section 3.7. As an example, assume we are to integrate some function of x between a and b. See Figure 3.10.

We must divide the line segment $\overline{ab}$ into n number of parts, thus establishing Δx. The larger n the more arithmetic involved, but this is no problem for a computer, so let us choose our n of such a size so that $\Delta x = 0.00000000001$. Then let the length of line segment $\overline{ab}$ equal $b - a$ and call it L.

Now by some computer language we must tell the computer the following things:

1. $x = a$
2. $\Delta x = 0.00000000001$ ⎫
3. $b = L + a$ ⎬ Store
4. $A = 0.0000000000$ ⎭
5. $A = (\Delta x) f[x]$ ⎫
10. $A = A + A$ ⎬ Execute
15. $x = x + (\Delta x)$ ⎭
20. If $x < b$ Go to 5   ⎫ Check
25. If $x = b$ Go to 30   ⎭
30. Print A Printout

If all is correct the printout should be the area between $x = a$ and $x = b$ under $y = f(x)$, which is the definite integral between a and b. The information listed above should be put into a computer program in Fortran or machine language by the mathematician or a programmer.

Simpson's Rule

Simpson's rule is not as popular today as it has been in the past, mainly because of the computer. In the preceding computer program the individual strip areas are calculated on the assumption that the strips are rectangles, which they are not. This error becomes less and less important as Δx gets smaller and smaller. Keeping Δx small is easy with a computer because all that is involved is a few more minutes of execution time. Simpson's rule uses the concept of fitting parabolas to the top of the strips instead of straight lines, thus forming trapezoids with curved lines at the top.

The rule passes a parabola of the form $y = ax^2 + bx + c$ through the first three points (x_0, y_0), (x_1, y_1), and (x_2, y_2), and then calculates the area under this parabola. Then a parabola is passed through (x_2, y_2), (x_3, y_3), and (x_4, y_4) and the area calculated here. This process is repeated until the entire required area is obtained. All of this sounds involved and the derivation is, but we will not concern ourselves with the derivation, just the use of the rule.

$$\int f(x)\, dx = \frac{x}{3}(y_0 + 4y_1 + 2y_2 + 4y_3 + 2y_4 + \cdots + 4y_{(n-1)} + y_n) \qquad (3.34)$$

Since the points are taken three at a time, it is necessary that n be an even number.

Example 3.57.   Calculate the area under $y = -x^2 + 10x$ between $x = 0$ and $x = 10$ using Simpson's rule.
Letting $n = 10$, $x = 1$, and

$$\int_0^{10} (-x^2 + 10x)\,dx = \tfrac{1}{3}\,[0 + 4(9) + 2(16) + 4(21) + 2(24) + 4(25)$$

$$+\ 2(24) + 4(21) + 2(16) + 4(9) + 0]$$

$$=\tfrac{1}{3}\,(36 + 32 + 84 + 48 + 100 + 48 + 84 + 32 + 36)$$

$$=\tfrac{1}{3}\,500 = \tfrac{500}{3} = 166.66$$

Exercise 3.16. Unless the method is specified, integrate by any method you choose.

1. $\int (x^2\,dx)/(3 + 2x^2) =$ 2. $\int \sin^3 x\,dx =$

3. $\int \cos^3 x\,dx =$ 4. $\int dx/\cos^2 x =$

5. $\int x^5 \sin x\,dx =$

6. $\int_0^1 [1 + (1/x^2)]^{\frac{1}{2}} =$ (use binomial expansion)

7. $\int_0^5 (x^2 + 10x)\,dx =$ (use Simpson's rule)

8. $\int_0^5 (x^2 + 10x)\,dx =$ (use rectangular method)

9. $\int_3^7 x(1 + 3x)^{\frac{1}{2}}\,dx =$ 10. $\int_2^5 (x^2\,dx)/(3x + 5)^{\frac{1}{2}} =$

11. $\int_{0.2}^{0.4} (x\,dx)/(3 - 4x) =$

12. $\displaystyle\int_0^{0.5} \left(\frac{1 + x}{1 - x}\right)^{\frac{1}{2}} dx =$

13. $\int x(2 + 3x)^3\,dx =$ 14. $\int dx/(1 + 3x + 2x^2) =$

15. $\int x^2 \sqrt{1 + x}\,dx =$ 16. $\int (x\,dx)/\sqrt{25 - x^2} =$

17. $\int \sqrt{1 - \cos x}\,dx =$ 18. $\int (\sin 3x)(\sin 2x)\,dx =$

19. $\int \cos^4 x\,dx =$ 20. $\int \tan^4 x\,dx =$

3.18 LENGTH OF A CURVED LINE

Recall the formula for the distance between two points P_1 and P_2:

$$\overline{P_1 P_2} = \sqrt{(x_2 - x_1)^2 + (y_2 - y_1)^2}$$

A look at this formula and Figure 3.43 shows that nothing more complicated than the Pythagorean theorem is used. If we let $\Delta x = x_2 - x_1$ and $\Delta y = y_2 - y_1$, we have

$$\overline{P_1 P_2} = \sqrt{(\Delta x)^2 + (\Delta y)^2}$$

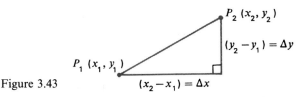

Figure 3.43

If the two points in question are on a curved line (see Figure 3.44), then we have

$$\overline{P_1 P_2} = \sqrt{(\Delta x)^2 + (\Delta y)^2}$$

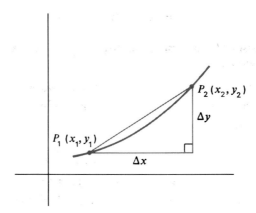

Figure 3.44

If we are striving to find the length of a curved-line segment, we first find the lengths of many straight-line segments connecting points on the curved line. See Figure 3.45, where the curved-line segment is broken up into five segments by six points, P_1, P_2, P_3, P_4, P_5, and P_6, from which the length L becomes:

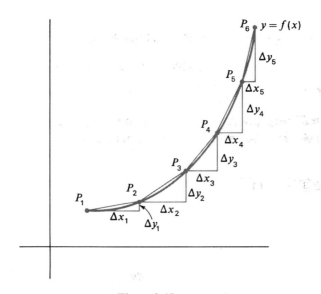

Figure 3.45

$$L \approx \overline{P_1P_2} + \overline{P_2P_3} + \overline{P_3P_4} + \overline{P_4P_5} + \overline{P_5P_6}$$

where

$$\overline{P_1P_2} = \sqrt{(\Delta x_1)^2 + (\Delta y_1)^2}$$

$$\overline{P_2P_3} = \sqrt{(\Delta x_2)^2 + (\Delta y_2)^2}$$

$$\overline{P_3P_4} = \sqrt{(\Delta x_3)^2 + (\Delta y_3)^2}$$

$$\overline{P_4P_5} = \sqrt{(\Delta x_4)^2 + (\Delta y_4)^2}$$

$$\overline{P_5P_6} = \sqrt{(\Delta x_5)^2 + (\Delta y_5)^2}$$

And in general:

$$\sqrt{(\Delta x)^2 + (\Delta y)^2} = \sqrt{\left[\frac{(\Delta x)^2}{(\Delta x)^2} + \frac{(\Delta y)^2}{(\Delta x)^2}\right](\Delta x)^2}$$

$$= \sqrt{1 + \left(\frac{\Delta y}{\Delta x}\right)^2}\,(\Delta x)$$

So

$$L \approx \sqrt{1 + \left(\frac{\Delta y_1}{\Delta x_1}\right)^2}\,(\Delta x_1) + \sqrt{1 + \left(\frac{\Delta y_2}{\Delta x_2}\right)^2}\,(\Delta x_2)$$

$$+ \cdots + \sqrt{1 + \left(\frac{\Delta y_5}{\Delta x_5}\right)^2}\,(\Delta x_5)$$

And

$$L \approx \sum_{i=1}^{n} \sqrt{1 + \left(\frac{\Delta y_i}{\Delta x_i}\right)^2}\,(\Delta x_i)$$

If we now apply our limit ideas we have:

$$L = \lim_{\substack{a \to b \\ \Delta x \to 0}} \sum_{i=1}^{n} \sqrt{1 + \left(\frac{\Delta y_i}{\Delta x_i}\right)^2}\,(\Delta x_i)$$

$$= \int_a^b \sqrt{1 + \left(\frac{dy}{dx}\right)^2}\,dx \tag{3.35}$$

or

$$L = \int_{c \to d}^{\,d} \sqrt{1 + \left(\frac{dx}{dy}\right)^2}\,dy$$

Example 3.58. Calculate the length of the curved line $y = \frac{2}{3}(x)^{3/2}$ between $x = 3$ and $x = 8$.

Here $y = \frac{2}{3}(x)^{3/2} = 2x^{3/2}/3$, and $dy/dx = (\frac{2}{3})(\frac{3}{2})x^{1/2} = x^{1/2}$, so $(dy/dx)^2 = x$.

Therefore

$$L = \int_3^8 (1 + x)^{1/2}\, dx$$

$$= \frac{(1 + x)^{3/2}}{3/2}\Bigg]_3^8 = \frac{2(1 + x)^{3/2}}{3}\Bigg]_3^8$$

$$= \frac{2(1 + 8)^{3/2}}{3} - \frac{2(1 + 3)^{3/2}}{3} = \frac{54}{3} - \frac{16}{3}$$

$$= \frac{38}{3}$$

In all fairness to the student it should be noted here that this example is one of the few that work out so easily, most others will offer a true test of your persistence.

Example 3.59. Calculate the length of $y = x^2$ between $x = 0$ and $x = \sqrt{3/2}$.

Here $y = x^2$ so $dy/dx = 2x$, and $(dy/dx)^2 = 4x^2$. Therefore

$$L = \int_0^{\sqrt{3/2}} \sqrt{1 + 4x^2}\, dx$$

If $u = 1 + 4x^2$, then $du = 8x\, dx$, and a standard formula for integration will not work. Integral tables show:

$$\int \sqrt{x^2 + a^2}\, dx = \tfrac{1}{2}\, [x \sqrt{x^2 + a^2} + a^2 \ln (x + \sqrt{x^2 + a^2})]$$

Our job now is to some way manipulate $1 + 4x^2$ into the form $x^2 + a^2$. Note that

$$1 + 4x^2 = \tfrac{4}{4} + 4x^2 = 4(\tfrac{1}{4} + x^2)$$

$$= 4(x^2 + \tfrac{1}{4})$$

Therefore

$$\sqrt{1 + 4x^2} = \sqrt{4(x^2 + \tfrac{1}{4})}$$

$$= 2\sqrt{x^2 + \tfrac{1}{4}}$$

So $$L = 2 \int_0^{\sqrt{3/2}} \sqrt{x^2 + \tfrac{1}{4}}\, dx$$

$$= 2\tfrac{1}{2}\, [x \sqrt{x^2 + \tfrac{1}{4}} + \tfrac{1}{4} \ln (x + \sqrt{x^2 + \tfrac{1}{4}})]\Bigg]_0^{\sqrt{3/2}}$$

$$= \left[\frac{\sqrt{3}}{2} \sqrt{1} + \frac{1}{4} \ln\left(\frac{\sqrt{3}}{2} + \sqrt{1}\right)\right] - \left[0\sqrt{\frac{1}{4}} + \ln\left(\frac{\sqrt{3}}{2} + \frac{1}{4}\right)\right]$$

$$= \left[\frac{\sqrt{3}}{2} + \frac{1}{4}\ln\left(\frac{\sqrt{3}}{2} + 1\right)\right] - \left[\frac{1}{4}\ln\left(\frac{\sqrt{3}}{2} + \frac{1}{2}\right)\right]$$

$$= (0.866 + \tfrac{1}{4}\ln 1.866) - (\tfrac{1}{4}\ln 1.366)$$

$$= 0.866 + 0.156 - \tfrac{1}{4}(0.312)$$

$$= 1.022 - 0.078 = 0.944$$

Exercise 3.17. Calculate the length of the following curved lines between the limits given.

1. $y = 4 - 2x^{3/2}$ between $x = 0$ and $x = 4$.
2. $y^{3/2} = x$ between $x = -1$ and $x = 1$.
3. $y = (x^3/6) + (1/2x)$ between $x = 1$ and $x = 3$.
4. $x^2 + y^2 = 4$ between $x = 0$ and $x = 4$.
5. $y = 5 + 8x^{3/2}$ between $x = 0$ and $x = 4$.
6. $y = (x^4 + 3)/6x$ between $x = 2$ and $x = 5$.
7. $y = 4/x$ between $x = 2$ and $x = 4$.

3.19 TRIPLE INTEGRALS—VOLUMES

Double integration was discussed in Section 3.9 and volumes in Sections 3.12 and 3.13. We now carry these ideas one step further and calculate volume using the triple integral. Triple integration is little different than double integration.

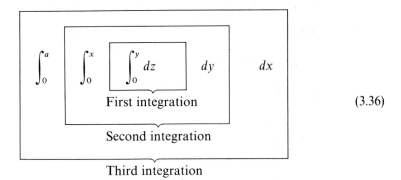

(3.36)

Care must be exercised in setting up the limits for triple integration. Some examples will illustrate this point.

Example 3.60. Calculate the volume of a right circular cylinder whose radius is R and altitude a. Use the triple integral.

Orient the cylinder as shown in Figure 3.46. Align the axis of the cylinder on the x axis and place one of the bases in the yz plane. Only the portion of the cylinder in the first octant will be considered since this will be exactly one-quarter of the entire cylinder.

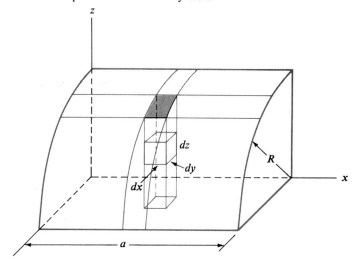

Figure 3.46

In Figure 3.46 we see the elemental cube which is $dz \times dy \times dx$.

First Integration: On the z axis the volume lies between the xy plane or surface $z = 0$ and the surface $z = \sqrt{R^2 - y^2}$ obtained from the equation of a base $z^2 + y^2 = R^2$. The limits are 0 and $\sqrt{R^2 - y^2}$.

Second Integration: On the y axis the volume lies between the xz plane or surface $y = 0$ and surface $y = R$. The limits are 0 and R.

Third Integration: On the x axis the volume lies between the yz plane or surface $x = 0$ and the surface $x = a$. The limits are 0 and a.
From all of this then:

$$V = 4 \int_0^a \int_0^R \int_0^{\sqrt{R^2+y^2}} dz \, dy \, dx = 4 \int_0^a \int_0^R \left[z \right]_0^{\sqrt{R^2+y^2}} dy \, dx$$

$$= 4 \int_0^a \int_0^R \sqrt{R^2 - y^2} \, dy \, dx$$

$$= 4 \int_0^a \left(\frac{y}{2} \sqrt{R^2 - y^2} + \frac{R^2}{2} \sin^{-1} \frac{y}{R} \right) \Bigg]_0^R dx$$

$$= 4 \int_0^a \left(\frac{R}{2} \sqrt{R^2 - R^2} + \frac{R^2}{2} \sin^{-1} \frac{R}{R} \right) - \left(\frac{0}{2} \sqrt{R^2} + \frac{R^2}{2} \sin^{-1} \frac{0}{R} \right) dx$$

$$= 4 \int_0^a \frac{R^2}{2} \cdot \frac{\pi}{2} \, dx = \pi R^2 \int_0^a dx$$

$$= \pi R^2 (x) \Bigg]_0^a = \pi R^2 a$$

Example 3.61. Calculate the volume of a right circular cone with radius of the base R and altitude a. Use triple integration.

Figure 3.47 shows one-quarter of the cone in the first octant. R is the radius of the base and r the radius at any point x. From this we obtain the following relationship:

$$\frac{R}{a} = \frac{r}{x} \quad \text{or} \quad r = \frac{Rx}{a}$$

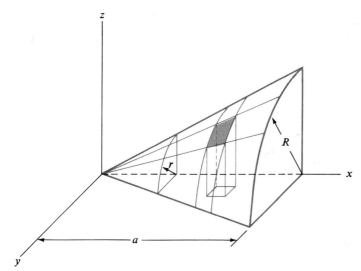

Figure 3.47

First Integration: On the z axis the volume lies between the xy plane or surface $z = 0$ and the surface $z = \sqrt{r^2 - y^2}$.

Second Integration: On the y axis the volume lies between the xz plane or surface $y = 0$ and the surface $y = r$. The limits are 0 and r.

Third Integration: On the x axis the volume lies between the yz plane or $x = 0$ and $x = a$. The limits are 0 and a.

From all of this then:

$$V = 4 \int_0^a \int_0^r \int_0^{\sqrt{r^2 - y^2}} dz\, dy\, dx = 4 \int_0^a \int_0^r \left[z \right]_0^{\sqrt{r^2 - y^2}} dy\, dx$$

$$= 4 \int_0^a \int_0^r \sqrt{r^2 - y^2}\, dy\, dx$$

$$= 4 \int_0^a \left[\frac{y}{2} \sqrt{r^2 - y^2} + \frac{y^2}{2} \sin^{-1} \frac{y}{r} \right]_0^r dx$$

$$= 4 \int_0^a \left(\frac{r}{2} \sqrt{0} + \frac{r^2}{2} \sin^{-1} \frac{r}{r} \right) - \left(\frac{0}{2} \sqrt{r^2} + \frac{0}{2} \sin^{-1} \frac{0}{r} \right) dx$$

$$= 4 \int_0^a \frac{r^2}{2} \cdot \frac{\pi}{2}\, dx = 4 \int_0^a \frac{\pi r^2}{4}\, dx$$

but $r = Rx/a$ so

$$= 4 \int_0^a \frac{\pi R^2 x^2}{4a^2}\, dx = \frac{\pi R^2}{a^2} \int_0^a x^2\, dx = \frac{\pi R^2}{a^2} \cdot \frac{x^3}{3}\Big]_0^a$$

$$= \frac{\pi R^2 a^3}{3a^2} = \frac{\pi R^2 a}{3}$$

Example 3.62.   Calculate the volume of a sphere with radius R. Use the triple integral.

Figure 3.48 shows one-eighth of the sphere in the first octant. The center of the sphere is at the origin.

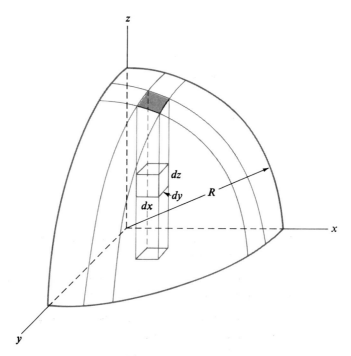

Figure 3.48

First Integration: On the z axis the volume lies between the xy plane or surface $z = 0$ and surface $z = \sqrt{R^2 - x^2 - y^2}$ from $x^2 + y^2 + z^2 = R^2$. The limits are 0 and $\sqrt{R^2 - x^2 - y^2}$.

Second Integration: On the y axis the volume lies between the xz plane or surface $y = 0$ and the surface $y = \sqrt{R^2 - x^2}$. The latter is obtained by letting $z = 0$. The limits are 0 and $\sqrt{R^2 - x^2}$.

Third Integration: On the x axis the volume lies between the yz plane or $x = 0$ and $x = R$. From all of this then:

$$V = 8 \int_0^R \int_0^{\sqrt{R^2-x^2}} \int_0^{\sqrt{R^2-x^2-y^2}} dz\, dy\, dx$$

$$= 8 \int_0^R \int_0^{\sqrt{R^2-x^2}} z \Big]_0^{\sqrt{R^2-x^2-y^2}} dy\, dx$$

$$= 8 \int_0^R \int_0^{\sqrt{R^2-x^2}} \sqrt{R^2-x^2-y^2}\, dy\, dx$$

From integration tables:

$$\int \sqrt{a^2-x^2}\, dx = \frac{1}{2}\left(x\sqrt{a^2-x^2} + a^2 \sin^{-1}\frac{x}{a} \right)$$

$$= \frac{x}{2}\sqrt{a^2-x^2} + \frac{a^2}{2}\sin^{-1}\frac{x}{a}$$

In our problem we let $k = R^2 - x^2$ and $y = x$.

$$V = 8 \int_0^R \int_0^{\sqrt{R^2-x^2}} (k^2-y^2)^{\frac{1}{2}}\, dy\, dx$$

$$= 8 \int_0^R \frac{y}{2}\sqrt{k^2-y^2} + \frac{k^2}{2}\sin^{-1}\frac{y}{k}\Big]_0^{\sqrt{R^2-x^2}} dx$$

$$= 8 \int_0^R \frac{y}{2}\sqrt{R^2-x^2-y^2} + \frac{R^2-x^2}{2}\sin^{-1}\frac{y}{\sqrt{R^2-x^2}}\Big]_0^{\sqrt{R^2-x^2}} dx$$

$$= 8 \int_0^R \frac{\sqrt{R^2-x^2}}{2}\sqrt{R^2-x^2-R^2+x^2} + \frac{R^2-x^2}{2}\sin^{-1}\frac{\sqrt{R^2-x^2}}{\sqrt{R^2-x^2}}$$

$$- \left(\frac{0}{2}\sqrt{R^2-x^2-0} + \frac{R^2-x^2}{2}\sin^{-1}\frac{0}{\sqrt{R^2-x^2}} \right) dx$$

$$= 8 \int_0^R \frac{\pi}{4}(R^2-x^2)\, dx = 2\pi \int_0^R (R^2-x^2)\, dx$$

$$= 2\pi \left(R^2 x - \frac{x^3}{3} \right)\Big]_0^R = 2\pi \left(R^2 R - \frac{R^3}{3} \right) - 0$$

$$= 2\pi \left(R^3 - \frac{R^3}{3} \right) = 2\pi \left(\frac{3R^3}{3} - \frac{R^3}{3} \right)$$

$$= 2\pi \left(\frac{2R^3}{3} \right) = \frac{4\pi R^3}{3}$$

Exercise 3.18.   Find by the triple integral the volumes as asked for.

1. The volume common to the two cylinders $x^2 + y^2 = R^2$ and $y^2 + z^2 = R^2$.
2. The volume cut from the elliptic paraboloid $z = x^2 + 4y^2$ by the plane $z = 1$.

3. The volume bounded by $x = 0$, $y = 0$, $z = 0$, and

$$\frac{x}{a} + \frac{y}{b} + \frac{z}{c} = 1$$

(see Figure 3.49).

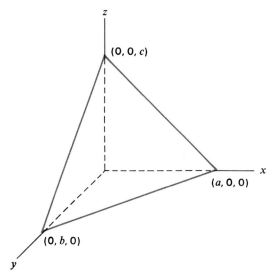

Figure 3.49

4. The ellipsoid

$$\frac{x^2}{a^2} + \frac{y^2}{b^2} + \frac{z^2}{c^2} = 1$$

(see Figure 3.50).

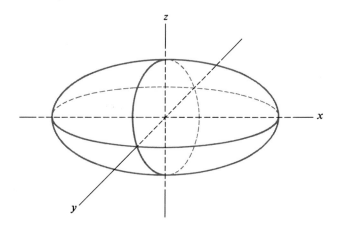

Figure 3.50

5. The volume cut off from the parabaloid $z = x^2 + y^2$ by the plane $z - y = 0$.

SUMMARY OF INTEGRALS

(3.1) $\int kx^n \, dx = \dfrac{kx^{n+1}}{n+1} + C \qquad n \neq -1.$

(3.2) $\int (kx^n \pm Kx^m) \, dx = \int kx^n \, dx \pm \int Kx^m \, dx + C.$

(3.3) $\int ku^n \, du = \dfrac{ku^{n+1}}{n+1} + C \qquad n \neq -1.$

(3.4) $\int_a^b f(x) \, dx = g(x) + C \Big]_a^b = g[b] - g[a].$

(3.8) $\int ku^{-1} \, du = k \ln u + C.$

(3.9) $\int k \sin u \, du = -k \cos u + C.$

(3.10) $\int k \cos u \, du = k \sin u + C.$

(3.11) $\int k \tan u \, du = k \ln (\sec u) + C.$

(3.12) $\int ke^u \, du = ke^u + C.$

REVIEW PROBLEMS

1. If differentiation is a precise mathematical process, sum up integration in a few words.

2. What is the origin of the indefinite integral sign?

3. List four special methods for determining the integral of a function for which no regular rule exists.

4. In $\lim\limits_{x \to 0} \sum\limits_{i=1}^{n} y_i(\Delta x) = \int_a^b y \, dx$, what is the relationship, if any, between the limits 1 and n, and a and b?

5. For what does $\sum$ stand? Why is the indefinite integral sign called indefinite?

6. $\int \sqrt{6x} \, dx = ?$

7. $\int 6\sqrt{x} \, dx = ?$

8. $\int 5\sqrt[3]{x^4}\,dx = ?$

9. $3\int x^{-1/5}\,dx = ?$

10. $\int (x^3 + x^2)\,dx = ?$

11. $\int \sin(x^2 + 1)x\,dx = ?$

12. Outline two methods for determining the value of the constant of integration.

13. $\int x^4(5 - x^5)^3\,dx = ?$

14. Calculate the area under $y = \sqrt{2x}$ between $x = 0$ and $x = 4$.

15. Calculate the area under $y = (x^3 + 3)^2 x^2$ between $x = 0$ and $x = 2$.

16. Calculate the area under $y = 2\cos 2x$ between $x = 0$ and $x = \pi/2$.

17. Calculate the area under $y = \cos^2 x$ between $x = 0$ and $x = \pi/2$.

18. $\displaystyle\int \frac{x^2\,dx}{\sqrt{5 + 3x^2}} = ?$

19. $\displaystyle\int \frac{dx}{x^2\sqrt{25 - x^2}} = ?$

20. $\int x \sin^2 x\,dx = ?$

21. $\displaystyle\int_0^{\pi/2} \int_0^x h\sin(h)^2\,dh\,dy = ?$ If $h = x$ and $y = x^2$.

22. $\displaystyle\int_0^1 \int_0^{\frac{\sqrt{1-x^2}}{2}} \int_{x^2+4y^2}^1 dz\,dy\,dx = ?$

4

Moments and
Centroids

The study of moments is an important part of physics and engineering and can get quite complicated. We shall start out rather intuitively and build up slowly to our goal. In general then:

The moment of a force is a distance times that force.

The moment of a line segment is a distance times the length of that line segment.

The moment of an area is a distance times that area.

The moment of a volume is a distance times that volume.

Like moments may be added or subtracted.

4.1 CENTER OF GRAVITY

Note that in every instance above, distance entered into moment, and if we are to discuss distance intelligently we must know where or how this distance is to be measured. All of this leads us to *center of gravity*. Center of gravity is involved with mass, since it is the point at which the entire mass is said to be concentrated. If the mass is homogeneous and we always work under that assumption, then the center of gravity is the exact center of the mass. Thus the center of gravity of a cube with sides s is $s/2$ from all faces. See Figure 4.1.

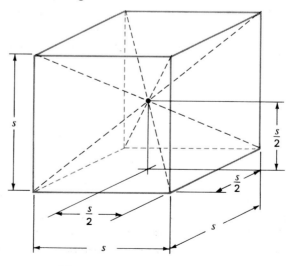

Figure 4.1

The center of gravity of a cube may also be located at the intersection of the diagonals of the cube.

The center of gravity of a mass *L* long, *W* wide, and *D* thick is located at the exact center. See Figure 4.2. This point would also be at the intersection of the

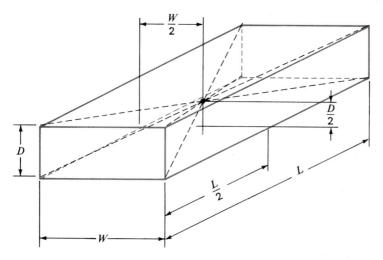

Figure 4.2

diagonals. To see how all this fits into a physical situation, suppose we have a homogeneous bar of steel 2 by 4 by 10 inches. If we balance this bar on a knife edge that is parallel to the planes of the ends, we would find that a plane through the knife edge parallel to the planes of the ends would pass through the center of gravity. It turns out that a requirement for static stability or equilibrium (balancing with no external force) is that the balance must occur at the center of gravity or the plane of the center of gravity. See Figure 4.3. Since the weight or mass acts at the center of gravity and the center of gravity is at or in the plane of the knife edge, we would expect balance and therefore no motion. The moment will be mass times distance, but distance will be zero, so the moment is zero—thus no motion.

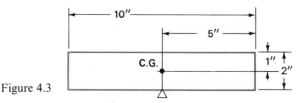

Figure 4.3

If we try to analyze a situation in which the knife edge is not at the center of gravity, it is obvious we will not be in static equilibrium. See Figure 4.4. The moment will be clockwise in nature and its magnitude will be the mass times the distance $[(10/2) - x]$ or moment will be the mass times this distance $[(10/2) - x]$.

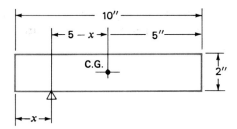

Figure 4.4

Example 4.1.   Calculate the moment of the bar in Figure 4.4, if $x = 2$ inches and the mass is 15 pounds.

Clockwise moment

$$M = 15\left(\frac{10}{2} - 2\right)$$

$$= 15(5 - 2)$$

$$= 15(3)$$

$$= 45 \text{ in.-lb}$$

Note that this one calculation is sufficient for the total solution even though part of the bar hangs over the left side of the knife edge. To show that our answer is correct, we can make a more complicated problem of it and compare answers. In Figure 4.5 we assume two smaller bars, one on either side of the

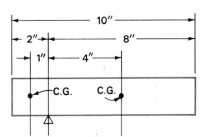

Figure 4.5

knife edge, calculate their mass and center of gravity and finally their moments. Here the left member has mass of 3 pounds and the right hand member has a mass of 12 pounds.

$$M = \text{distance times mass} = 4(12) = 48$$

$$M = \text{distance times mass} = 1(3) = 3$$

$$\sum M = M - M = 48 - 3 = 45 \text{ in.-lb}$$

The answers compare favorably but note that the latter method required three operations while the former only took one operation.

From what we have said we can easily see that the center of gravity of a rectangle of any sheet material is located at one-half the length, one-half the width, and one-half the thickness. Likewise the center of gravity of a piece of circular material is on the plane passing through the midpoint of the material at the center of the cross-sectional area. See Figure 4.6.

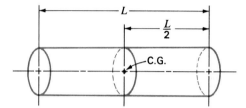

Figure 4.6

In conclusion then, the center of gravity of a mass is located at its exact center and is the one point where all of the mass can be considered to be acting.

4.2 CENTROIDS

Many do not realize that in mathematics a circle is not a disc, even though we talk about the "area of a circle." What we should say is "area enclosed by a circle," which is the tipoff that a circle is much closer to a loop of fine wire than a disc of material. Likewise a mathematical rectangle is not a rectangular piece of something, but rather space surrounded by the intersection of four straight lines. And a mathematical rectangular parallelepiped is the space enclosed by the intersection of six planes. From all of this then it should be obvious that mathematical plane figures or solids are not solids and have no mass. If they have no mass then our use of the word center of gravity is invalid because a mathematical solid has no mass to be concentrated. We wish to use this point in mathematics, so we simply give it a new name—we call it a *centroid*. A centroid is to a mathematical solid as a center of gravity is to a corresponding mass. Many times these names are incorrectly interchanged, but if one really understands their true meaning then little harm is done.

Now if we are to discuss moments of a line segment, area, or volume we must measure a distance, that is, the distance to the centroid.

4.3 FIRST MOMENTS

If we are to further analyze moments, we must locate the second reference point from which the distance is to be measured. This requires further definition of moment. When we discuss moments we must always discuss them with reference to some axis or straight line and it is this reference axis from which the distance is measured. Further, the measurement must be perpendicular to this reference axis.

If we are asked the moment of line segment $\overline{ab}$ in Figure 4.7 with respect to the x axis, we must first establish the distance k which we call the "moment arm."

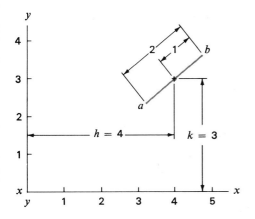

Figure 4.7

This must be the perpendicular distance from the x axis to the centroid. The moment with respect to the x axis is:

$$M_{xx} = 3(2) = 6 \text{ in.}^2$$

The moment with respect to the y axis (M_{yy}) requires a moment arm which is the perpendicular distance from the y axis to the centroid. In Figure 4.7 this moment arm is dimensioned h. Here $h = 4$ inches, so the moment with respect to the y axis is: $M_{yy} = 4(2) = 8 \text{ in.}^2$

To further advance our knowledge of moments we call both of these answers first moments because the first power of the moment arm is used.

Example 4.2. Calculate M_{xx} and M_{yy} of the area in Figure 4.8.

Here we see that the moment arm, which is the perpendicular distance from the x axis to the centroid, is correctly labeled $\bar{y}$. $\bar{y} = 4$, so

$$M_{xx} = \bar{y}A = 4(3) = 12 \text{ in.}^3$$

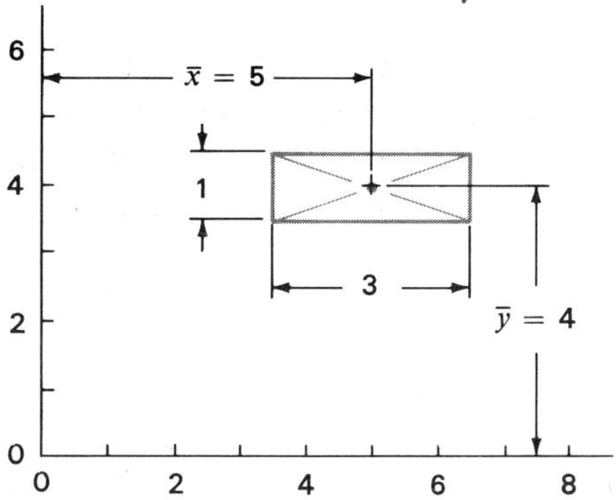

Figure 4.8

In Figure 4.8 the perpendicular distance from the y axis to the centroid is properly labeled $\bar{x}$. $\bar{x} = 5$, so

$$M_{yy} = \bar{x}A = 5(3) = 15 \text{ in.}^3$$

Example 4.3. Calculate M_{xx} and M_{yy} of the volume shown in Figure 4.9.

$$M_{xx} = \bar{y}V = 2(1 \cdot 1 \cdot 3) = 2 \cdot 3 = 6 \text{ in.}^4$$

$$M_{yy} = \bar{x}V = 4(1 \cdot 1 \cdot 3) = 4 \cdot 3 = 12 \text{ in.}^4$$

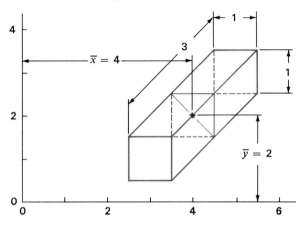

Figure 4.9

4.4 CENTROIDS OF COMPOSITE GEOMETRIC FIGURES

If $M_{xx} = \bar{y}A = \bar{y}V = \bar{y}L$

$$\text{(4.1)}$$

Then $\bar{y} = \dfrac{M_{xx}}{A} = \dfrac{M_{xx}}{V} = \dfrac{M_{xx}}{L}$

If $M_{yy} = \bar{x}A = \bar{x}V = \bar{x}L$

$$\text{(4.2)}$$

Then $\bar{x} = \dfrac{M_{yy}}{A} = \dfrac{M_{yy}}{V} = \dfrac{M_{yy}}{L}$

Now if moments with like units can be added and subtracted, we should be able to take a composite figure, calculate the moments of the individual parts and add them for total moment, and divide this total moment by the total area to locate the centroid of the composite figure.

Example 4.4. Calculate $\bar{x}$ and $\bar{y}$ of the geometric figure pictured in Figure 4.10.

	Area	Moment Arm
$\sum M_{xx} = (4 \cdot 1)(\tfrac{1}{2}) = 4$		$(\tfrac{1}{2}) = 2$
$(4 \cdot 1)3 = 4$		$3 = 12$
$(1 \cdot 1)(\tfrac{9}{2}) = \underline{1}$		$(\tfrac{9}{2}) = \underline{\tfrac{9}{2}}$
9		$18\tfrac{1}{2}$

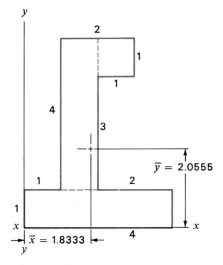

Figure 4.10

Thus $M_{xx} = 18\frac{1}{2}$ and $A = 9$, so $\bar{y} = M_{xx}/A$, and $\bar{y} = (18.5)/8 = 2.055$.

	Area		Moment Arm	
$\sum M_{yy} = (4 \cdot 1)2$	$= 4$		$2 =$	8
$(4 \cdot 1)(1\frac{1}{2}) = 4$			$1\frac{1}{2} =$	6
$(1 \cdot 1)(2\frac{1}{2}) = 1$			$2\frac{1}{2} =$	$2\frac{1}{2}$
	9			$16\frac{1}{2}$

Thus $M_{yy} = 16\frac{1}{2}$ and $A = 9$, so $\bar{x} = M_{yy}/A$, and $\bar{x} = (16.5)/9 = 1.833$.

Example 4.5. Calculate $\bar{x}$ and $\bar{y}$ of the configuration shown in Figure 4.11 if the smaller portion is considered removed from the larger.

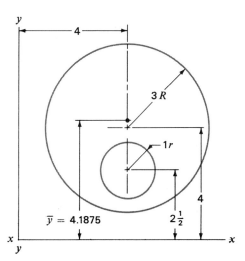

Figure 4.11

$$\sum M_{xx} = (\pi 3^2)4 \ = \ 9\pi(4) \ = \ 36\pi$$

$$(\pi 1^2)2\tfrac{1}{2} \ = \ \underline{\pi(2\tfrac{1}{2}) \ = \ 2\tfrac{1}{2}\pi}$$
$$8\pi \qquad 33\tfrac{1}{2}\pi$$

$$\bar{y} \ = \ \frac{M_{xx}}{A} \ = \ (33.5)\,\frac{\pi}{8\pi} \ = \ 4.1875$$

$$\sum M_{yy} = (\pi 3^2)4 = 9\pi(4) = 36\pi$$

$$(\pi 1^2)4 \ = \ \underline{\pi(4) \ = \ 4\pi}$$
$$8\pi \qquad 32\pi$$

$$\bar{x} \ = \ \frac{M_{yy}}{A} \ = \ \frac{32\pi}{8\pi} \ = \ 4.000$$

It should be noted here that the calculation of $\bar{x}$ was in reality a waste of time since it was obvious by looking at the picture that $\bar{x}$ had to be 4.000. It is good to know, however, that if the answer is not apparent, it can be obtained by applying the rules and procedures.

Exercise 4.1.   Calculate $\bar{x}$ and $\bar{y}$ for each part (*a–h*) in Figure 4.12.

4.5 CENTROIDS OF TWO OR MORE AREAS

Now that we have mastered adjacent or overlapping geometric figures, let us try our hand at geometric configurations with separate parts or areas.

Example 4.6.   Determine $\bar{x}$ and $\bar{y}$ of the system shown in Figure 4.13.

$$\sum M_{xx} = 3 \quad (4) \quad = 12$$

$$1 \quad (\pi) \ = \ 3.1416$$
$$\overline{4 + \pi \quad 15.1416}$$

$$\bar{y} = \frac{M_{xx}}{A} = \frac{15.1416}{7.1416} = 2.121$$

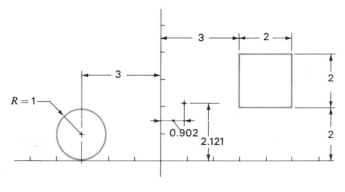

Figure 4.13

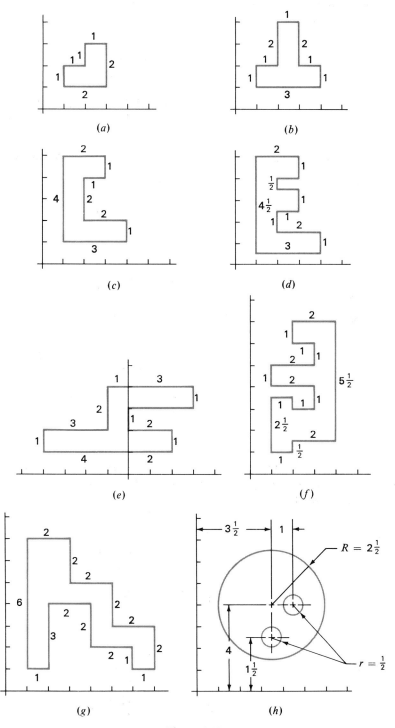

Figure 4.12

$$\sum M_{yy} = \quad 4 \ (4) \quad = \quad 16$$

$$-3 \ (\pi) \quad = \quad \frac{-3\pi}{4 + \pi} \quad \frac{-3\pi}{16 - (3\pi)}$$

$$\bar{x} = \frac{M_{yy}}{A} = \frac{6.5752}{7.1416} = 0.902$$

Example 4.7.   Determine $\bar{x}$ and $\bar{y}$ of the system shown in Figure 4.14.

$$\sum M_{xx} = \quad 3 \ (2) = \quad 6.0$$

$$(-\tfrac{3}{2}) \ (2) = \quad -3.0$$

$$-3 \ (4) = \quad \frac{-12.0}{-9}$$

$$\bar{y} = \frac{M_{xx}}{A} = \frac{-9}{8} = -1.125$$

$$\sum M_{yy} = \quad (\tfrac{7}{2}) \ (2) = \quad 7.0$$

$$3 \ (4) = \quad 12.0$$

$$-3 \ (2) = \quad \frac{-6.0}{13.0}$$

$$\bar{x} = \frac{M_{yy}}{A} = \frac{13}{8} = 1.625$$

Example 4.8.   Determine $\bar{x}$ and $\bar{y}$ of the system shown in Figure 4.15. The centroid of a triangle is located one-third the altitude from the base. See Example 4.12.

$$\sum M_{xx} = \quad 2 \ (3) \quad = \quad 6.0$$

$$-2 \ (\pi) \quad = \quad \frac{-2.0\pi}{3 + \pi} \quad \frac{-2.0\pi}{6 - 2\pi}$$

$$\bar{y} = \frac{M_{xx}}{A} = \frac{-0.2832}{6.1416} = -0.0461$$

$$\sum M_{yy} = \quad 2 \ (3) \quad = \quad 6$$

$$-2 \ (\pi) \quad = \quad \frac{-2\pi}{3 + \pi} \quad \frac{-2\pi}{6 - 2\pi}$$

$$\bar{x} = \frac{M_{yy}}{A} = \frac{-0.2832}{6.1416} = -0.0461$$

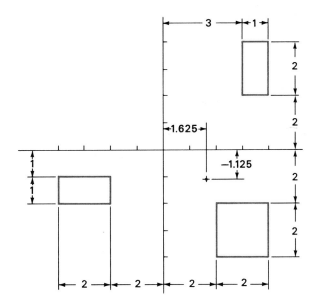

Figure 4.14

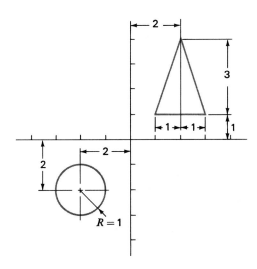

Figure 4.15

Example 4.9.   Determine $\bar{x}$ and $\bar{y}$ of the system shown in Figure 4.16.

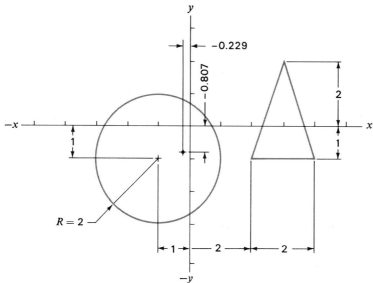

Figure 4.16

$$\sum M_{xx} = -1 \;\; (4\pi) \;\; = \;\; -4\pi$$

$$\frac{0 \;\; (3)}{3 + 4\pi} \;\; = \;\; \frac{0}{-4\pi}$$

$$\bar{y} = \frac{M_{xx}}{A} = \frac{-12.5662}{15.5662} = -0.807$$

$$\sum M_{yy} = -1 \;\; (4\pi) \;\; = \;\; -4\pi$$

$$\frac{3 \;\; (3)}{3 + 4\pi} \;\; = \;\; \frac{9}{9 - 4\pi}$$

$$\bar{x} = \frac{M_{yy}}{A} = \frac{-3.5662}{15.5662} = -0.229$$

Exercise 4.2.   Calculate $\bar{x}$ and $\bar{y}$ for each system (a–e) given in Figure 4.17.

4.6 CENTROIDS USING CALCULUS

Suppose now we wish to calculate the moment of an area under a curve. In

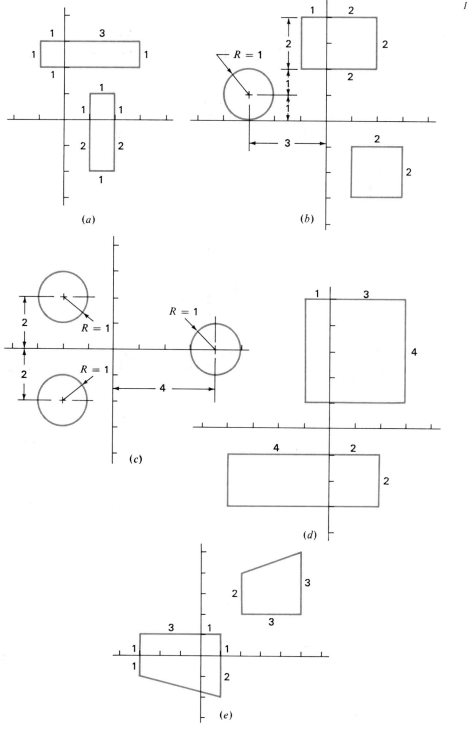

Figure 4.17

Figure 4.18 we are given the curve $y = f(x)$ with the limits $x = a$ and $x = b$, and are asked to calculate the moment of that area with respect to the y axis.

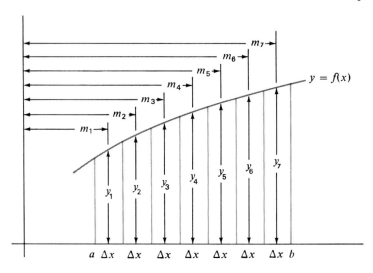

Figure 4.18

The area in question is divided into seven elemental strips as shown. Then to get the moment of each strip the moment arms are introduced. Now each individual moment is calculated and summed:

$$M_{yy} \approx m_1(\Delta A_1) + m_2(\Delta A_2) + m_3(\Delta A_3) + m_4(\Delta A_4) + m_5(\Delta A_5)$$
$$+ \, m_6(\Delta A_6) + m_7(\Delta A_7)$$

From this

$$M_{yy} \approx m_1 y_1(\Delta x) + m_2 y_2(\Delta x) + m_3 y_3(\Delta x) + m_4 y_4(\Delta x) + m_5 y_5(\Delta x)$$
$$+ \, m_6 y_6(\Delta x) + m_7 y_7(\Delta x)$$

or $$M_{yy} \approx \sum_{i=1}^{7} m_i y_i(\Delta x)$$

From this, by applying our limit ideas, we have:

$$M_{yy} = \lim_{\Delta x \to 0} \sum_{i=1}^{n} m_i y_i(\Delta x)$$

$$= \int_a^b my \, dx$$

(4.3)

Note: $y \, dx = dA$.

Equation (4.3) is used with a picture setup as shown in Figure 4.19.

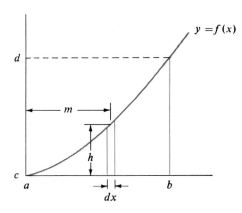

Figure 4.19

From all of this and Figure 4.20 we arrive at an equation for M_{xx}.

$$M_{xx} = \int_c^d mx\,dy \qquad (4.4)$$

Note: $x\,dy = dA$.

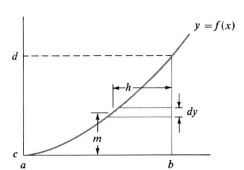

Figure 4.20

It is not absolutely necessary to set the picture up as in Figures 4.19 and 4.20. There are two other picture possibilities. Before showing these methods, let us keep in mind that the M_{xx} tells us that the moment arm m must be perpendicular to the x axis and M_{yy} tells us that the moment arm m must be perpendicular to the y axis. Therefore the M_{xx} or M_{yy} will establish how the moment arm m is to enter into the picture. If the integration is to be with respect to y, the limits must be along the y axis and the differential dy is used. If the integration is to be with respect to x, then the limits of integration must be along the x axis and the differential

dx is used. Figure 4.21a–d shows the four situations properly set up with the correct equations.

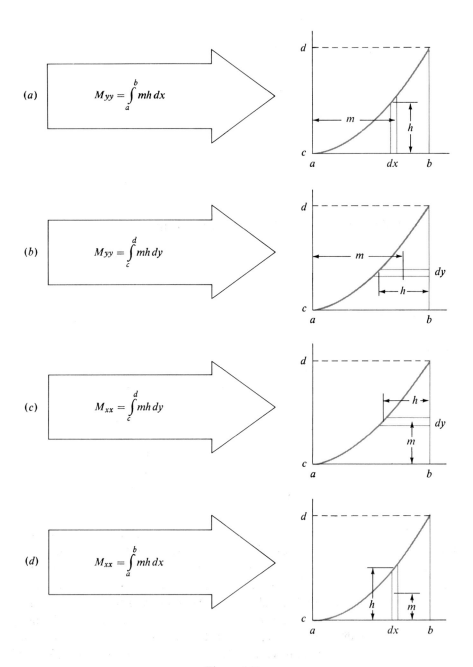

Figure 4.21

Example 4.10. Calculate both M_{xx} and M_{yy} first with respect to x and then with respect to y of the area bounded by $y = x^2/2$, $y = 0$, $x = 0$, $x = 3$.

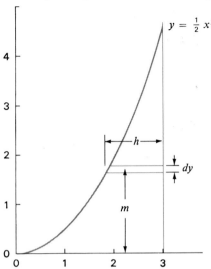

Figure 4.22

For M_{xx} with respect to y, we use Figure 4.22, and

$$M_{xx} = \int_0^{9/2} mh \, dy$$

where $h = (3 - x) = (3 - \sqrt{2y}) = 3 - (2y)^{1/2}$, so

$$M_{xx} = \int_0^{9/2} y(3 - (2y)^{1/2}) \, dy$$

$$= \int_0^{9/2} (3y - \sqrt{2} \, y^{3/2}) \, dy$$

$$= \frac{3y^2}{2} - \frac{\sqrt{2} \, y^{5/2}}{5/2} \Bigg]_0^{9/2} = \frac{3y^2}{2} - \frac{2\sqrt{2} \, y^{5/2}}{5} \Bigg]_0^{9/2}$$

$$= \frac{3(9/2)^2}{2} - \frac{2\sqrt{2}(9/2)^{5/2}}{5}$$

$$= \frac{3(81)}{2(4)} - \frac{2\sqrt{2}(3/\sqrt{2})^5}{5}$$

$$= \frac{243}{8} - \frac{2(2)^{1/2} \, 3 \cdot 3 \cdot 3 \cdot 3 \cdot 3/(2)^{5/2}}{5}$$

$$= \frac{243}{8} - \frac{2 \cdot 3 \cdot 3 \cdot 3 \cdot 3 \cdot 3}{5 \cdot 2 \cdot 2}$$

$$= \frac{2430}{80} - \frac{1944}{80} = \frac{486}{80} = \frac{243}{40}$$

For M_{xx} with respect to x, we use Figure 4.23 and:

$$M_{xx} = \int_0^3 mh \, dx$$

where $m = h/2 = y/2 = x^2/4$ and $h = y = x^2/2$, so

$$M_{xx} = \int_0^3 \frac{x^2}{4} \frac{x^2}{2} dx$$

$$= \frac{1}{8} \int_0^3 x^4 \, dx$$

$$= \frac{1 \cdot x^5}{8 \cdot 5}\bigg]_0^3 = \frac{3 \cdot 3 \cdot 3 \cdot 3 \cdot 3}{40} = \frac{243}{40}$$

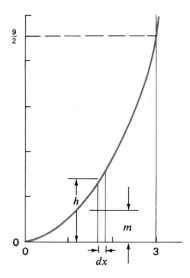

Figure 4.23

For M_{yy} with respect to x we use Figure 4.24 and:

$$M_{yy} = \int_0^3 mh \, dx$$

where $m = x$ and $h = y = x^2/2$, so

$$M_{yy} = \int_0^3 x \frac{x^2}{2} dx$$

$$= \frac{1}{2} \int_0^3 x^3 \, dx$$

$$= \frac{1 \cdot x^4}{2 \cdot 4}\bigg]_0^3 = \frac{3 \cdot 3 \cdot 3 \cdot 3}{8} = \frac{81}{8}$$

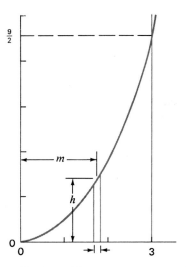

Figure 4.24

For M_{yy} with respect to y we use Figure 4.25 and:

$$M_{yy} = \int_0^{9/2} mh \, dy$$

where $m = x + (h/2) = 2x/2 + (3 - x)/2 = (3 + x)/2$, $h = 3 - x$, and $mh = [(3 - x)/1][(3 + x)/2] = (9 - x^2)/2 = (9 - 2y)/2$, so

$$M_{yy} = \frac{1}{2} \int_0^{9/2} (9 - 2y) \, dy$$

$$= \frac{1}{2} 9y - \frac{1}{2} \frac{2y^2}{2} \Big]_0^{9/2}$$

$$= \frac{9y}{2} - \frac{y^2}{2} \Big]_0^{9/2} = \frac{9(9/2)}{2} - \frac{(9/2)(9/2)}{2}$$

$$= \frac{81}{4} - \frac{81}{8} = \frac{162}{8} - \frac{81}{8} = \frac{81}{8}$$

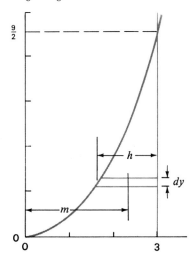

Figure 4.25

Example 4.11.   Calculate $\bar{x}$ and $\bar{y}$ for the area bounded by $y = x^2 + 4$, $y = 0$, $x = 2$, and $x = 6$.

One solution: See Figure 4.26 for a picture of the area in question as well as the setup for calculating the area.

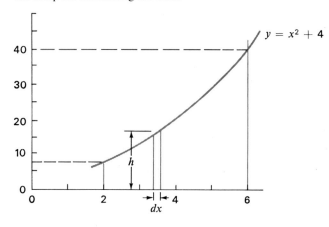

Figure 4.26

$$A = \int_2^6 h\,dx = \int_2^6 y\,dx = \int_2^6 (x^2 + 4)\,dx$$

$$= \frac{x^3}{3} + 4x \Big]_2^6$$

$$= \left(\frac{6 \cdot 6 \cdot 6}{3} + 4 \cdot 6\right) - \left(\frac{2 \cdot 2 \cdot 2}{3} + 4 \cdot 2\right)$$

$$= (72 + 24) - \left(\frac{8}{3} + 8\right) = 96 - \frac{32}{3}$$

$$= \frac{288}{3} - \frac{32}{3} = \frac{256}{3} = 85.333$$

Figure 4.27 is set up for calculating M_{yy}.

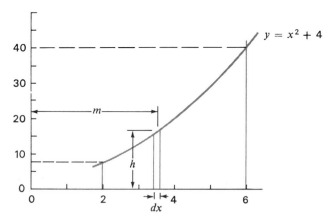

Figure 4.27

$$M_{yy} = \int_2^6 mh\,dx = \int_2^6 x(x^2 + 4)\,dx$$

$$= \int_2^6 (x^3 + 4x)\,dx$$

$$= \frac{x^4}{4} + \frac{4x^2}{2}\bigg]_2^6$$

$$= \left(\frac{6\cdot 6\cdot 6\cdot 6}{4} + \frac{4\cdot 6\cdot 6}{2}\right) - \left(\frac{2\cdot 2\cdot 2\cdot 2}{4} + \frac{4\cdot 2\cdot 2}{2}\right)$$

$$= (324 + 72) - (4 + 8) = 396 - 12 = 384$$

And

$$\bar{x} = \frac{M_{yy}}{A} = \frac{384}{(256/3)} = \frac{384}{1}\cdot\frac{3}{256} = \frac{1152}{256} = 4.5$$

Figure 4.28 is set up for calculating M_{xx}.

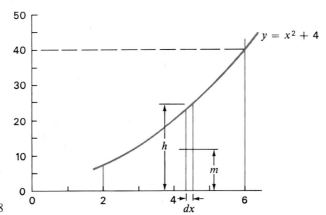

Figure 4.28

$$M_{xx} = \int_2^6 mh\,dx = \int_2^6 \frac{y}{2}\,dx$$

but $y = x^2 + 4$, so $y^2 = (x^2 + 4)^2 = x^4 + 8x^2 + 16$, and

$$M_{xx} = \frac{1}{2}\int_2^6 (x^4 + 8x^2 + 16)\,dx$$

$$= \frac{1}{2}\left(\frac{x^5}{5} + \frac{8x^3}{3} + 16x\right)\bigg]_2^6$$

$$= \frac{x^5}{10} + \frac{4x^3}{3} + 8x\bigg]_2^6$$

$$= \left(\frac{6^5}{10} + \frac{4(6)^3}{3} + 8(6)\right) - \left(\frac{2^5}{10} + \frac{4(2)^3}{3} + 8(2)\right)$$

$$= \left(\frac{7776}{10} + \frac{864}{3} + 48\right) - \left(\frac{32}{10} + \frac{32}{3} + 16\right)$$

$$= (777.6 + 288 + 48) - (3.2 + 10.66 + 16)$$

$$= 1113.6 - 29.86 = 1083.74$$

$$\bar{y} = \frac{M_{xx}}{A} = \frac{1083.74}{(256/3)} = \frac{(1083.74)(3)}{256} = 12.7$$

Second solution: Figure 4.29 shows our problem set up for M_{yy}.

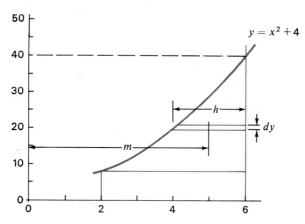

$$M_{yy} = \int_8^{40} mh\,dy$$

Figure 4.29

where $h = 6 - x$ and $m = x + (h/2) = x + (6 - x)/2 = 2x/2 + (6 - x)/2 = (6 + x)/2$, so $mh = [(6 - x)/1] \cdot [(6 + x)/2] = (36 - x^2)/2$, and if $y = x^2 + 4$ then $x^2 = y - 4$, and $mh = [36 - (y - 4)/2] = (40 - y)/2$, therefore

$$M_{yy} = \frac{1}{2} \int_8^{40} (40 - y)\,dy$$

$$= \frac{1}{2} \left. 40y - \frac{y^2}{4} \right]_8^{40} = \left. 20y - \frac{y^2}{4} \right]_8^{40}$$

$$= \left(20 \cdot 40 - \frac{40 \cdot 40}{4}\right) - \left(20 \cdot 8 - \frac{8 \cdot 8}{4}\right)$$

$$= (800 - 400) - (160 - 16) = 400 - 144 = 256$$

It must be remembered that we integrated from $y = 8$ to $y = 40$ which did not include the 8-by-4 rectangle. The moment of this rectangle about the y axis is $M_{yy} = 4(8 \cdot 4) = 128$, therefore the total

$$M_{yy} = 256 + 128 = 384$$

For the second solution of M_{xx} see Figure 4.30.

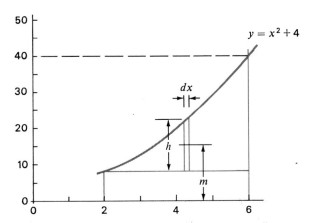

Figure 4.30

$$M_{xx} = \int_2^6 mh \, dx$$

where $h = y - 8$ and $m = y - (h/2) = (y + 8)/2$, so $mh = [(y - 8)/1] \cdot [(y + 8) /2] = (y^2 - 64)/2$, but $y = x^2 + 4$ and $y^2 = x^4 + 8x^2 + 16$, therefore $mh = (x^4 + 8x^2 - 48)/2$ and

$$M_{xx} = \frac{1}{2} \int_2^6 (x^4 + 8x^2 - 48) \, dx$$

$$= \frac{1}{2} \cdot \frac{x^5}{5} + \frac{8x^3}{2 \cdot 3} - \frac{48x}{2} \Big]_2^6 = \frac{x^5}{10} + \frac{4x^3}{3} - 24x \Big]_2^6$$

$$= \left(\frac{(6)^5}{10} + \frac{4(6)^3}{3} - 24(6) \right) - \left(\frac{(2)^5}{10} + \frac{4(2)^3}{3} - 24(2) \right)$$

$$= (777.6 + 288 - 144) - (3.2 + 10.6 - 48)$$

$$= 921.6 + 34.2 = 955.8$$

The moment of the 8-by-4 rectangle with moment arm 4 is $M_{xx} = 4(8)(4) = 4(32) = 128$, therefore total moment is $M_{xx} = 955.8 + 128 = 1083.8$.
From all of this then:

$$M_{xx} = 1083.74 \qquad M_{yy} = 384$$

$$\bar{x} = 4.5 \qquad \bar{y} = 12.7$$

Figure 4.31 shows the centroid properly located.

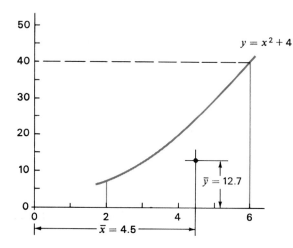

Figure 4.31

Example 4.12. Calculate $\bar{y}$ for any triangle with base b and altitude a. See Figure 4.32.

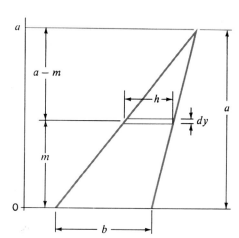

Figure 4.32

$$M_{xx} = \int_0^a mh\, dy$$

Since the elemental strip is parallel to the base, we have two similar triangles, and $h/(a - m) = b/a$ so $h = [b(a - m)]/a$, but $m = y$, so $h = [b(a - y)]/a$, therefore

$$M_{xx} = \int_0^a y\, \frac{b(a - y)}{a}\, dy$$

$$= \frac{1}{a} \int_0^a (aby - by^2)\, dy$$

$$= \frac{aby^2}{2a} - \frac{by^3}{3a}\Big]_0^a = \frac{by^2}{2} - \frac{by^3}{3a}\Big]_0^a = \frac{ba^2}{2} - \frac{ba^3}{3a}$$

$$= \frac{a^2b}{2} - \frac{a^2b}{3} = \frac{3a^2b - 2a^2b}{6} = \frac{a^2b}{6}$$

The area of a triangle is $A = ab/2$, so

$$\bar{y} = \frac{M_{xx}}{A} = \frac{a^2b}{6} \cdot \frac{2}{ab} = \frac{a}{3}$$

Thus we see that the centroid of any triangle is located one-third the altitude from the base.

Example 4.13. In Figure 4.33, show that the moment of area I with respect to the y axis is the same as the moment of area II with respect to the y axis.

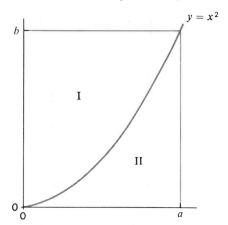

Figure 4.33

From Figure 4.34:

$$\text{(I)} \quad M_{yy} = \int_0^b mh\,dy$$

where $h = x = y^{1/2}$ and $m = h/2 = y^{1/2}/2$, so

$$\text{(I)} \quad M_{yy} = \frac{1}{2}\int_0^b y\,dy = \frac{y^2}{4}\Big]_0^b = \frac{b^2}{4}$$

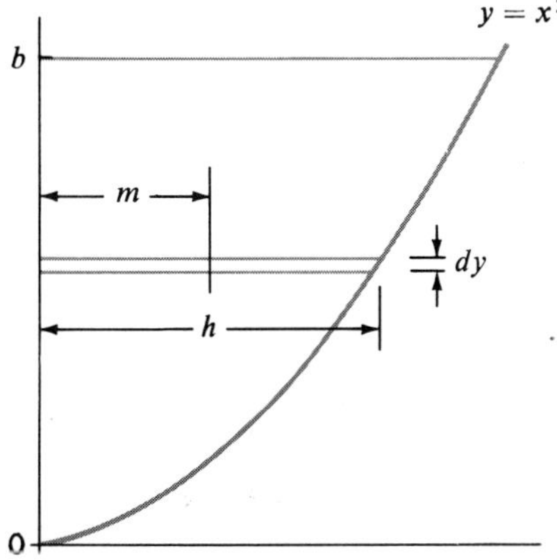

Figure 4.34

From Figure 4.35:

$$(II) \ M_{yy} = \int_0^a mh \, dx$$

where $m = x$ and $h = y = x^2$, so

$$(II) \ M_{yy} = \int_0^a x^3 \, dx = \left. \frac{x^4}{4} \right]_0^a = \frac{a^4}{4}$$

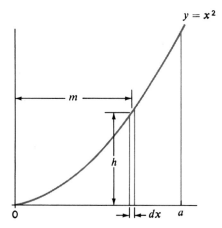

Figure 4.35

Now if (I) $M_{yy} = b^2/4$ and (II) $M_{yy} = a^4/4$, our job is to try to show that (I) M_{yy} is equal to (II) M_{yy}. From $y = x^2$ we find $b = a^2$, so (I) $M_{yy} = (a^2)^2/4 = a^4/4$, therefore (I) $M_{yy} = $ (II) M_{yy}.

Exercise 4.3

1. Repeat Example 4.13 for moments with respect to the x axis.
2. From Figure 4.36 calculate M_{yy} of area abc with respect to x.
3. From Figure 4.36 calculate M_{yy} of area abc with respect to y.
4. From Figure 4.36 calculate M_{xx} of area abc with respect to y.

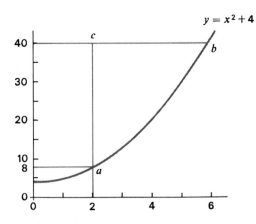

Figure 4.36

5. From Figure 4.36 calculate M_{xx} of area *abc* with respect to x.
6. Calculate $\bar{x}$ and $\bar{y}$ of a semicircle with radius R, if the semicircle is in quadrants I and II with center at the origin.
7. Calculate $\bar{x}$ and $\bar{y}$ of a quarter-circle with radius 10 in the first quadrant with center at the origin.
8. Calculate $\bar{x}$ and $\bar{y}$ of the area shown in Figure 4.37.

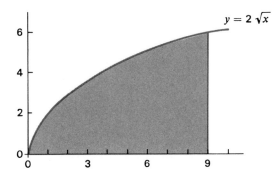

$y = 2\sqrt{x}$

Figure 4.37

9. Calculate $\bar{x}$ and $\bar{y}$ of the area bounded by $y = 10 - x$, $x = 0$ and $y = 0$.
10. Calculate $\bar{x}$ and $\bar{y}$ of the area bounded by $y = x$, $x = 10$ and $y = 0$.
11. Show that the moment of area I with respect to x is equal to the moment of area II with respect to x, in Figure 4.38.

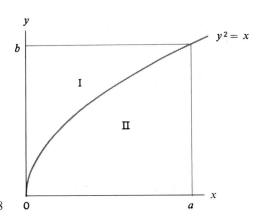

$y^2 = x$

Figure 4.38   0

12. Compare the area and $\bar{y}$ of areas I and II in Figure 4.38.

4.7 CENTROIDS OF VOLUMES

Recall that moment of volume has been defined as moment arm times the

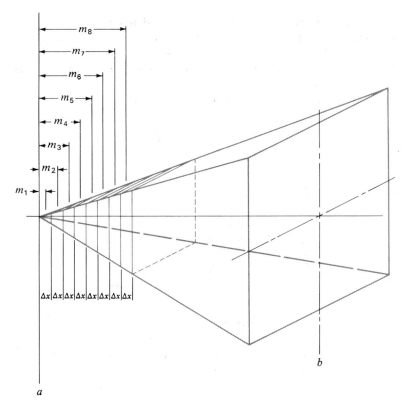

a   Figure 4.39

volume and that moments may be added. Looking at the right square pyramid in Figure 4.39, we divide it into n elemental square volumes Δx thick. Then:

$$M_{yy} \approx m_1 v_1 + m_2 v_2 + m_3 v_3 + \cdots + m_n v_n$$

$$M_{yy} \approx m_1 A_1(\Delta x) + m_2 A_2(\Delta x) + m_3 A_3(\Delta x) + \cdots + m_n A_n(\Delta x)$$

Therefore

$$M_{yy} \approx \sum_{i=1}^{n} m_i A_i(\Delta x)$$

and applying our limit ideas, we obtain:

$$M_{yy} = \lim_{\Delta x \to 0} \sum_{i=1}^{n} m_i A_i(\Delta x) = \int_a^b mA \, dx \qquad (4.5)$$

Note: $A \, dx = dV$. Likewise:

$$M_{xx} = \int_c^d mA \, dy \qquad (4.6)$$

Here $A \, dy = dV$.

Before attempting a problem of this nature, a sketch similar to Figure 4.40 should be made.

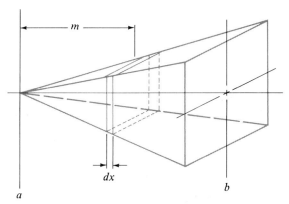

Figure 4.40

Example 4.14. Calculate M_{yy} of the right square pyramid shown in Figure 4.41.

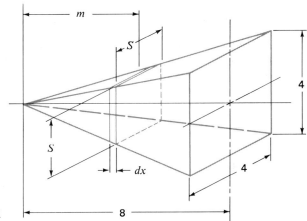

Figure 4.41

$$M_{yy} = \int_0^8 mA\,dx$$

where $m = x$ and $A = (s)(s) = s^2$, but $s = 2y$ and from similar triangles $x/2y = 8/4$, so $16y = 4x$, $y = x/4$, and $2y = x/2$, therefore $A = s^2 = (2y)^2 = x^2/4$, so

$$M_{yy} = \int_0^8 x\,\frac{x^2}{4}\,dx = \frac{1}{4}\int_0^8 x^3\,dx = \frac{x^4}{4\cdot 4}\Big]_0^8$$

$$= \frac{(8)^4}{16} = 256$$

If $M_{yy} = \bar{x} \cdot V$ then:

$$\bar{x} = \frac{M_{yy}}{V} \qquad (4.7)$$

and

$$\bar{y} = \frac{M_{xx}}{V} \qquad (4.8)$$

Example 4.15. Calculate $\bar{x}$ for Example 4.14.

Since $\bar{x} = M_{yy}/V$, we must calculate the volume of the pyramid.

$$V = \int_0^8 A \, dx = \int_0^8 \frac{x^2}{4} \, dx = \frac{1}{4} \int_0^8 x^2 \, dx$$

$$= \frac{x^3}{3 \cdot 4} \Big]_0^8 = \frac{8 \cdot 8 \cdot 8}{3 \cdot 4} = \frac{128}{3}$$

So

$$\bar{x} = \frac{M_{yy}}{V} = \frac{256}{128/3} = \frac{256}{1} \cdot \frac{3}{128} = 6.0$$

This places the centroid six-eighths or three-quarters of the altitude from the vertex or one-quarter of the altitude from the base.

Example 4.16. Calculate $\bar{x}$ for the volume generated by revolving area A about the x axis if area A is bounded by $y = x/2$, $x = 0$ and $x = 8$.

The volume generated is a right circular cone as illustrated in Figure 4.42.

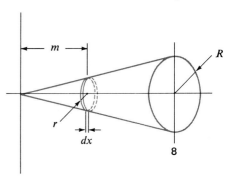

Figure 4.42   0

$$V = \int_0^8 \pi r^2 \, dx$$

but $r = y = x/2$, therefore $r^2 = x^2/4$, so

$$V = \frac{\pi}{4} \int_0^8 x^2 \, dx = \frac{\pi x^3}{4 \cdot 3} \Big]_0^8 = \frac{\pi \cdot 8 \cdot 8 \cdot 8}{4 \cdot 3} = \frac{128\pi}{3}$$

And

$$M_{yy} = \int_0^8 mA \, dx$$

where $m = x$, so

$$M_{yy} = \frac{\pi}{4} \int_0^8 x \cdot x^2 \, dx = \frac{\pi}{4} \int_0^8 x^3 \, dx$$

$$= \frac{\pi x^4}{4 \cdot 4} \Big]_0^8 = \frac{8 \cdot 8 \cdot 8 \cdot 8 \cdot \pi}{4 \cdot 4} = 256\pi$$

and

$$\bar{x} = \frac{M_{yy}}{V} = \frac{256\pi}{128\pi/3} = \frac{256\pi}{1} \cdot \frac{3}{128\pi} = 6.0$$

Example 4.17. Calculate $\bar{x}$ for the volume generated by revolving area A about the x axis if area A is bounded by $y = x/2 + 1$, $x = 2$, $x = 6$, and $y = 0$.

Figure 4.43*a* shows the area in question and Figure 4.43*b* shows the volume generated.

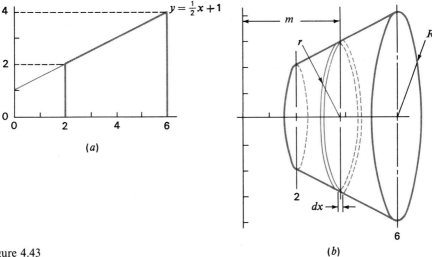

Figure 4.43

(a)

(b)

$$V = \pi \int_2^6 r^2 \, dx$$

where $r = y = (x/2) + 1$, so $r^2 = y^2 = (x^2/4) + x + 1$, therefore

$$V = \pi \int_2^6 \left(\frac{x^2}{4} + x + 1 \right) dx$$

$$= \frac{\pi x^3}{4 \cdot 3} + \frac{\pi x^2}{2} + \pi x \Big]_2^6 = \pi(18 + 18 + 6) - \pi(\tfrac{2}{3} + 2 + 2)$$

$$= 42\pi - \frac{14\pi}{3} = \frac{112\pi}{3}$$

$$M_{yy} = \int_2^6 m(\pi r^2) \, dx = \pi \int_2^6 m r^2 \, dx$$

where $m = x$, so

$$M_{yy} = \pi \int_2^6 x\left(\frac{x^2}{4} + x + 1\right) dx$$

$$= \pi \int_2^6 \left(\frac{x^3}{4} + x^2 + x\right) dx$$

$$= \pi\left(\frac{x^4}{4 \cdot 4} + \frac{x^3}{3} + \frac{x^2}{2}\right)\Bigg]_2^6$$

$$= \pi(81 + 72 + 18) - \pi\left(1 + \frac{8}{3} + 2\right) = 171\pi - \frac{17\pi}{3}$$

$$= \frac{496\pi}{3}$$

And $$\bar{x} = \frac{M_{yy}}{V} = \frac{496\pi}{3} \div \frac{112\pi}{3} = \frac{496\pi}{3} \cdot \frac{3}{112\pi} = \frac{496}{112}$$

$$= 4.428$$

Example 4.18.   Calculate $\bar{y}$ for the volume generated by revolving the area in Example 4.17 about the y axis. See Figure 4.44.

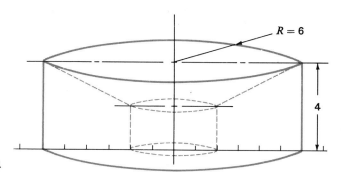

Figure 4.44

We first calculate the volume between $y = 2$ and $y = 4$.

$$V_{2 \to 4} = \pi \int_2^4 (R^2 - r^2) \, dy$$

where $R = 6$, $R^2 = 36$, and $r = x$, so $r^2 = x^2$, but $y = (x/2) + 1$ so $x = 2y - 2$ and $x^2 = 4y^2 - 4y + 4$, therefore

$$V = \pi \int_2^4 (36) - (4y^2 - 4y + 4) \, dy$$

$$= \pi \int_2^4 (-4y^2 + 4y + 32) \, dy$$

$$= \pi\left(\frac{4y^3}{-3} + \frac{4y^2}{2} + 32y\right)\Bigg]_2^4$$

$$= \left(\frac{256\pi}{-3} + 32\pi + 128\pi\right) - \left(\frac{32\pi}{-3} + 8\pi + 64\pi\right)$$

$$= \frac{224\pi}{3} - \frac{184\pi}{3} = \frac{40\pi}{3}$$

And the volume between 0 and 2:

$$\underset{0 \to 2}{V} = \pi(36 - 4)2 = 64\pi$$

Total volume then: $V = 40\pi/3 + 64\pi = 232\pi/3$.

$$\underset{0 \to 2}{M_{xx}} = (64\pi)(1) = 64\pi$$

$$\underset{2 \to 4}{M_{xx}} = \pi \int_2^4 m(R^2 - r^2)\,dy$$

$$= \pi \int_2^4 (-4y^3 + 4y^2 + 32y)\,dy$$

$$= \pi\left(-y^4 + \frac{4y^3}{3} + 16y^2\right)\Bigg]_2^4$$

$$= \pi\left(-256 + \frac{256}{3} + 256\right) - \pi\left(-16 + \frac{32}{3} + 64\right)$$

$$= \frac{256\pi}{3} - \frac{176\pi}{3} = \frac{80\pi}{3}$$

$$\underset{0 \to 4}{M_{xx}} = 64\pi + \frac{80\pi}{3} = \frac{272\pi}{3}$$

$$\bar{y} = \frac{M_{xx}}{V} = \frac{272\pi}{3} \cdot \frac{3}{232\pi} = 1.172$$

Exercise 4.4

1. Locate the centroid of any right circular cone.
2. Locate the centroid of the volume generated by revolving area A about the x axis if area A is bounded by $y = 3$, $y = 0$, $x = 0$, and $x = 10$.
3. Locate the centroid of the volume generated by revolving area A about the y axis if area A is bounded by $x^2 + y^2 = 10$, $x = 0$, and $y = 0$.
4. Locate the centroid of the volume generated by revolving area A about the y axis if area A is bounded by $y = x^2$, $y = 0$, $x = 0$, and $x = 3$.
5. Locate the centroid of the volume generated by revolving area A in problem 4 about the y axis.

6. Locate the centroid of the volume generated by revolving area A about the x axis if area A is bounded by $y = x^2$, $y = 9$, and $x = 0$.

7. Locate the centroid of the volume generated by revolving area A in problem 6 about the y axis.

8. Locate the centroid of the volume generated by revolving area A about the x axis if area A is bounded by $y = (x^2/2) + 2$, $x = 0$, and $y = 4$.

9. Locate the centroid of the volume generated by revolving area A in problem 8 about the y axis.

10. Locate the centroid of the volume generated by revolving area A about the x axis if area A is bounded by $y = (x^2/2) + 2$, $x = 0$, $x = 2$, and $y = 0$.

11. Locate the centroid of the volume generated by revolving the area in problem 10 about the y axis.

12. Locate the centroid of the volume generated by revolving area A about the y axis if area A is bounded by $y = -x + 6$, $y = 3$, and $x = 0$.

13. Locate the centroid of the volume generated by revolving area A in problem 12 about the x axis.

14. Locate the centroid of the volume generated by revolving area A about the x axis if area A is bounded by $(x^2/16) + (y^2/9) = 1$, $x = 0$, and $y = 0$.

15. Locate the centroid of the volume generated by revolving area A in problem 14 about the y axis.

16. Locate the centroid of the volume generated by revolving area A about the x axis if area A is bounded by $(x^2/4) - (y^2/1) = 1$, $x = 2$, $x = 5$, and $y = 0$.

17. Locate the centroid of the volume generated by revolving area A in problem 16 about the y axis.

18. Locate the centroid of the volume generated by revolving area A about the x axis if area A is bounded by $y = x^2/4$, $x = y^2/4$, $x = 0$, and $y = 0$.

19. Locate the centroid of the volume generated by revolving area A in problem 18 about the y axis.

4.8 A PAPPUS THEOREM

Pappus of Alexandria was a Greek mathematician responsible for two famous theorems of mechanics. The Pappus theorem we are to use says:

> *The volume generated by revolving an area about an axis is calculated by multiplying the area by the distance through which the centroid of that area moves.*   (4.9)

Consider a square of side s revolved about the x axis as shown in Figure 4.45. Here we have the area of the square to be revolved equal to $s \cdot s = s^2$. The distance from the axis of revolution to the centroid of the area involved is $R = \bar{y}$. The distance through which the centroid travels is then the circumference of a circle with radius R, so $C = 2\pi R = 2\pi \bar{y}$.

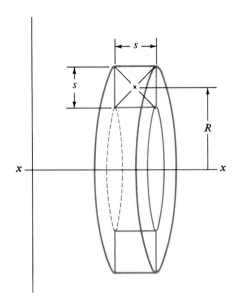

Figure 4.45

From Pappus then,

$$V = s^2(2\pi\bar{y}) = 2\pi\bar{y}s^2 = 2\pi\bar{y}A$$

But if $V = 2\pi\bar{y}A$, we see that $\bar{y}A$ is in fact M_{xx} of area A, so the most effective use of this Pappus theorem is:

$$V = 2\pi(M_{xx})$$
$$= 2\pi(M_{yy})$$

(4.10)

Example 4.19. Calculate the volume generated by revolving a circle of radius 2 about the x axis if the center of the circle is 3 units from the x axis. See Figure 4.46.

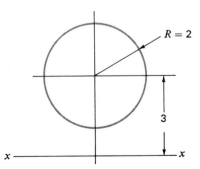

Figure 4.46

First solution:

$$V = 2\pi \bar{y}(A) = 2\pi 3(4\pi) = 24\pi^2$$

Second solution:

$$V = 2\pi(M_{xx})$$

where $M_{xx} = \bar{y}A = 3(4\pi) = 12\pi.$

$$V = 2\pi(12\pi) = 24\pi^2$$

Example 4.20. Calculate the volume generated by revolving the area in Figure 4.43*a* about the *x* axis. See Figure 4.47.

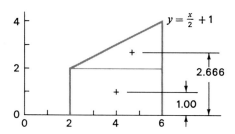

Figure 4.47

First solution:

$$M_{xx}(\text{rectangle}) = 1.0(2)(4) = 8.0$$

$$M_{xx}(\text{triangle}) = 2.666[4(2/2)] = 10.664$$

$$M_{xx}(\text{total}) = 8.0 + 10.664 = 18.664$$

$$V = 2\pi(M_{xx}) = 2\pi(18.664) = 37.34\pi$$

Compare this answer with the answer to Example 4.17.
  Second solution:

$$\bar{y} = \frac{M_{xx}}{A} = \frac{18.664}{3.666} = 5.09 \qquad \text{and } A = 4\pi$$

$$V = 2\pi\bar{y}A = 2\pi(5.09)(3.666) = 2\pi(18.664) = 37.34\pi$$

Exercise 4.5. Use the theorem of Pappus to calculate the volumes asked for in Exercise 4.4.

4.9 CENTROIDS OF CURVED-LINE SEGMENTS

In looking at the centroid of a curved-line segment, we shall use an approach that should be familiar by now. Divide the curved-line segment into small elemental lengths, then look at the chords (ΔL) and set up moment arms *m* for each, calculate each individual moment, and sum. Figure 4.48 shows such a picture.

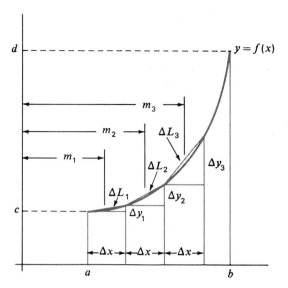

Figure 4.48

$$M_{yy} \approx m_1(\Delta L)_1 + m_2(\Delta L)_2 + \cdots + m_n(\Delta L)_n$$

$$\approx \sum_{i=1}^{n} m_i(\Delta L)_i$$

But $\quad (\Delta L)_i = (\sqrt{1 + (\Delta y/\Delta x)^2})_i(\Delta x)$

therefore

$$M_{yy} \approx \sum_{i=1}^{n} m_i \left(\sqrt{1 + \left(\frac{\Delta y}{\Delta x}\right)^2}\right)_i (\Delta x)$$

$$M_{yy} = \lim_{\substack{a \to b \\ \Delta x \to 0}} \sum_{i=1}^{n} m_i \left(\sqrt{1 + \left(\frac{\Delta y}{\Delta x}\right)^2}\right)_i (\Delta x)$$

$$= \int_a^b m \sqrt{1 + \left(\frac{dy}{dx}\right)^2} \, dx \qquad (4.11)$$

$$M_{xx} = \int_{c \to d}^{d} m \sqrt{1 + \left(\frac{dx}{dy}\right)^2} \, dy \qquad (4.12)$$

And since $M_{yy} = \bar{x}L$

$$\bar{x} = \frac{M_{yy}}{L} \qquad (4.13)$$

$$\bar{y} = \frac{M_{xx}}{L} \qquad (4.14)$$

Example 4.21.   Calculate $\bar{x}$ for the line segment $y = \frac{2}{3}\sqrt{x^3}$ between $x = 3$ and $x = 8$.

$$L = \int_3^8 \sqrt{1 + \left(\frac{dy}{dx}\right)^2}\, dx$$

If $y = \frac{2}{3}x^{3/2}$, then $dy/dx = (\frac{3}{2})(\frac{2}{3})x^{1/2} = x^{1/2}$ and $(dy/dx)^2 = x$, so

$$L = \int_3^8 (1 + x)^{1/2}\, dx = \frac{(1 + x)^{3/2}}{3/2}\Bigg]_3^8$$

$$= \frac{2(1 + x)^{3/2}}{3}\Bigg]_3^8 = \frac{2(1 + 8)^{3/2}}{3} - \frac{2(1 + 3)^{3/2}}{3}$$

$$= \frac{2(27)}{3} - \frac{2(8)}{3} = \frac{54}{3} - \frac{16}{3} = \frac{38}{3}$$

$$M_{yy} = \int_3^8 m\sqrt{1 + \left(\frac{dy}{dx}\right)^2}\, dx = \int_3^8 x\left(1 + \left(\frac{dy}{dx}\right)^2\right)^{1/2} dx$$

$$= \int_3^8 x(1 + x)^{1/2}\, dx$$

From a table of integrals:

$$\int x(a + bx)^n\, dx = \frac{1}{b^2(n + 2)}(a + bx)^{n+2} - \frac{a}{b^2(n + 1)}(a + bx)^{n+1}$$

So

$$\int_3^8 x(1 + x)^{1/2}\, dx = \frac{1}{1[(1/2) + 2]}(1 + x)^{(1/2)+2}$$

$$- \frac{1}{1[(1/2) + 1]}(1 + x)^{(1/2)+1}\Bigg]_3^8$$

$$= \frac{1}{5/2}(1 + x)^{5/2} - \frac{1}{3/2}(1 + x)^{3/2}\Bigg]_3^8$$

$$= [\tfrac{2}{5}(9)^{5/2} - \tfrac{2}{3}(9)^{3/2}] - [\tfrac{2}{5}(4)^{5/2} - \tfrac{2}{3}(4)^{3/2}]$$

$$= 84.4 + 5.33 - 18$$

$$= 71.73$$

$$\bar{x} = \frac{M_{yy}}{L} = \frac{71.73}{38/3} = 5.66$$

Exercise 4.6

1. Locate the centroid of the line segment $x^2 + y^2 = 400$ in quadrant I.
2. Locate the centroid of the line segment $x^2 + y^2 = 100$ in quadrant II.

4.10 SECOND MOMENTS—MOMENT OF INERTIA

So far our work has been with first moments or with moments that were first moments without so saying because the first power of the moment arm entered into the calculations. We now wish to discuss second moments or moments in which the second power of the moment arm is used. Second moments are called *moment of inertia* and, instead of using M_{xx} and M_{yy} as with first moments, we use I_{xx} and I_{yy} as the identifying symbols. Moment arm in moment of inertia is measured exactly as it is measured in first moments, that is, from and perpendicular to the axis of reference to the centroid of the configuration. In order to eliminate confusion between first and second moment, we shall designate the moment arm for moment of inertia problems with the letter l.

Figure 4.49 shows a simple rectangle properly set up for finding I_{xx}, the moment

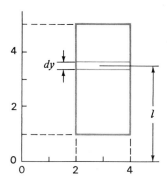

Figure 4.49

of inertia with respect to the x axis. Since the only difference between M and I is the power of the moment arm, we write

$$I_{xx} = \int_1^5 l^2 h \, dy$$

where l is the moment arm, h the length of the elemental strip, and dy the width of the strip.

Similarly, Figure 4.50 is set up for finding I_{yy} the moment of inertia with respect to the y axis, and

$$I_{yy} = \int_2^4 l^2 h \, dx$$

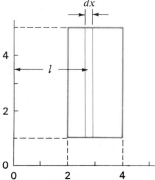

Figure 4.50

In general then:

$$I_{xx} = \int_c^d l^2 h \, dy \qquad (4.15)$$

$$I_{yy} = \int_a^b l^2 h \, dx \qquad (4.16)$$

Example 4.22.   Calculate I_{xx} and I_{yy} for the rectangle in Figures 4.49 and 4.50.

$$I_{yy} = \int_2^4 l^2 h \, dx$$

where $l = x$, so $l^2 = x^2$ and $h = 5 - 1 = 4$, therefore:

$$I_{yy} = \int_2^4 x^2 4 \, dx = 4 \int_2^4 x^2 \, dx$$

$$= \frac{4x^3}{3} \Big]_2^4 = \frac{4 \cdot 4 \cdot 4 \cdot 4}{3} - \frac{4 \cdot 2 \cdot 2 \cdot 2}{3}$$

$$= \frac{264}{3} - \frac{32}{3} = \frac{232}{3}$$

$$= 77.33 \text{ units to the fourth power}$$

Similarly for

$$I_{xx} = \int_1^5 l^2 h \, dy$$

where $l = y$, so $l^2 = y^2$, and $h = 4 - 2 = 2$, therefore

$$I_{xx} = \int_1^5 y^2 2 \, dy = 2 \int_1^5 y^2 \, dy$$

$$= \frac{2y^3}{3} \Big]_1^5$$

$$= \frac{2 \cdot 5 \cdot 5 \cdot 5}{3} - \frac{2 \cdot 1 \cdot 1 \cdot 1}{3} = \frac{250}{3} - \frac{2}{3}$$

$$= \frac{248}{3} = 82.66 \text{ units to the fourth power.}$$

When working with first moments we were concerned with $\bar{x}$ and $\bar{y}$, the distance from the centroid to the respective axes of reference. When discussing moment of inertia we concern ourselves with the radius of gyration (r). The radius of gyration of an area about the x axis is implied by

$$I_{xx} = (r_x)^2 A \tag{4.17}$$

and defined by

$$r_x = \sqrt{\frac{I_{xx}}{A}} \tag{4.18}$$

Similarly, the radius of gyration of an area about the y axis is implied by

$$I_{yy} = (r_y)^2 A \tag{4.19}$$

and defined by

$$r_y = \sqrt{\frac{I_{yy}}{A}} \tag{4.20}$$

This concept of radius of gyration is of extreme importance to engineering approaches in strength of materials and static mechanics problems. We shall treat it as a mathematical entity defined by (4.18) and (4.20).

Example 4.23.   Calculate r_x and r_y from Example 4.22.
Here the area $A = 2 \cdot 4 = 8$, and $I_{xx} = 82.66$, so

$$r_x = \sqrt{\frac{82.66}{8}} = \sqrt{10.332} = 3.21$$

and

$$r_y = \sqrt{\frac{77.33}{8}} = \sqrt{9.666} = 3.11$$

There seems to be an analogy between r_x, r_y and $\bar{x}$, $\bar{y}$ and in fact there is a remote connection. There are many differences too, however. Recall that $\bar{x}$ and $\bar{y}$ locate the centroid of a given area, and that if that area is moved with respect to the reference axes, $\bar{x}$ and $\bar{y}$ will change just enough to locate the centroid in exactly the same position relative to the boundaries of the area itself. Now while it is true that the point (r_y, r_x) can be plotted, the radius of gyration is not a function of the area itself but is a function of the area and the environment of the area, that is, the axes of reference. To illustrate this point we all agree that the centroid of the 2-by-4 rectangle we have been working with in Examples 4.22 and 4.23 is located one unit from either four-unit edge and two units from either two-unit edge regardless of where this rectangle is located.

If, however, we move the rectangle and recalculate r_x and r_y, we find the point (r_y, r_x) shifts relative to the boundaries of the rectangle itself.

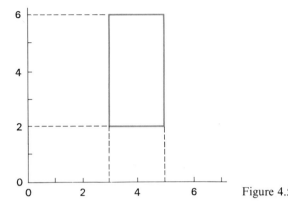

Figure 4.51

Suppose we move the same rectangle, as shown in Figure 4.51, then:

$$I_{yy} = \int_3^5 l^2 h \, dx = 4 \int_3^5 x^2 \, dx = \frac{4x^3}{3}\Bigg]_3^5$$

$$= \frac{4 \cdot 5 \cdot 5 \cdot 5}{3} - \frac{4 \cdot 3 \cdot 3 \cdot 3}{3} = 130.66$$

$$I_{xx} = \int_2^6 l^2 h \, dy = 2 \int_2^6 y^2 \, dy = \frac{2y^3}{6}\Bigg]_2^6$$

$$= \frac{2 \cdot 6 \cdot 6 \cdot 6}{3} - \frac{2 \cdot 2 \cdot 2 \cdot 2}{3} = \frac{432}{3} - \frac{16}{3} = 138.66$$

Thus

$$r_x = \sqrt{\frac{I_{xx}}{A}} = \sqrt{\frac{138.66}{8}} = \sqrt{17.33} = 4.16$$

and

$$r_y = \sqrt{\frac{I_{yy}}{A}} = \sqrt{\frac{130.66}{8}} = \sqrt{16.33} = 4.06$$

Figure 4.52a shows (r_y, r_x) with respect to the area's own boundaries if

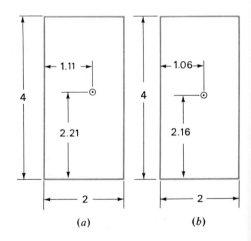

Figure 4.52   (a)   (b)

calculated according to Figures 4.49 and 4.50, and Figure 4.52b shows (r_y, r_x) with respect to the area's boundaries if calculated according to Figure 4.51.

In problems involving moment of inertia by integration the same four possibilities exist as existed in Figure 4.21. In each sketch substitute l for m and in each formula substitute l^2 for m, I_{yy} for M_{yy}, and I_{xx} for M_{xx}.

Example 4.24.   Calculate r_x and r_y for the area bounded by $y = x^2/2$, $y = 0$, $x = 0$, and $x = 3$.

For I_{xx} we use Figure 4.53.

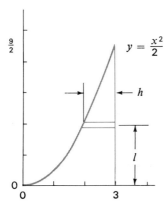

Figure 4.53

$$I_{xx} = \int_0^{9/2} l^2 h \, dy$$

where $l = y$ so $l^2 = y^2$ and $h = 3 - x = 3 - (2y)^{1/2}$, and

$$I_{xx} = \int_0^{9/2} y^2 (3 - (2y)^{1/2}) \, dy$$

$$= \int_0^{9/2} (3y^2 - \sqrt{2}(y)^{5/2}) \, dy$$

$$= \frac{3y^3}{3} - \frac{\sqrt{2}(y)^{7/2}}{7/2} \Bigg]_0^{9/2} = y^3 - \frac{2\sqrt{2}(y)^{7/2}}{7} \Bigg]_0^{9/2}$$

$$= \frac{729}{8} - \frac{2187}{28} = 13.01$$

For I_{yy} we use Figure 4.54.

$$I_{yy} = \int_0^3 l^2 h \, dx$$

where $l = x$ so $l^2 = x^2$ and $h = y = x^2/2$, so

$$I_{yy} = \int_0^3 x^2 \frac{x^2}{2} \, dx = \frac{1}{2} \int_0^3 x^4 \, dx$$

$$= \frac{1}{2} \cdot \frac{x^5}{5} \Big]_0^3 = 24.3$$

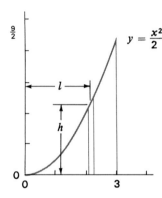

$$y = \frac{x^2}{2}$$

Figure 4.54

Using Figure 4.54 we calculate the area.

$$A = \int_0^3 h \, dx = \frac{1}{2} \int_0^3 x^2 \, dx$$

$$= \frac{1}{2} \cdot \frac{x^3}{3} \Big]_0^3 = \frac{9}{2} = 4.5$$

$$r_x = \sqrt{\frac{13.01}{4.5}} = \sqrt{2.89} = 1.70$$

$$r_y = \sqrt{\frac{24.3}{4.5}} = \sqrt{5.4} = 2.32$$

Example 4.25.   Calculate the formula for the moment of inertia of a rectangle about a centroidal axis.

Set up the problem as in Figure 4.55 with the x axis passing through the centroid.

$$I_{xx} = \int_a^c l^2 b \, dy$$

where $l = y$, $a = -d/2$, and $c = d/2$, therefore

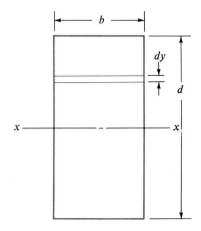

Figure 4.55

$$I_{xx} = \int_{-d/2}^{d/2} by^2 \, dy = b \int_{-d/2}^{d/2} y^2 \, dy = \frac{by^3}{3} \bigg]_{-d/2}^{d/2}$$

$$= \frac{b(d/2)(d/2)(d/2)}{3} - \frac{b(-d/2)(-d/2)(-d/2)}{3}$$

$$= \frac{bd^3}{24} - \left(-\frac{bd^3}{24} \right) = \frac{2bd^3}{24} = \frac{bd^3}{12}$$

$$I_{xx} = \frac{bd^3}{12} \quad \text{(rectangle about the centroidal axis)} \qquad (4.21)$$

Example 4.26. Calculate the formula for the moment of inertia of a rectangle about a side.

Set the problem up as in Figure 4.56 with the x axis coinciding with a side.

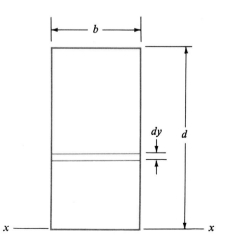

Figure 4.56

$$I_{xx} = \int_a^c l^2 b\, dy$$

where $a = 0$, $c = d$, $l = y$, so $l^2 = y^2$, therefore

$$I_{xx} = \int_0^d y^2 b\, dy = b \int_0^d y^2\, dy = \frac{by^3}{3}\Bigg]_0^d$$

$$= \frac{bddd}{3} = \frac{bd^3}{3}$$

$$I_{xx} = \frac{bd^3}{3} \text{ (rectangle about a side)} \qquad (4.22)$$

Example 4.27. Calculate the moment of inertia of a triangle about a base. Set the problem up as in Figure 4.57.

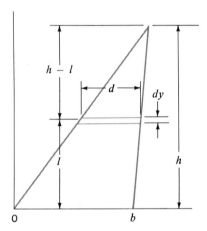

Figure 4.57

$$I_{xx} = \int_a^c l^2 d\, dy$$

where $l = y$, so $l^2 = y^2$ and, by similar triangles, $d/b = (h - l)/h$, so $d = [(h - l)/h]b = [(h - y)/h]b$, and $a = 0$, $c = h$, therefore

$$I_{xx} = \int_0^h y^2 \frac{h - y}{h} b\, dy = \frac{b}{h} \int_0^h (hy^2 - y^3)\, dy$$

$$= \frac{by^3}{3} - \frac{by^4}{4h}\Bigg]_0^h = \frac{bh^3}{3} - \frac{bh^4}{4h}$$

$$= \frac{4bh^3}{12} - \frac{3bh^3}{12} = \frac{bh^3}{12}$$

$$I_{xx} = \frac{bh^3}{12} \text{ (triangle about base)} \qquad (4.23)$$

It would seem logical at this point to develop the formula for the moment of inertia of a triangle about its centroidal axis, but we lack the necessary tools, so we will stop and discuss what is needed.

4.11 TRANSLATION FORMULA— MOMENT OF INERTIA

We have noted while working Example 4.23 that r_x and r_y are not only functions of the area involved but the location of that area with respect to the reference axis. In Example 4.23 we moved the area, but the axes could be moved also. For instance, we know the formula for the moment of inertia of a rectangle about its centroidal axis.

Suppose then we wish to calculate the moment of inertia of a rectangle about a line parallel to the centroidal axis if the distance between axes is D. Figure 4.58 illustrates such a situation. For this we have:

$$I_p = I_c + AD^2 \tag{4.24}$$

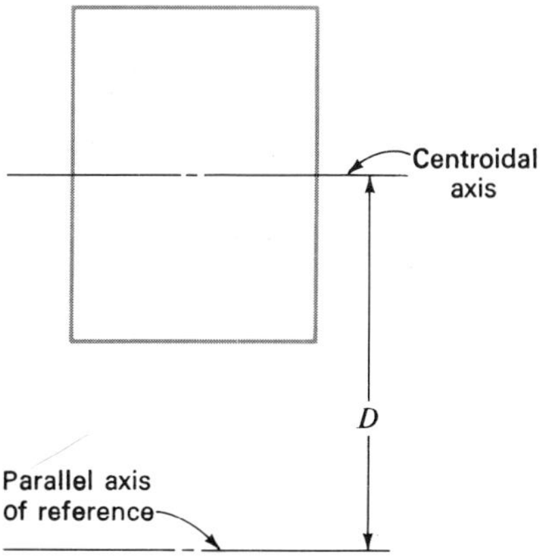

Centroidal axis

D

Parallel axis of reference

Figure 4.58

In (4.24) I_p is the moment of inertia about the axis parallel to the centroidal axis, and I_c is the moment of inertia about the centroidal axis. A is the area of the geometric figure and D is the distance between the two parallel axes. And since $r_y = \sqrt{(I_{yy})/A}$, we have

$$r_y = \sqrt{\frac{I_c + AD^2}{A}} \tag{4.25}$$

$$r_x = \sqrt{\frac{I_c + AD^2}{A}} \tag{4.26}$$

We know that the moment of inertia of a rectangle about its centroidal axis is $I_c = (bd^3)/12$, and the moment of inertia of a rectangle about a side is $I_{xx} = (bd^3)/3$.

With a proper sketch let us see if we can derive $I_{xx} = (bd^3)/3$. See Figure 4.59.

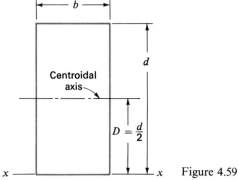

Figure 4.59

$$I_{xx} = I_c + AD^2$$

$$= \frac{bd^3}{12} + (bd)\frac{d^2}{2} = \frac{bd^3}{12} + \frac{bd^3}{4}$$

$$= \frac{bd^3}{12} + \frac{3bd^3}{12} = \frac{4bd^3}{12} = \frac{bd^3}{3}$$

Example 4.28.   Calculate the moment of inertia of a triangle about a centroidal axis parallel to the base.

See Figure 4.60. We know $I_{xx} = (bh^3)/12$, so if $I_{xx} = I_c + AD^2$, then

$$I_c = I_{xx} - AD^2$$

where $A = bh/2$ and $D = h/3$, so $D^2 = h^2/9$.

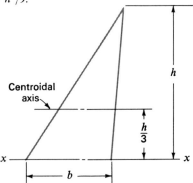

Figure 4.60

$$I_c = \frac{bh^3}{12} - \frac{bh}{2}\cdot\frac{h^2}{9} = \frac{bh^3}{12} - \frac{bh^3}{18}$$

$$= \frac{3bh^3}{36} - \frac{2bh^3}{36} = \frac{bh^3}{36}$$

$$I_c = \frac{bh^3}{36} \text{ (triangle about centroidal axis)} \qquad (4.27)$$

Example 4.29. Calculate the moment of inertia of a semicircle about a diameter, and then using the translation formula calculate the moment of inertia of a semicircle about an axis through the centroid parallel to the diameter.

See Figure 4.61.

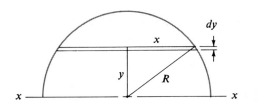

Figure 4.61

$$I_{xx} = \int_0^R y^2 \, dA$$

where $dA = 2x \, dy$, so

$$I_{xx} = \int_0^R y^2 \, 2x \, dy$$

but $R^2 = x^2 + y^2$, so $x^2 = R^2 - y^2$, and $x = \sqrt{R^2 - y^2}$, therefore

$$I_{xx} = 2 \int_0^R y^2 \sqrt{R^2 - y^2} \, dy$$

From a table of integrals we find

$$\int x^2 \sqrt{a^2 - x^2} \, dx = -\frac{\pi}{4} \sqrt{(a^2 - x^2)^3} + \frac{a^2}{8} \left(x \sqrt{a^2 - x^2} + a^2 \sin^{-1} \frac{x}{a} \right)$$

$$I_{xx} = 2 \left(-\frac{\pi}{4} \sqrt{(R^2 - y^2)^3} + \frac{y^2}{8} \left(y \sqrt{R^2 - y^2} + R^2 \sin^{-1} \frac{y}{R} \right) \right)_0^R$$

$$= 2 \left(-\frac{\pi}{4} \sqrt{(R^2 - R^2)^3} + \frac{R^2}{8} \left(R \sqrt{R^2 - R^2} + R^2 \sin^{-1} \frac{R}{R} \right) \right)$$

$$= 2 \left(\frac{R^2}{8} \left[R^2 \sin^{-1} (1) \right] \right)$$

$$= \frac{R^4}{4} \sin^{-1} (1) = \frac{R^4}{4} \cdot \frac{\pi}{2} = \frac{\pi R^4}{8}$$

$$I_{xx} = \frac{\pi R^4}{8} \text{ (semicircle about diameter)} \qquad (4.28)$$

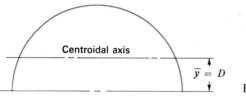

Figure 4.62

For I_c we use Figure 4.62. From problem 6, Exercise 4.3:

$$\bar{y} = D = \frac{4R}{3\pi} \quad \text{and} \quad D^2 = \frac{16R^2}{9\pi^2}$$

$$I_c = I_{xx} - AD^2 \quad \text{and} \quad A = \frac{\pi R^2}{2}$$

therefore

$$I_c = \frac{\pi R^4}{8} - \frac{\pi R^2}{2} \cdot \frac{16R^2}{9\pi^2} = \frac{\pi R^4}{8} - \frac{16R^4}{18\pi} = \frac{\pi R^4}{8} - \frac{8R^4}{9\pi}$$

$$\frac{9\pi^2 R^4}{72\pi} - \frac{64R^4}{72\pi} = \frac{9\pi^2 R^4 - 64R^4}{72\pi}$$

$$= \frac{R^4(9\pi^2 - 64)}{72\pi}$$

$$I_c = \frac{R^4(9\pi^2 - 64)}{72\pi} \quad \text{(semicircle about centroidal axis parallel to a diameter)}$$

$$(4.29)$$

Moments of inertia may be added and subtracted in much the same way that first moments are manipulated. For instance, the square in Figure 4.63 has a

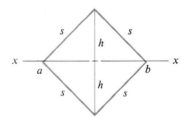

Figure 4.63

second moment about the x axis which is equal to the sum of the second moments of the two triangles. I_{xx} for a triangle according to (4.23) is:

$$I_{xx} = \frac{bh^3}{12} = \frac{(\bar{a}\bar{b})h^3}{12}$$

but since $(\bar{a}\bar{b})^2 = s^2 + s^2 = 2s^2$, $\bar{a}\bar{b} = \sqrt{2s^2} = \sqrt{2}\,s$, and $s^2 = h^2 + (\bar{a}\bar{b}/2)^2 = h^2 + (\sqrt{2}\,s/2)^2 = h^2 + (2s^2/4)$, so $h^2 = s^2 - (s^2/2) = (s^2/2)$, and $h = s/\sqrt{2}$, therefore

$$I_{xx} = \frac{\sqrt{2}\, s(s^3/\sqrt{2^3})}{12} = \frac{s^4}{24}$$

But there are two identical triangles, so

$$I_{xx} = \frac{s^4}{24} + \frac{s^4}{24} = \frac{s^4}{12}$$

$$I_{xx} = \frac{s^4}{12}\ \text{(square about a diagonal)} \tag{4.30}$$

Example 4.30. Calculate the moment of inertia of the composite channel as shown in Figure 4.64.

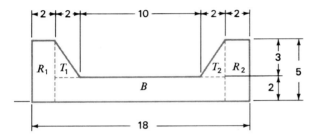

Figure 4.64

We will divide the total area into smaller areas whose moment of inertia we can calculate, and then for the total moment of inertia we will sum all of these.

Rectangles R_1 and R_2 are identical and are so placed that the axis of reference coincides with a side of each rectangle.

$$I_{xxR} = \frac{bd^3}{3} = \frac{2 \cdot 5 \cdot 5 \cdot 5}{3} = \frac{250}{3} = 83.33$$

and

$$I_{xxR_1R_2} = 2(83.33) = 166.66$$

Rectangle B has a side that coincides with the axis of reference, so

$$I_{xxB} = \frac{bd^3}{3} = \frac{14 \cdot 2 \cdot 2 \cdot 2}{3} = \frac{112}{3} = 37.33$$

Triangles T_1 and T_2 are identical and have the same relationship to the axis of reference, but we will have to use the translation formula since the axis of reference is removed from them:

$$I_{cT_1} = \frac{bh^3}{36} = \frac{2 \cdot 3 \cdot 3 \cdot 3}{36} = \frac{3}{2}$$

$$I_{xxT_1} = I_c + AD^2$$

where $A = (2 \cdot 3)/2 = 3$ and $D = 3$, therefore

$$I_{xxT_1} = \tfrac{3}{2} + 3(3 \cdot 3) = 1.5 + 27 = 28.5$$

and

$$I_{xxT_1T_2} = 2(28.5) = 57.0$$

Finally we sum:

$$I_{xx} = I_{xxR_1R_2} + I_{xxB} + I_{xxT_1T_2}$$
$$= 166.66 + 37.33 + 57.00 = 260.99$$

4.12 SUMMARY OF MOMENT-OF-INERTIA FORMULAS

(4.21) Rectangle, centroidal axis (Figure 4.65).

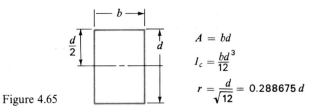

Figure 4.65

$$A = bd$$
$$I_c = \frac{bd^3}{12}$$
$$r = \frac{d}{\sqrt{12}} = 0.288675\,d$$

(4.22) Rectangle, axis on a side (Figure 4.66).

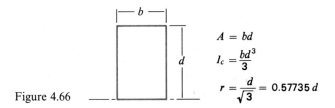

Figure 4.66

$$A = bd$$
$$I_c = \frac{bd^3}{3}$$
$$r = \frac{d}{\sqrt{3}} = 0.57735\,d$$

(4.23) Triangle, axis on a base (Figure 4.67).

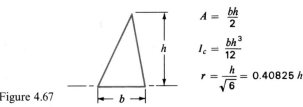

Figure 4.67

$$A = \frac{bh}{2}$$
$$I_c = \frac{bh^3}{12}$$
$$r = \frac{h}{\sqrt{6}} = 0.40825\,h$$

(4.27) Triangle, centroidal axis (Figure 4.68).

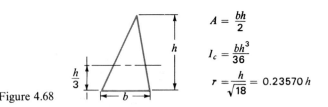

Figure 4.68

$$A = \frac{bh}{2}$$
$$I_c = \frac{bh^3}{36}$$
$$r = \frac{h}{\sqrt{18}} = 0.23570\,h$$

(4.28) Semicircle, axis on diameter (Figure 4.69).

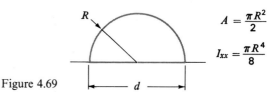

$$A = \frac{\pi R^2}{2}$$

$$I_{xx} = \frac{\pi R^4}{8}$$

Figure 4.69

(4.29) Semicircle, centroidal axis (Figure 4.70).

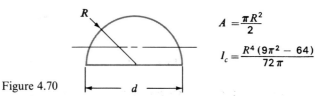

$$A = \frac{\pi R^2}{2}$$

$$I_c = \frac{R^4 (9\pi^2 - 64)}{72\pi}$$

Figure 4.70

(4.30) Square, axis on diagonal (Figure 4.71).

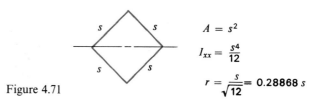

$$A = s^2$$

$$I_{xx} = \frac{s^4}{12}$$

$$r = \frac{s}{\sqrt{12}} = 0.28868\, s$$

Figure 4.71

(4.31) Rectangle, axis on diagonal (Figure 4.72).

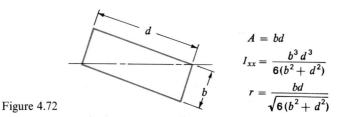

$$A = bd$$

$$I_{xx} = \frac{b^3 d^3}{6(b^2 + d^2)}$$

$$r = \frac{bd}{\sqrt{6(b^2 + d^2)}}$$

Figure 4.72

(4.32) Circle, axis on diameter (Figure 4.73).

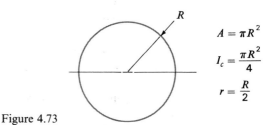

$$A = \pi R^2$$

$$I_c = \frac{\pi R^2}{4}$$

$$r = \frac{R}{2}$$

Figure 4.73

(4.33) Equal, parallel rectangles, axis through centroid parallel to edge (Figure 4.74).

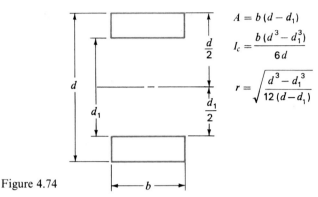

$$A = b(d - d_1)$$

$$I_c = \frac{b(d^3 - d_1^3)}{6d}$$

$$r = \sqrt{\frac{d^3 - d_1^3}{12(d - d_1)}}$$

Figure 4.74

(4.34) Circular ring, axis on diameter (Figure 4.75).

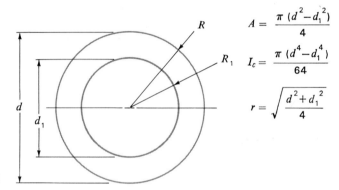

$$A = \frac{\pi(d^2 - d_1^2)}{4}$$

$$I_c = \frac{\pi(d^4 - d_1^4)}{64}$$

$$r = \sqrt{\frac{d^2 + d_1^2}{4}}$$

Figure 4.75

Exercise 4.7

1. Calculate r_x and r_y for the area bounded by $y = x^2/2$, $y = 0$, $y = 9/2$, and $x = 0$.
2. Calculate r_x and r_y for the area bounded by $y = x^2$, $y = 0$, $x = 0$, and $x = 3$.
3. Calculate r_x and r_y for the area bounded by $y = x^2$, $y = 0$, $x = 0$, and $y = 9$.
4. Calculate r_x and r_y for the area bounded by $y = \sqrt{x}$, $y = 0$, $x = 0$, and $x = 9$.
5. Calculate r_x and r_y for the area bounded by $y = \sqrt{x}$, $y = 3$, and $x = 0$.
6. Calculate r_x and r_y for the area bounded by $y = x^2 + 10$, $y = 0$, $x = 2$, and $x = 6$.
7. Calculate r_x and r_y for the area bounded by $y = x^2 + 10$, $y = 14$, $x = 2$, and $x = 6$.
8. Calculate r_x and r_y for the area bounded by $y = x^2 + 10$, $y = 14$, $y = 46$, and $x = 0$.

Exercise 4.8

1. Calculate I_c and r for a rectangle 3 by 5, if the centroidal axis is parallel to the side 3.
2. Calculate I_{xx} and r for a rectangle 3 by 5, if the axis of reference coincides with a side 5.
3. Calculate I_{xx} and r for a triangle with base 5 and height 9, if the axis of reference coincides with the base.
4. Calculate I_c and r for a triangle with base 5 and height 9, if the axis of reference passes through the centroid parallel to the base.
5. Calculate I_{xx} and r for a semicircle with radius 10 and axis of reference coinciding with a base.
6. Calculate I_c and r for a semicircle with radius 10 and axis of reference through the centroid parallel to the diameter.
7. Calculate I_{xx} and r for a square with side 4 and axis of reference on a diagonal.

Exercise 4.9

1. Derive formula (4.31).
2. Calculate I_{xx} and r for a rectangle 3 by 5, if the axis of reference is a diagonal.
3. Derive formula (4.32).
4. Calculate I_{xx} and r for a circle with radius 20 and axis of reference passing through the center.
5. Derive formula (4.33).
6. Calculate I_c and r for parallel equal rectangles as in formula (4.33) where $d = 8$, $d_1 = 4$, and $b = 6$.
7. Derive formula (4.34).
8. Calculate I_c and r for a circular ring as in formula (4.34), where $R = 12$ and $R_1 = 8$.

Exercise 4.10

1. Calculate I_{xx} and r for the shape shown in Figure 4.76.

Figure 4.76

2. Calculate I_c and r for the shape shown in Figure 4.76.

3. Calculate I_c for the shape shown in Figure 4.77.

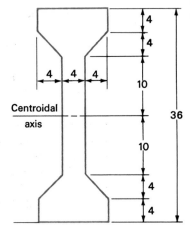

Figure 4.77

4. Calculate I_{xx} for the shape shown in Figure 4.77.
5. Calculate I_{xx} for the shape shown in Figure 4.78.

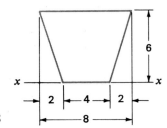

Figure 4.78

6. Calculate I_c for the shape shown in Figure 4.78.
7. Calculate I_{xx} for the shape shown in Figure 4.79.

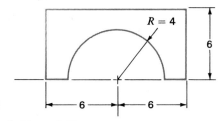

Figure 4.79

8. Calculate I_c for the shape shown in Figure 4.79.
9. Calculate I_{xx} for the shape shown in Figure 4.80.

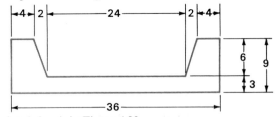

Figure 4.80

10. Calculate I_c for the shape shown in Figure 4.80.

4.13 DOUBLE INTEGRATION AND MOMENT OF INERTIA

Many times double integration is useful in calculating moment of inertia, and occasionally it is required.

Let us use double integration to calculate I_{xx} for the area in Figure 4.81.

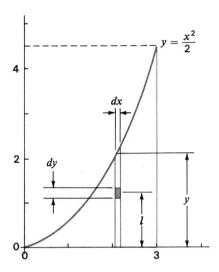

Figure 4.81

Here $\quad I_{xx} = \displaystyle\int_0^3 \int_0^y l^2 d\, dx$

$$= \int_0^3 \frac{l^3}{3} \Big]_0^y dx = \int_0^3 \frac{y^3}{3} dx$$

But $y = x^2/2$, so $y^3 = x^6/8$, and

$$I_{xx} = \frac{1}{24} \int_0^3 x^6 dx$$

$$= \frac{3^7}{7 \cdot 24} = \frac{3^7}{7 \cdot 24} = \frac{729}{56} = 13.01$$

Compare this result with Example 4.24.

Exercise 4.11

1. Using double integration calculate I_{yy} for the area shown in Figure 4.81.
2. Using double integration calculate I_{yy} for the area bounded by $y = x^2/2$, $y = 9/2$, $x = 0$, and $x = 3$.
3. Using double integration calculate I_{xx} for the area in problem 2.

5 Sequence and Series

In this unit we shall involve ourselves with the writing of a given function as a series expansion. If this can be accomplished for the transcendental functions, for instance, we see how these functions could be evaluated for given values of the variable. We could calculate the tabular values for such functions as sine, cosine, tangent, natural logarithms, and others.

In writing these series expansions we shall call on our knowledge of the derivative and the integral.

In order to discuss a series expansion intelligently, we shall begin with some simple concepts and proceed intuitively.

5.1 SEQUENCE

A number sequence is a set of numbers that are arranged in order according to some prearranged plan or rule. For example, 1, 2, 3, 4, 5, 6, 7, 8 is a sequence. Also 2, 5, 8, 11, 14, 17 is a sequence, and $a_1, a_2, a_3, \ldots a_n$ is a general sequence. Sometimes a sequence is called a *progression*.

The terms of a sequence are the numbers in the sequence.

An *arithmetic sequence* is a sequence of terms arranged so that each term, after the first term a, equals the sum of the preceding term and a constant d called the common difference. Thus,

$$a, a + d, a + 2d, \ldots, a + (n - 1)d \tag{5.1}$$

is an arithmetic sequence, whose nth or last term is $a + (n - 1)d$.

A *geometric sequence* is a sequence of terms arranged so that each term after the first is the product of the preceding term and a constant r, called the common ratio. Thus,

$$a, ar, ar^2, ar^3, \ldots, ar^{n-1} \tag{5.2}$$

is a geometric sequence whose nth or last term is ar^{n-1}.

> **Exercise 5.1.** In problems 1 through 10 the given numbers are terms of an arithmetic sequence. Identify a and d and write the next five terms.
>
> 1. 2, 4, 6, ...   2. 3, 6, 9, ...
> 3. 5, 9, 13, ...   4. 19, 26, 33, ...

5. 27, 23, 19, ...   6. $-8, -2, 4, \ldots$
7. $a, a + 3, a + 6, \ldots$ 8. $-m, 0, m, \ldots$
9. $b, -b, -3b, \ldots$ 10. $x, 2x, 3x, \ldots$

11. In a given geometric sequence $a = \frac{1}{2}, r = \frac{2}{3}$. What is the ninth term?
12. If $r = 2, n = 5$, and the fifth term is 24, what is the first term?
13. What is the seventh term of the geometric sequence $10, 0.1, 0.001, \ldots$?
14. What are the next five terms of the geometric sequence $10, -5, 2\frac{1}{2}, \ldots$?

5.2 SERIES

A series is the indicated sum of the terms of a sequence. We will use S for the sum of an infinite number of terms and S_n for the sum of n terms.

The sum of the terms of a general arithmetic sequence with n terms then becomes:

$$S_n = a + (a + d) + (a + 2d) + \cdots + [a + (n - 1)d] \tag{5.3}$$

And the sum of the terms of a general geometric sequence with n terms becomes:

$$S_n = a + ar + ar^2 + ar^3 + \cdots + ar^{n-1} \tag{5.4}$$

5.3 INFINITE SERIES

When the terms of a sequence continue indefinitely without limit, the sequence is called *infinite*. The sum of the terms of an infinite sequence is called an *infinite series*.

Calculating the sum of an infinite series requires a little thought since the number of terms is infinite.

Suppose we look at the series:

$$S_5 = \frac{1}{2} + \frac{1}{4} + \frac{1}{8} + \frac{1}{16} + \frac{1}{32} = \frac{31}{32}$$

Here we have obtained the sum by arithmetically adding the fractions, but we could use the standard formula for summing a geometric series

$$S_n = \frac{a - ar^n}{1 - r} \tag{5.5}$$

So $\quad S_5 = \dfrac{\frac{1}{2} - (\frac{1}{2})(\frac{1}{2})^5}{1 - \frac{1}{2}} = \dfrac{\frac{1}{2} - (\frac{1}{2})^6}{\frac{1}{2}}$

$$= \frac{\frac{1}{2} - \frac{1}{64}}{\frac{1}{2}} = \frac{\frac{32}{64} - \frac{1}{64}}{\frac{1}{2}} = \frac{\frac{31}{64}}{\frac{1}{2}} = \frac{31}{32}$$

Thus we see the formula gives the correct answer for $n = 5$. In our move toward an infinite number of terms let us now increase n from 5 to 100, then

$$S_{100} = \frac{\frac{1}{2} - (\frac{1}{2})(\frac{1}{2})^{100}}{1 - \frac{1}{2}} = \frac{\frac{1}{2} - (\frac{1}{2})^{101}}{\frac{1}{2}} = 1 - (\frac{1}{2})^{100}$$

Now since $(\frac{1}{2})^{100}$ will be extremely small, we see that the sum will be close to 1. By similar reasoning we can show that if $n = 1000$ the sum will be

$$S_{1000} = 1 - (\tfrac{1}{2})^{1000}$$

which is still closer to 1 than when $n = 100$. We have seen n go from 5 to 100 and then to 1000. Now what will happen when n gets even larger or when n approaches an infinitely large number. Symbolically we write $n \to \infty$.

If we manipulate (5.5) we can help our thinking:

$$S_n = \frac{a - ar^n}{1 - r} = \frac{a}{1 - r} - \frac{ar^n}{1 - r} \tag{5.6}$$

If we now let $n \to \infty$ when $|r| > 1$, the second term of (5.6) $(ar^n)/(1 - r)$ increases without limit and it is impossible to define S_n. However, if $n \to \infty$ when $|r| < 1$, the second term of (5.6) approaches its limit zero. Symbolically then

$$S = \lim_{n \to \infty} S_n = \frac{a}{1 - r} \tag{5.7}$$

when $|r| < 1$.

When summing an infinite series it is impossible to write down or include all terms, since the number of terms is infinite. Therefore we must think of this sum in a new or slightly different way. If S is to be the sum of an infinite series, S must be greater than the sum of any finite number of terms or $|S - S_n|$ becomes and remains less than any small positive number. Symbolically:

$$\lim_{n \to \infty} S_n = S \tag{5.8}$$

Equation (5.8) is read: "The limit of S_n as n approaches an infinitely large number equals S."

As shown above a series may have a limit, but it is also true that a sequence may have a limit. For example, the sequence making up the above series $\frac{1}{2}$, $\frac{1}{4}$, $\frac{1}{8}$, $\frac{1}{16}$, $\frac{1}{64}$, . . . has a limit of zero as n approaches an infinitely large number. We are saying here that each successive term is smaller than its predecesor. Symbolically:

$$\lim_{n \to \infty} a_n = 0 \tag{5.9}$$

Here a_n is the nth term of the sequence. Equation (5.9) is read: "The limit of the nth term as n approaches an infinitely large number is zero."

Convergence: *If the sum of the first* n *terms of an infinite series approaches some finite value as a limit, as* n $\to \infty$*, the series is said to*   (5.10) *converge.*

Divergence: *If an infinite series does not converge, it is said to diverge.*   (5.11)

If an infinite series is convergent and a_n is the nth term, then $\lim_{n \to \infty} a_n = 0$. The converse of this is not necessarily true, however, because even though $\lim_{n \to \infty} a_n = 0$, the series may not converge. Thus the zero limit of the a_nth term is a necessary but not sufficient condition for convergence.

Some basic properties of limits of infinite convergent sequences are listed here as a guide.

In each instance let

$$\lim_{n \to \infty} a_n = A \qquad \lim_{n \to \infty} b_n = B$$

Limit of the product of a constant and a sequence:

$$\lim_{n \to \infty} (ka_n) = k \lim_{n \to \infty} a_n = kA \tag{5.12}$$

Limit of the sum of two sequences:

$$\lim_{n \to \infty} (a_n \pm b_n) = \lim_{n \to \infty} a_n \pm \lim_{n \to \infty} b_n = A \pm B \tag{5.13}$$

Limit of the product of two sequences:

$$\lim_{n \to \infty} (a_n b_n) = \left(\lim_{n \to \infty} a_n \right) \left(\lim_{n \to \infty} b_n \right) = AB \tag{5.14}$$

Limit of the quotient of two sequences:

$$\lim_{n \to \infty} \frac{a_n}{b_n} = \frac{\lim_{n \to \infty} a_n}{\lim_{n \to \infty} b_n} = \frac{A}{B} \tag{5.15}$$

One useful test for convergence or divergence of a series is the ratio test. To use this test we write the expression for the general or nth term (u_n). Then we write the expression for the next term (u_{n+1}). In writing this term, we substitute $(n + 1)$ for (n) in the general term. We now take the ratio:

$$\frac{u_{n+1}}{u_n}$$

and see what happens when n becomes infinitely large. In other words, we take the limit:

$$\lim_{n \to \infty} \frac{u_{n+1}}{u_n} = L$$

There are three possibilities for L:

If $L < 1$, the series converges.
If $L > 1$, the series diverges.
If $L = 1$, the test fails.

Example A.   Test the series:

$$\frac{1}{3} + \frac{1 \cdot 2}{3 \cdot 5} + \frac{1 \cdot 2 \cdot 3}{3 \cdot 5 \cdot 7} + \cdots + \frac{1 \cdot 2 \cdot 3 \cdots n}{3 \cdot 5 \cdot 7 \cdots (2n + 1)} + \cdots$$

for convergence.

$$u_{n+1} = \frac{1 \cdot 2 \cdot 3 \cdots n(n + 1)}{3 \cdot 5 \cdot 7 \cdots (2n + 1)(2n + 3)}$$

and

$$u_n = \frac{1 \cdot 2 \cdot 3 \cdots n}{3 \cdot 5 \cdot 7 \cdots (2n + 1)}$$

and

$$\frac{u_{n+1}}{u_n} = \frac{\dfrac{1 \cdot 2 \cdot 3 \cdots n(n + 1)}{3 \cdot 5 \cdot 7 \cdots (2n + 1)(2n + 3)}}{\dfrac{1 \cdot 2 \cdot 3 \cdots n}{3 \cdot 5 \cdot 7 \cdots (2n + 1)}} = \frac{n + 1}{2n + 3}$$

Now taking the limit:

$$\lim_{n \to \infty} \frac{u_{n+1}}{u_n} = \lim_{n \to \infty} \frac{n + 1}{2n + 3} = \frac{1}{2}$$

From this we see that the series converges.

Example B.   Test the series

$$\frac{1}{3} + \frac{1}{5} + \frac{1}{7} + \cdots + \frac{1}{2n + 1}$$

for convergence.

$$\mathrm{Lim}_{n \to \infty} \frac{u_{n+1}}{u_n} = \lim_{n \to \infty} \frac{\dfrac{1}{2n + 3}}{\dfrac{1}{2n + 1}} = \lim_{n \to \infty} \frac{2n + 1}{2n + 3} = 1$$

Here the test fails and we do not know whether the series converges or diverges.

Example C.   Test the series

$$\frac{2}{1!} + \frac{4}{2!} + \frac{8}{3!} + \frac{16}{4!} + \frac{32}{5!} + \frac{64}{6!} + \cdots + \frac{2^n}{n!}$$

for convergence.

$$\mathrm{Lim}_{n \to \infty} \frac{u_{n+1}}{u_n} = \lim_{n \to \infty} \frac{\dfrac{2n + 1}{(n + 1)!}}{\dfrac{2^n}{n!}} = \lim_{n \to \infty} \frac{2}{n + 1} = 0$$

This series converges.

Many series can be cataloged as convergent or divergent quite easily and others require considerable effort. A textbook on the theory of calculus should be consulted if the student wishes to pursue the use of tests for convergency of infinite series.

Exercise 5.2

1. Find the limiting value of the infinite series $\frac{2}{3} + \frac{1}{3} + \frac{1}{6} + \frac{1}{12} + \frac{1}{24} + \frac{1}{48}$ + $\cdots$.

2. For $1 + \frac{2}{5} + \frac{4}{25} + \frac{8}{125} + \cdots$, find S.

3. For $\frac{1}{2} + \frac{1}{4} + \frac{1}{8} + \frac{1}{16} + \cdots$, find S.

4. For $\frac{1}{3} + \frac{1}{9} + \frac{1}{27} + \frac{1}{81} + \cdots$, find S.

5. For $12 + 4 + \frac{4}{3} + \cdots$, find S.

For problems 6 through 10 assume $\lim_{n \to \infty} (1/n) = 0$ and evaluate.

6. $\lim_{n \to \infty} (1/n^2)$

7. $\lim_{n \to \infty} [(1/n) + (1/n^2)]$

8. $\lim_{n \to \infty} [1/(n + 1)]$

9. $\lim_{n \to \infty} [(1/(n^2 + n)]$

10. $\lim_{n \to \infty} [(2n + 1)/(3n - 2)]$

5.4 MACLAURIN SERIES

From our discussion so far we see that an algebraic function may be written in the form of an infinite series or power series.

$$f(x) = a_0 + a_1x + a_2x^2 + a_3x^3 + \cdots \tag{5.16}$$

The question now arises as to whether functions other than algebraic may be written as a power series. That is, could transcendental functions such as $\sin x$ and $\cos x$ be written as a power series?

The functions with which we shall deal may be written as power series, though proving this is beyond the scope of this book.

Let us proceed by writing a power series and then taking successive differentiations.

$$f(x) = a_0 + a_1x + a_2x^2 + a_3x^3 + a_4x^4 + a_5x^5 + \cdots$$
$$+ a_nx^n + \cdots$$

$$f'(x) = a_1 + 2a_2x + 3a_3x^2 + 4a_4x^3 + 5a_5x^4 + \cdots$$
$$+ na_nx^{n-1} + \cdots$$

$$f''(x) = 2a_2 + 6a_3x + 12a_4x^2 + 20a_5x^3 + \cdots + (n - 1)na_nx^{n-2}$$
$$+ \cdots$$

$$f'''(x) = 6a_3 + 24a_4x + 60a_5x^2 + \cdots + (n - 2)(n - 1)na_nx^{n-3}$$
$$+ \cdots$$

$$f''''(x) = 24a_4 + 120a_5x + \cdots + (n - 3)(n - 2)(n - 1)na_nx^{n-4} + \cdots$$

No matter what values the coefficients of a_n take on, if $x = 0$ all the terms on the right side will be zero except the first. Therefore

$$f[0] = a_0 \qquad f'[0] = a_1 \qquad f''[0] = 2a_2$$
$$f'''[0] = 6a_3 \qquad \text{and} \qquad f^{iv}[0] = 24a_4$$

and solving each of the above for the a_n we have

$$a_0 = f[0] \qquad a_1 = f'[0] \qquad a_2 = (f''[0]/2)$$
$$a_3 = \frac{f'''[0]}{6} \qquad \text{and} \qquad a_4 = \frac{f^{iv}[0]}{24}$$

Now if these values are substituted into the original power series $f(x)$, we have

$$f(x) = f[0] + f'[0]x + \frac{f''[0]x^2}{2} + \frac{f'''[0]x^3}{6} + \frac{f^{iv}[0]x^4}{24} + \cdots$$

or

$$f(x) = f[0] + f'[0]x + \frac{f''[0]x^2}{2!} + \frac{f'''[0]x^3}{3!} + \frac{f^{iv}[0]x^4}{4!} + \cdots$$

$$+ \frac{f^n[0]x^n}{n!} + \cdots \quad (5.17)$$

Equation (5.17) is the *Maclaurin series expansion* of a function. The Maclaurin expansion can be written only if the function and all its derivatives exist when $x = 0$.

Example 5.1. Write the first four terms of the Maclaurin expansion for $f(x) = 2/(2 - x)$.

By simple division $f(x) = 1 + \frac{1}{2}x + \frac{1}{4}x^2 + \frac{1}{8}x^3 + \cdots$. Using the Maclaurin expansion:

$$f(x) = \frac{2}{2 - x} \qquad f[0] = 1$$

$$f'(x) = \frac{2}{(2 - x)^2} \qquad f'[0] = \tfrac{1}{2}$$

$$f''(x) = \frac{4}{(2 - x)^3} \qquad f''[0] = \tfrac{1}{2}$$

$$f'''(x) = \frac{12}{(2 - x)^4} \qquad f'''[0] = \tfrac{3}{4}$$

Substituting these values into the expansion:

$$f(x) = 1 + \frac{1}{2}x + \frac{1}{2}\frac{x^2}{2!} + \frac{3}{4}\frac{x^3}{3!} + \cdots$$

$$= 1 + \tfrac{1}{2}x + \tfrac{1}{4}x^2 + \tfrac{1}{8}x^3 + \cdots$$

which is the same expression that was obtained by division.

Example 5.2. Write the first four terms of the Maclaurin expansion for $f(x) = e^x$.

$$f(x) = e^x \qquad f[0] = 1$$
$$f'(x) = e^x \qquad f'[0] = 1$$
$$f''(x) = e^x \qquad f''[0] = 1$$
$$f'''(x) = e^x \qquad f'''[0] = 1$$

By substitution:

$$f(x) = e^x = 1 + x + \frac{x^2}{2!} + \frac{x^3}{3!} + \frac{x^4}{4!} + \cdots$$

Example 5.3. Write the first four terms of the Maclaurin expansion for $f(x) = e^{-x}$.

$$f(x) = e^{-x} \qquad f[0] = 1$$
$$f'(x) = -e^{-x} \qquad f'[0] = -1$$
$$f''(x) = e^{-x} \qquad f''[0] = 1$$
$$f'''(x) = -e^{-x} \qquad f'''[0] = -1$$

By substitution:

$$f(x) = e^{-x} = 1 - x + \frac{x^2}{2!} - \frac{x^3}{3!} + \cdots$$

Example 5.4. Write the first four terms of the Maclaurin expansion for $f(x) = \sin x$.

$$f(x) = \sin x \qquad f[0] = 0$$
$$f'(x) = \cos x \qquad f'[0] = 1$$
$$f''(x) = -\sin x \qquad f''[0] = 0$$
$$f'''(x) = -\cos x \qquad f'''[0] = -1$$
$$f^{iv}(x) = \sin x \qquad f^{iv}[0] = 0$$
$$f^{v}(x) = \cos x \qquad f^{v}[0] = 1$$
$$f^{vi}(x) = -\sin x \qquad f^{vi}[0] = 0$$
$$f^{vii}(x) = -\cos x \qquad f^{vii}[0] = -1$$

By substitution:

$$f(x) = 0 + 1 \cdot x + \frac{0 \cdot x^2}{2!} - \frac{1 \cdot x^3}{3!} + \frac{0 \cdot x^4}{4!} + \frac{1 \cdot x^5}{5!} + \frac{0 \cdot x^6}{6!}$$

$$- \frac{1 \cdot x^7}{7!} + \cdots$$

Therefore $\sin x = x - \dfrac{x^3}{3!} + \dfrac{x^5}{5!} - \dfrac{x^7}{7!} + \cdots$

Example 5.5.   Write the first four terms of the Maclaurin expansion for $f(x) = \cos x$.

$$
\begin{aligned}
f(x) &= \cos x & f[0] &= 1 \\
f'(x) &= -\sin x & f'[0] &= 0 \\
f''(x) &= -\cos x & f''[0] &= -1 \\
f'''(x) &= \sin x & f'''[0] &= 0 \\
f''''(x) &= \cos x & f''''[0] &= 1 \\
f'''''(x) &= -\sin x & f'''''[0] &= 0 \\
f''''''(x) &= -\cos x & f''''''[0] &= -1
\end{aligned}
$$

By substitution:

$$f(x) = 1 + 0 \cdot x - \frac{1 \cdot x^2}{2!} + \frac{0 \cdot x^3}{3!} + \frac{1 \cdot x^4}{4!} + \frac{0 \cdot x^5}{5!} - \frac{1 \cdot x^6}{6!} + \cdots$$

$$\cos x = 1 - \frac{x^2}{2!} + \frac{x^4}{4!} - \frac{x^6}{6!} + \cdots$$

Example 5.6.   Write the first four terms of the Maclaurin expansion for $f(x) = \ln(1 + x)$.

$$f(x) = \ln(1 + x) \qquad f[0] = 0$$

$$f'(x) = \frac{1}{1 + x} \qquad f'[0] = 1$$

$$f''(x) = \frac{-1}{(1 + x)^2} \qquad f''[0] = -1$$

$$f'''(x) = \frac{2}{(1 + x)^3} \qquad f'''[0] = 2$$

$$f''''(x) = \frac{-6}{(1 + x)^4} \qquad f''''[0] = -6$$

By substitution:

$$f(x) = 0 + 1 \cdot x - \frac{1 \cdot x^2}{2!} + \frac{2 \cdot x^3}{3!} - \frac{6 \cdot x^4}{4!} + \cdots$$

or

$$\ln (1 + x) = x - \frac{x^2}{2} + \frac{x^3}{3} - \frac{x^4}{4} + \cdots$$

Example 5.7. Write the first four terms of the Maclaurin expansion of $f(x) = \cos (4x)$.

$$f(x) = \cos 4x \qquad f[0] = 1$$
$$f'(x) = -4 \sin 4x \qquad f'[0] = 0$$
$$f''(x) = -16 \cos 4x \qquad f''[0] = -16$$
$$f'''(x) = 64 \sin 4x \qquad f'''[0] = 0$$
$$f^{iv}(x) = 256 \cos 4x \qquad f^{iv}[0] = 256$$
$$f^{v}(x) = -1024 \sin 4x \qquad f^{v}[0] = 0$$
$$f^{vi}(x) = -4096 \cos 4x \qquad f^{vi}[0] = -4096$$

By substitution:

$$f(x) = 1 + 0 \cdot x - \frac{16x^2}{2!} + \frac{0 \cdot x^3}{3!} + \frac{256x^4}{4!} + \frac{0 \cdot x^5}{5!} - \frac{4096x^6}{6!} + \cdots$$

$$\cos 4x = 1 - 8x^2 + \frac{32x^4}{3} - \frac{512x^6}{90} + \cdots$$

Exercise 5.3. In problems 1 through 8 find the first three nonzero terms of the Maclaurin expansion for the given function.

1. $\sin 2x$
2. $x \cdot e^x$
3. $\sqrt{1 + x}$
4. $1/(1 + x)^2$
5. $e^x \sin x$
6. $\frac{1}{2}(e^x - e^{-x})$
7. $\cos 3x$
8. $\sin 3x$

In problems 9 through 16 find the first two nonzero terms of the Maclaurin expansion for the function given.

9. $\tan x$
10. $\ln (\cos x)$
11. $\sec x$
12. $\cos x^2$
13. $x e^{\sin x}$
14. $\csc x$
15. $\cos 2x^3$
16. $\ln (1 + x^2)$

5.5 TAYLOR SERIES

An even more general expansion than the Maclaurin is the *Taylor expansion series*. In a Taylor expansion the polynomial is assumed to take the form:

$$f(x) = C_0 + C_1(x - a) + C_2(x - a)^2 + \cdots \qquad (5.18)$$

If we proceed exactly as we did with the Maclaurin development we will evaluate the C_n by successive differentiation and substitute the C_n in (5.18), which yields:

$$f(x) = f[a] + f'[a](x + a) + \frac{f''[a](x - a)^2}{2!} + \cdots \qquad (5.19)$$

Example 5.8.   Write the Taylor expansion for $f(x) = e^x$ with $a = 1$.

$$f(x) = e^x \qquad f[1] = e$$
$$f'(x) = e^x \qquad f'[1] = e$$
$$f''(x) = e^x \qquad f''[1] = e$$
$$f'''(x) = e^x \qquad f'''[1] = e$$
$$f^{iv}(x) = e^x \qquad f^{iv}[1] = e$$

By substitution:

$$f(x) = e + e(x - 1) + e\frac{(x - 1)^2}{2!} + e\frac{(x - 1)^3}{3!} + \cdots$$

$$f(x) = e^x = e\left[1 + (x - 1) + \frac{(x - 1)^2}{2!} + \frac{(x - 1)^3}{3!} + \cdots\right]$$

This series is useful in evaluating e^x when x is near 1.

Example 5.9.   Write a Taylor expansion for $\ln x$, using powers of $(x - 1)$. Note there is no Maclaurin expansion for $\ln x$ since $\ln x$ is not defined at $x = 0$.

$$f(x) = \ln x \qquad f[1] = 0$$
$$f'(x) = x^{-1} \qquad f'[1] = 1$$
$$f''(x) = -x^{-2} \qquad f''[1] = -1$$
$$f'''(x) = 2x^{-3} \qquad f'''[1] = 2$$

By substitution:

$$f(x) = 0 + (x - 1) + \frac{-1(x - 1)^2}{2!} + \frac{2(x - 1)^3}{3!} + \cdots$$

$$\ln x = (x - 1) - \frac{(x - 1)^2}{2!} + \frac{2}{3!}(x - 1)^3 + \cdots$$

Example 5.10.   Write a Taylor expansion for $\sin x$ at $x = \pi/6$.

$$f(x) = \sin x \qquad f[\pi/6] = 1/2$$
$$f'(x) = \cos x \qquad f'[\pi/6] = \sqrt{3}/2$$
$$f''(x) = -\sin x \qquad f''[\pi/6] = -1/2$$
$$f'''(x) = -\cos x \qquad f'''[\pi/6] = -\sqrt{3}/2$$

By substitution:

$$f(x) = \frac{1}{2} + \frac{\sqrt{3}}{2}\left(x - \frac{\pi}{6}\right) - \frac{1}{2}\frac{[x - (\pi/6)]^2}{2!} - \frac{\sqrt{3}}{2}\frac{[x - (\pi/6)]^3}{3!} + \cdots$$

Example 5.11.   Write the Taylor expansion for $\sqrt{x}$ in powers of $(x - 2)$.

$$
\begin{aligned}
f(x) &= x^{1/2} & f[2] &= \sqrt{2} \\
f'(x) &= \tfrac{1}{2}x^{-1/2} & f'[2] &= \sqrt{2}/4 \\
f''(x) &= -\tfrac{1}{4}x^{-3/2} & f''[2] &= -\sqrt{2}/16 \\
f'''(x) &= \tfrac{3}{8}x^{-5/2} & f'''[2] &= 3\sqrt{2}/64
\end{aligned}
$$

By substitution:

$$f(x) = \sqrt{x} = \sqrt{2} + \frac{\sqrt{2}}{4}(x - 2) - \frac{\sqrt{2}}{16}\frac{(x - 2)^2}{2!} + \frac{3\sqrt{2}}{64}\frac{(x - 2)^3}{3!} + \cdots$$

$$= \sqrt{2} + \frac{\sqrt{2}}{4}(x - 2) - \frac{\sqrt{2}}{32}(x - 2)^2 + \frac{\sqrt{2}}{128}(x - 2)^3 + \cdots$$

Exercise 5.4.   In problems 1 through 6 use expansion series.

1. Evaluate $e^{1.2}$.
2. Evaluate $e^{0.7}$.
3. Evaluate $\sqrt{4.2}$.
4. Evaluate $\sqrt{3.7}$.
5. Evaluate $\sin 32°$.
6. Evaluate $\sin 44°$.

In problems 7 through 12 write the first three nonzero terms of the Taylor expansion for the given function and a.

7. e^{-2}, $a = 2$.
8. $\cos x$, $a = \pi/4$.
9. $\sin x$, $a = \pi/3$.
10. $\ln x$, $a = 4$.
11. $\sqrt[3]{x}$, $a = 11$.
12. $1/x$, $a = 3$.

5.6 FOURIER SERIES

Use of Maclaurin and Taylor series allows good approximate evaluation near the values used in the expansion. For an expansion that allows a wider range of values for evaluation, we try to express the function in terms of sine and cosine. Thus,

$$f(x) = a_0 + a_1 \cos x + a_2 \cos 2x + \cdots + a_n \cos nx$$

$$+ b_1 \sin x + b_2 \sin 2x + \cdots + b_n \sin nx \quad (5.20)$$

Equation (5.20) is known as the *Fourier expansion series*. The Fourier expansion has a period of 2π.

Recall that in the Maclaurin and Taylor series we used differentiation to evaluate the coefficients. With the Fourier series we will use integration to evaluate the coefficients.

$$a_0 = \frac{1}{2\pi} \int_{-\pi}^{\pi} f(x)\,dx$$

$$a_n = \frac{1}{\pi} \int_{-\pi}^{\pi} f(x) \cos(nx)\,dx$$

$$b_n = \frac{1}{\pi} \int_{-\pi}^{\pi} f(x) \sin(nx)\,dx$$

Note that the limits of integration $-\pi$ and $+\pi$ cover the 2π period of (5.20). The derivations of the three integral equations, although not too difficult, are lengthy and will not be presented here.

> ***Example 5.12.*** Write the Fourier expansion for the function defined as:
>
> $$f(x) = 0 \qquad \text{when } -\pi \le x < 0$$
>
> and $\qquad\qquad f(x) = 1 \qquad \text{when } 0 \le x < \pi$
>
> This function is obviously discontinuous by inspection as well as by plotting. See Figure 5.1.

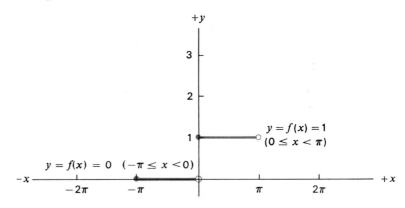

$$+y$$

$$3$$

$$2$$

$$y = f(x) = 1$$
$$(0 \le x < \pi)$$

$$1$$

$$y = f(x) = 0 \quad (-\pi \le x < 0)$$

$$-x \qquad\qquad -2\pi \qquad -\pi \qquad\qquad \pi \qquad 2\pi \qquad\qquad +x$$

Figure 5.1

Many functions expanded into Fourier series are discontinuous. Because of the discontinuity in this problem, each coefficient will require two integrals. For a_0, the first term, we have:

$$a_0 = \frac{1}{2\pi} \int_{-\pi}^{0} 0\,dx + \frac{1}{2\pi} \int_{0}^{\pi} 1\,dx = \frac{1}{2}$$

For all other a_n, we have:

$$a_n = \frac{1}{\pi} \int_{-\pi}^{0} 0\,dx + \frac{1}{\pi} \int_{0}^{\pi} \cos nx\,dx$$

$$= \frac{1}{nx} \sin nx \Big]_{0}^{\pi} = 0$$

Since $\sin nx = 0$, $a_n = 0$ for all values of x. For the b_n, we have:

$$b_1 = \frac{1}{\pi}\int_{-\pi}^{0} 0\,dx + \frac{1}{\pi}\int_{0}^{\pi}\sin x\,dx = -\frac{1}{\pi}\cos x \bigg]_{0}^{\pi}$$

$$= -\frac{1}{\pi}(-1-1) = \frac{2}{\pi}$$

$$b_2 = \frac{1}{\pi}\int_{-\pi}^{0} 0\,dx + \frac{1}{\pi}\int_{0}^{\pi}\sin 2x\,dx = -\frac{1}{2\pi}\cos 2x \bigg]_{0}^{\pi}$$

$$= -\frac{1}{2\pi}(1-1) = 0$$

$$b_3 = \frac{1}{\pi}\int_{-\pi}^{0} 0\,dx + \frac{1}{\pi}\int_{0}^{\pi}\sin 3x\,dx = -\frac{1}{3\pi}\cos 3x \bigg]_{0}^{\pi}$$

$$= -\frac{1}{3\pi}(-1-1) = \frac{2}{3\pi}$$

From b_1, b_2, and b_3 we see a pattern develop: If n is even, $b_n = 0$, and if n is odd, $b_n = 2/n\pi$. By substitution:

$$f(x) = \frac{1}{2} + \frac{2}{\pi}\sin x + \frac{2}{3\pi}\sin 3x + \frac{2}{5\pi}\sin 5x + \cdots \qquad (5.21)$$

If the function as defined by the first three terms only is plotted, Figure 5.2 results. Figure 5.2 shows one cycle of our function. Since the expansion is infinite and we used only the first three terms, we did not get an exact fit. Inclusion of more terms would produce a closer fit.

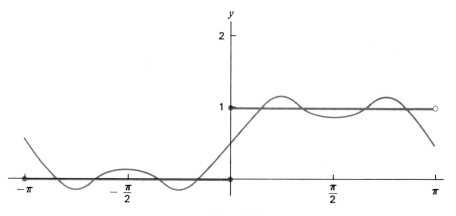

Figure 5.2

Recall from trigonometry that $\sin x$ was called the fundamental curve, while $\sin 2x$ was called its second harmonic. Sin $3x$ was called the third harmonic, etc. Thus we see that (5.21) can be referred to as a *harmonic series*.

Example 5.13. Write the Fourier expansion for the function $f(x) = x$, when $-\pi \leq x < \pi$.

This function is plotted on the interval $-\pi \leq x < \pi$ in Figure 5.3. Solving for the coefficients:

$$a_0 = \frac{1}{2\pi} \int_{-\pi}^{\pi} f(x)\, dx = \frac{1}{2\pi} \int_{-\pi}^{\pi} x\, dx$$

$$= \frac{1}{2\pi} \left. \frac{x^2}{2} \right]_{-\pi}^{\pi}$$

$$= \left. \frac{x^2}{4\pi} \right]_{-\pi}^{\pi}$$

$$= \frac{\pi \cdot \pi}{4\pi} - \frac{(-\pi)(-\pi)}{4\pi} = 0$$

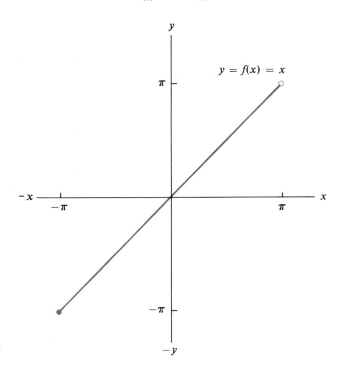

Figure 5.3

$$a_1 = \frac{1}{\pi} \int_{-\pi}^{\pi} f(x) \cos x\, dx = \frac{1}{\pi} \int_{-\pi}^{\pi} x \cos x\, dx$$

$$= \frac{1}{\pi} \left. (\cos x + x \sin x) \right]_{-\pi}^{\pi}$$

$$= \left[\frac{1}{\pi} \left(\cos \pi + \frac{1}{\pi} \pi \sin \pi \right) \right] - \left[\frac{1}{\pi} \cos (-\pi) + \frac{1}{\pi} (-\pi) \cos (-\pi) \right]$$

$$= \left[\frac{1}{\pi}(-1) + 0\right] - \left[\frac{1}{\pi}(-1) + (-1)(0)\right]$$

$$= \frac{-1}{\pi} - \left(\frac{-1}{\pi}\right) = 0$$

Similarly it can be shown that all $a_n = 0$.

$$b_1 = \frac{1}{\pi}\int_{-\pi}^{\pi} f(x) \sin x \, dx = \frac{1}{\pi}\int_{-\pi}^{\pi} x \sin x \, dx$$

$$= \frac{1}{\pi}(\sin x - x \cos x)\bigg]_{-\pi}^{\pi}$$

$$= \left[\frac{1}{\pi}(\sin \pi - \pi \cos \pi)\right] - \left[\frac{1}{\pi}(\sin(-\pi) - \pi \cos(-\pi))\right]$$

$$= \left[\frac{1}{\pi}(0) - \frac{1}{\pi}\pi(-1)\right] - \left[\frac{1}{\pi}(0) - \frac{1}{\pi}(-\pi)(-1)\right]$$

$$= 1 + 1 = 2$$

Similarly it can be shown that $b_1 = -1$ and $b_2 = \frac{2}{3}$. By substitution:

$$f(x) = x = 2 \sin x - \sin 2x + \tfrac{2}{3} \sin 3x - \cdots$$

$$= 2[\sin x - \tfrac{1}{2} \sin 2x + \tfrac{1}{3} \sin 3x - \cdots]$$

Once again we have a harmonic series. See Figure 0.7. If the three terms shown are summed and plotted, Figure 5.4 results. As with the previous

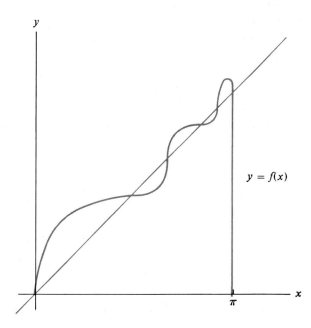

$y = f(x)$

Figure 5.4

example, if more terms are used the plot will more closely approach $y = x$, as shown in Figure 5.5. Note also in Figure 5.5 the total wave pattern when taken in cycles of 2π.

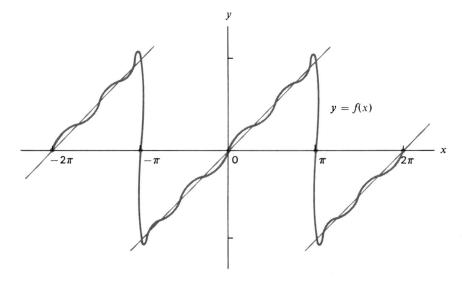

Figure 5.5

Let us pause a moment now to reflect a little on the Fourier expansions. Both examples here have contained sine terms only, with no cosine terms. This was not a coincidence because it turns out that if $f(x) = -f(x)$, then $y = f(x)$ is defined as an odd function and the expansion will contain sine terms only. If, on the other hand, $f(-x) = f(x)$, then $y = f(x)$ is an even function, so its expansion should contain cosine terms only.

The function $y = f(x) = |x|$ when $-\pi \leq x < \pi$ is an even function, so its expansion should contain cosine terms only. The Fourier expansion for $f(x) = |x|$ is:

$$|x| = \frac{\pi}{2} - \frac{4}{\pi}\left(\cos x + \frac{1}{3^2}\cos 3x + \frac{1}{5^2}\cos 5x + \cdots\right)$$

Figure 5.6 shows $y = f(x) = |x|$ plotted periodically.

One of the main advantages of a Fourier expansion over a Maclaurin or Taylor expansion is that the Fourier can be developed for a discontinuous function while the Taylor or Maclaurin series requires that the function be continuous and all derivatives exist. Note further that the Fourier series adapts well to periodic functions.

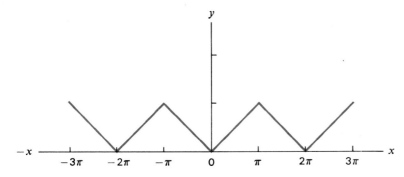

Figure 5.6

Exercise 5.5.   In problems 1 through 3 write four nonzero terms of the Fourier expansion for the functions given, and then sketch three or more periods of the given function.

1. $f(x) = 1$ when $-\pi \leq x < 0$, and $f(x) = 0$ when $0 \leq x < \pi$.
2. $f(x) = 1$ when $-\pi \leq x < 0$, and $f(x) = 2$ when $0 \leq x < \pi$.
3. $f(x) = -1$ when $-\pi \leq x < 0$, and $f(x) = 1$ when $0 \leq x < \pi$.
4. The Fourier expansion for the square waveform shown in Figure 5.7 is written symbolically:

$$f(x) = \frac{4c}{\pi} \sum_{n=1}^{\infty} \frac{\sin n\omega x}{n}$$

where n is a positive, odd integer and c is the amplitude constant. Write out the first five terms of the expansion.

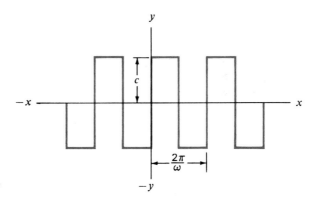

Figure 5.7

5. Write the Fourier expansion series representing a full-wave rectifier whose current function is: $f(x) = -\sin x$ when $-\pi < x \leq 0$, and $f(x) = \sin x$ when $0 < x < \pi$. See Figure 5.8.

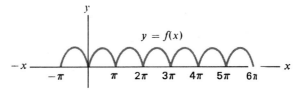

Figure 5.8

In problems 6 through 9 the plot and general equation for a Fourier expansion is given. In each instance write out the first five terms of the expansion.

6. $f(x) = \dfrac{2}{\pi} \displaystyle\sum_{n=1}^{\infty} \dfrac{(-1)^n}{n} \left(\cos \dfrac{n\pi l}{L} - 1 \right) \sin \dfrac{n\pi x}{L}$

See Figure 5.9.

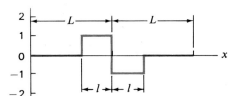

Figure 5.9

7. $f(x) = \dfrac{l}{L} + \dfrac{2}{\pi} \displaystyle\sum_{n=1}^{\infty} \dfrac{(-1)^n}{n} \sin \dfrac{n\pi l}{L} \cos \dfrac{n\pi x}{L}$

See Figure 5.10.

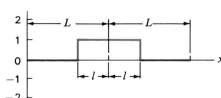

Figure 5.10

8. $f(x) = \dfrac{2}{\pi} \displaystyle\sum_{n=1}^{\infty} \dfrac{(-1)^{n+1}}{n} \sin \dfrac{n\pi x}{L}$

See Figure 5.11.

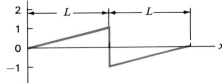

Figure 5.11

9. $f(x) = \dfrac{9}{\pi^2} \displaystyle\sum_{n=1}^{\infty} \dfrac{1}{n^2} \sin \dfrac{n\pi}{3} \sin \dfrac{n\pi x}{L}$

See Figure 5.12.

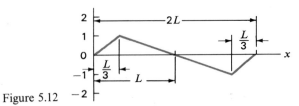

Figure 5.12

6

Differential Equations

One of the most important tools at the disposal of the technician is the differential equation (often referred to as D.E.). Differential equations form a vast field of mathematical study in which entire textbooks do not cover the material completely. We shall only birefly delve into differential equations. In spite of this brevity, we shall find solutions to many problems common to engineering situations today.

6.1 SOLVING DIFFERENTIAL EQUATIONS

A differential equation by definition is any equation containing a derivative. Examples of differential equations are:

(a) $\quad \dfrac{dy}{dx} + x = 1$

(b) $\quad dy = 2\,dx$

(c) $\quad \dfrac{dy}{dx} - 3 = 2y$

(d) $\quad L\dfrac{d^2q}{dt^2} + R\dfrac{dq}{dt} + \dfrac{q}{c} = 0$

(e) $\quad L\dfrac{d^2i}{dt^2} + R\dfrac{di}{dt} + \dfrac{i}{c} = \sin \omega t$

(f) $\quad \left(\dfrac{d^3y}{dx^3}\right)^2 + \dfrac{d^2y}{dx^2} - 2\left(\dfrac{dy}{dx}\right)^3 = 3x$

The order of a differential equation is the highest order of the derivative in the' equation. Thus a, b, and c above are first-order differential equations, d and e are second order, and f is third order.

The degree of a differential equation is the power of the highest-order derivative that occurs. Thus a, b, c, d, and e are of first degree while f is of second degree.

A solution to a differential equation is an equation that contains no derivatives or differentials and satisfies the given differential equation.

Example 6.1.   Show that $y = 3x^2 + 2x$ is a solution to the differential equation $dy/dx = 6x + 2$.

To show mathematically that $y = 3x^2 + 2x$ is a solution, we must substitute the solution into the given D.E. This substitution cannot be made directly since y does not show up in the D.E., but if we differentiate the suspected solution we get $dy/dx = 6x + 2$, and substituting in the given D.E. produces $6x + 2 = 6x + 2$ which is an identity. Therefore $y = 3x^2 + 2x$ is a solution to the D.E. $dy/dx = 6x + 2$.

Example 6.2.   Show that $x^2y + Ax + 2 = 0$ is a solution to $x^3(dy/dx) = 2 - x^2y$.

In order to make the substitution we must differentiate the suspected solution $x^2y + Ax + 2 = 0$.

$$x^2 \frac{dy}{dx} + y(2x) + A + 0 = 0$$

$$x^2 \frac{dy}{dx} + 2xy + A = 0$$

$$x^2 \frac{dy}{dx} = -2xy - A$$

$$\frac{dy}{dx} = \frac{-2xy - A}{x^2}$$

Substituting this into the given D.E., we get

$$x^3 \left(\frac{-2xy - A}{x^2} \right) = 2 - x^2y$$

$$x(-2xy - A) = 2 - x^2y$$

$$-2x^2y - Ax = 2 - x^2y$$

Solving the suspected solution for A:

$$Ax = -2 - x^2y \quad \text{and} \quad A = \frac{(-2 - x^2y)}{x}$$

Making this substitution for A we have

$$-2x^2y - \left(\frac{-2 - x^2y}{x} \right) x = 2 - x^2y$$

$$-2x^2y - (-2 - x^2y) = 2 - x^2y$$

$$-2x^2y + 2 + x^2y = 2 - x^2y$$

$$-x^2y + 2 = 2 - x^2y$$

$$2 - x^2y = 2 - x^2y$$

Thus $x^2y + Ax + 2 = 0$ is in fact a solution to the D.E. $x^3(dy/dx) = 2 - x^2y$.

Exercise 6.1

1. Prove that $y = x^2 + kx$ is a solution to $(dy/dx) - 2x = k$.
2. Prove that $A = xy$ is a solution to $(dy/dx) = -y/x$.
3. Prove that $y = Ae^{x^4}$ is a solution to $dy/dx = 4x^3y$.
4. Prove that $\cos\phi = A\cos\theta$ is a solution to $\cos\phi\sin\theta\,(d\theta/d\phi) = \sin\phi\cos\theta$.
5. Prove that $y = Ae^{kx}$ is a solution to $dy = ky\,dy$.
6. Prove that $x\ln(xy) + 1 - Ax = 0$ is a solution to $y = xy + x^2\,(dy/dx)$.
7. Prove that $x^2y + Ax = -2$ is a solution to $x^3(dy/dx) = 2 - x^2y$.

Many differential equations can be solved by direct integration. For example, if $dy/dx = 3x^2 - 2$, then $dy = (3x^2 - 2)\,dx$ and $\int dy = \int 3x^2 - 2\,dx$. So $y = x^3 - 2x + C$ is a solution to the given D.E. Note further that since the constant C is not evaluated, this solution is called a *general solution*. If enough pertinent information was available to evaluate the constant C, the solution would be called a *specific* or *exact solution*.

Even some higher-order differential equations can be solved by the direct-integration method.

Example 6.3.   Solve $d^3y/dx^3 = \sin 2x$.

First
$$\int \frac{d^3y}{dx^3} = \int \sin 2x\,dx$$

$$\frac{d^2y}{dx^2} = -\frac{1}{2}\cos 2x + C_1$$

Then
$$\int \frac{d^2y}{dx^2} = -\frac{1}{2}\int (\cos 2x + C_1)\,dx$$

$$\frac{dy}{dx} = -\frac{1}{4}\sin 2x + C_1x + C_2$$

Finally
$$\int dy = -\frac{1}{4}\int (\sin 2x + C_1x + C_2)\,dx$$

$$y = \frac{1}{8}\cos 2x + \frac{C_1x^2}{2} + C_2x + C_3$$

This then is the general solution to the given differential equation.

If additional information was available a specific or exact solution could be found. For instance, if $x = 0$ when $y = 2$, $dy/dx = 1$, and $d^2y/dx^2 = -3$, then

$$2 = \frac{1}{8}\cos{(2 \cdot 0)} + \frac{C_1(0)^2}{2} + C_2(0) + C_3$$

$$2 = \tfrac{1}{8} + C_3 \quad \text{and} \quad C_3 = \tfrac{15}{8}$$

and $\quad 1 = -\tfrac{1}{4}\sin{(2 \cdot 0)} + C_1(0) + C_2$

$$1 = 0 + 0 + C_2 \quad \text{so } C_2 = 1$$

finally $\quad -3 = -\tfrac{1}{2}\cos{(2 \cdot 0)} + C_1$

$$-3 = -\tfrac{1}{2} + C_1 \quad \text{so } C_1 = -3 + \tfrac{1}{2} = -\tfrac{5}{2}.$$

From this then the specific or exact solution becomes:

$$y = \tfrac{1}{8}\cos{(2x)} - \tfrac{5}{4}x^2 + x + \tfrac{15}{8}$$

Since all differential equations cannot be solved by direct integration, we cannot call the constants C_1, C_2, and C_3 constants of integration. Note further that the number of constants in a general solution will always be the same as the order of the differential equation being solved.

Recall that one method of approaching integration was to apply our knowledge of differentiation. It turns out that many differential equations can be solved by strong use of differentiation knowledge.

Recall: If $y = Ae^{\pm mx}$, then $dy/dx = \pm mAe^{\pm mx}$ and $dy/dx = \pm my$ by substitution. Therefore:

$$\text{If } \frac{dy}{dx} = \pm my, \quad \text{then } y = Ae^{\pm mx} \tag{6.1}$$

Recall: If $y = \sin{(mx + \phi)}$, then $dy/dx = m\cos{(mx + \phi)}$, and $dy/dx = m\sqrt{1 - \sin^2{(mx + \phi)}}$, but since $\cos{x} = \sqrt{1 - \sin^2{x}}$, $dy/dx = m\sqrt{1 - y^2}$ by substitution, therefore:

$$\text{If } \frac{dy}{dx} = m\sqrt{1 - y^2}, \quad \text{then } y = \sin{(mx + \phi)} \tag{6.2}$$

Recall: If $y = \cos{(mx + \phi)}$, then $dy/dx = -m\sin{(mx + \phi)}$ and $dy/dx = -m\sqrt{1 - \cos^2{(mx + \phi)}}$, but since $\sin{x} = \sqrt{1 - \cos^2{x}}$, $dy/dx = -m\sqrt{1 - y^2}$ by substitution, therefore:

$$\text{If } \frac{dy}{dx} = -m\sqrt{1 - y^2}, \quad \text{then } y = \cos{(mx + \phi)} \tag{6.3}$$

Example 6.4. Solve $dy/dx = -3y$.

From (6.1), $y = Ae^{-3x}$ with A an arbitrary constant.

Example 6.5.   Solve $Ri + L(di/dt) = 0$.

From the given equation $L(di/dt) = -Ri$ and $di/dt = -(R/L)i$. From (6.1), if $di/dt = -(R/L)i$, then $i = Ae^{-(R/L)t}$.

Note: The student should prove that this solution satisfies the given D.E.

Example 6.6.   Solve $dq/dt = 4\sqrt{1-q^2}$.

From (6.2), $q = \sin(4t + \phi)$. Here ϕ is the arbitrary constant. Once again the student should prove that this solution satisfies the given D.E.

Exercise 6.2.   In problems 1 through 11 calculate a general solution to the given differential equation. Prove each solution.

1. $dy = 5\sin 10t\, dt$
2. $di/dt = 3e^{-6t}$
3. $dy/dx = 2\cos 4x + (3/x)$
4. $dy/dx = 4e^{-8x}e^{-2}$
5. $dy = xe^{-x^2-5}\, dx$
6. $dy = te^{-50t}\, dt$
7. $dy/dx = 2\sqrt{9-4x^2}$
8. $dy/dx = -x/(x^2+6x+8)$
9. $dy/dx = -7y$
10. $v/C + R(dv/dt) = 0$
11. $di/dt = 50\sqrt{1-i^2}$

In problems 12 through 16 calculate an exact solution to the given D.E. Prove each solution.

12. $dy = 6\sin 3x\, dx + 6\cos 3x\, dx$; if $x = 30°$ when $y = 1$.
13. $dy = dt/(6 + 2t^2)$; if $t = 0$ when $y = -2$.
14. $dy = 2\ln 3t$; if $t = \frac{1}{3}$ when $y = 1$.
15. $dy = 5y\, dx$; if $x = 0$ when $y = 2$.
16. $q + RC(dq/dt) = 0$; if $t = 0$ when $q = EC$.

6.2 SEPARATION OF VARIABLES

In general, if the variables in a differential equation can be grouped together in groups of like variables, the equation can be solved by integration. Accomplishing this grouping is usually called *separation of variables*. *Caution*: Only certain differential equations are constructed so that separation of variables is possible.

If a differential equation can be written in the form

$$M\, dx + N\, dy = 0 \qquad (6.4)$$

where M is a function of x only, or a constant, and N is a function of y only, or a constant, it is said to have its variables separable and can be solved by integration.

Example 6.7.   Solve $(1/2x)(dy/dx) - y = 0$.

Multiplying through by $2x\, dx$ yields $dy - 2xy\, dx = 0$. Dividing through by y, $(dy/y) - 2x\, dx = 0$, which can be written $dy/y = 2x\, dx$, and thus the variables are separated and solution can be accomplished by integration:

$$\int \frac{dy}{y} = 2 \int x \, dx$$

$$\ln y + C_1 = x^2 + C_2$$

Combining constants we have $\ln y = x^2 + C$. If we let $C = \ln K$, we may write $\ln y = x^2 + \ln K$, or $\ln y - \ln K = x^2$, which can be written $Ky = e^{x^2}$ and is a general solution to the given D.E.

Example 6.8.   Solve the D.E. $L(di/dt) + Ri = E$ which yields the current i in a series RL circuit with constant emf E.

First $L(di/dt) = E - Ri$ or $di/dt = (E - Ri)/L$ or $di = (1/L)(E - Ri) dt$, from which

$$di = \frac{R}{L}\left(\frac{E}{R} - i\right) dt \qquad \text{and} \qquad \frac{di}{(E/R) - i} = \frac{R}{L} dt$$

Now with the variables separated we may integrate:

$$\int \frac{di}{(E/R) - i} = \frac{R}{L} \int dt$$

which yields $- \ln [(E/R) - i] = (R/L)t - C$. Letting $C = \ln K$ and multiplying through by -1, we have

$$\ln\left(\frac{E}{R} - i\right) = -\frac{R}{L}t + \ln K$$

which by taking antilogs yields $(E/R) - i = Ke^{-Rt/L}$ and

$$i = \frac{E}{R} - Ke^{-Rt/L}$$

which is a general solution to the given D.E. To obtain an exact solution we note that if the initial current is zero ($i = 0$), the time would be zero ($t = 0$), so by substitution $0 = (E/R) - Ke^{-R \cdot 0/L}$ or $0 = (E/R) - K$ and therefore $K = E/R$, thus the exact solution would be

$$i = \frac{E}{R} - \frac{E}{R} e^{-Rt/L} \qquad \text{or} \qquad i = \frac{E}{R}(1 - e^{-Rt/L})$$

Exercise 6.3.   Calculate the general solution to the following differential equations.

1. $dy/dx = x/y$
2. $x(dy/dx) = -y$
3. $x \, dy = y \, dx$
4. $e^x \, dy = \cos y \, dx$
5. $dy/dx = -3y$
6. $dy/d\theta = (\sin \theta)/2y$
7. $(y + 2) dx + (x - 1) dy = 0$
8. $dy/dx = y + 3$
9. $dy/dx + y = 3$
10. $dy/dx - 3y + 5 = 0$
11. $dy/dx + 3y = 5$
12. $RC(dv/dt) + v = E$
13. $2y(dy/dx) = 4 + y^2$
14. $di/d\theta = 4 + i^2$

15. $(dy/dx) - (4 - y^2)/y = 0$ 16. $dy = (y^2 + 5y + 6) dx$
17. $\cos 2y \, (dy/dx) = \sec^2 (x/2)$ 18. $dy/dx = e^{-3y+x}$
19. $dy/dx = xe^{-3y-x}$ 20. $dy/dx = y \ln x$

Calculate the exact solution to the following differential equations.

21. $2i + 0.002(di/dt) = 4$; if $t = 0$ when $i = 0$.
22. $dy/dt = 4 - 0.001y$; if $t = 0$ when $y = 500$.
23. $dv/d\theta = \sqrt{4 - v^2}$; if $\theta = 30°$ when $v = 2$.
24. $Ri + L(di/dt) = E$; if $t = 0$ when $i = 0$.
25. $dy = \sqrt{9 - y^2} \, dx$; if $x = 1$ when $y = 0$.

6.3 INTEGRATING CERTAIN COMBINATIONS

When one cannot separate the variables in a differential equation, simple methods of solution are not likely unless one recognizes some familiar combination of variables. A few of these combinations become apparent when recalling differentiation of certain combinations.

Recall the rule for differentiating a product:

$$\text{If } y = uv, \quad \text{then } \frac{dy}{dx} = \frac{d(uv)}{dx} = u \frac{dv}{dx} + v \frac{du}{dx}$$

or $d(uv) = u \, dv + v \, du$, from which comes a particular combination of variables x and y:

$$d(xy) = x \, dy + y \, dx \tag{6.5}$$

Recall from differentiation:

$$\text{If } y = u^2 + v^2, \quad \text{then } \frac{dy}{dx} = \frac{d(u^2 + v^2)}{dx} = 2u \frac{du}{dx} + 2v \frac{dv}{dx}$$

which yields the combination

$$d(x^2 + y^2) = 2(x \, dx + y \, dy) \tag{6.6}$$

Recall the differentiation of a quotient:

$$\text{If } y = \frac{u}{v}, \quad \text{then } \frac{dy}{dx} = \frac{d(u/v)}{dx} = \frac{v(du/dx) - u(dv/dx)}{v^2}$$

or

$$d\left(\frac{u}{v}\right) = \frac{v \, du - u \, dv}{v^2}$$

This yields the combinations:

$$d\left(\frac{y}{x}\right) = \frac{x \, dy - y \, dx}{x^2} \tag{6.7}$$

$$d\left(\frac{x}{y}\right) = \frac{y\,dx - x\,dy}{y^2} \tag{6.8}$$

Now if we have a differential equation resembling the right side of Equations (6.5) through (6.8), we must suspect that the solution will resemble the corresponding left side.

Example 6.9. Solve $x\,dy + y\,dx = -xy\,dy$.
Dividing by xy:

$$\frac{x\,dy + y\,dx}{xy} = -dy$$

From (6.5) we see the left side of our equation has a numerator that is the derivative of the denominator, therefore we have $\ln xy = -y + C$ or

$$(\ln xy) + y = \ln K$$

Example 6.10. Solve $y\,dx - x\,dy + x\,dx = 0$.
The $y\,dx - x\,dy$ suggests either (6.7) or (6.8). Division by y^2 makes the third term $x\,dx/dy^2$, which cannot be integrated, but division by x^2 produces:

$$\frac{y\,dx - x\,dy}{x^2} + \frac{dx}{x} = 0 \quad \text{or} \quad \frac{-(x\,dy - y\,dx)}{x^2} + \frac{dx}{x} = 0$$

from which $-(y/x) + \ln x = \ln K$.

Example 6.11. Solve $x\,dx + (x^2 + y^2 + y)\,dy = 0$.
Rearranging, we have:

$$x\,dx + (x^2 + y^2)\,dy + y\,dy = 0$$

or

$$x\,dx + y\,dy + (x^2 + y^2)\,dy = 0$$

and dividing through by $x^2 + y^2$:

$$\frac{x\,dx + y\,dy}{x^2 + y^2} + dy = 0$$

From (6.6) we see the numerator misses being the derivative of the denominator by a multiple of 2. Making that adjustment and compensating for the multiplication by 2, we have:

$$\frac{1}{2}\left(\frac{2(x\,dx + y\,dy)}{x^2 + y^2}\right) + dy = 0$$

from which

$$\tfrac{1}{2}\ln(x^2 + y^2) + y = C_1$$

or

$$\ln(x^2 + y^2) + 2y = C$$

or

$$\ln(x^2 + y^2) + 2y = \ln K$$

Example 6.12. Solve $(y^3 + x^2y + 2x)dy + (x^3 + xy^2 + 2y)dx = 0$ for an exact solution if $x = 2$ when $y = 1$.

Expanding the given equation, we have:

$$y^3 dy + x^2y dy + 2x dy + x^3 dx + xy^2 dx + 2y dx = 0$$

or $\qquad x^3 dx + xy^2 dx + x^2y dy + y^3 dy + 2y dx + 2x dy = 0$

or $\qquad x(x^2 + y^2)dx + y(x^2 + y^2)dy + 2(y dx + x dy) = 0$

or $\qquad (x^2 + y^2)(x dx + y dy) + 2(y dx + x dy) = 0$

From (6.6) we see the second factor of the first term needs a multiple of 2 to make it the derivative of the first factor $(x^2 + y^2)$. Supplying this factor and compensating for it we have:

$$\tfrac{1}{2}(x^2 + y^2)(2)(x dx + y dy) + 2(y dx + x dy) = 0$$

From which we get:

$$\frac{1}{2}\frac{(x^2 + y^2)^2}{2} + 2xy + C_1 = 0$$

The integral of the second term comes from (6.5). Multiplying by four produces the general solution:

$$(x^2 + y^2)^2 + 8xy + C = 0$$

If $x = 2$ when $y = 1$, we have:

$$(2^2 + 1^2)^2 + 8(2)(1) + C = 0$$

$$5^2 + 16 + C = 0$$

$$25 + 16 + C = 0$$

$C = -41$, and the exact solution becomes:

$$(x^2 + y^2)^2 + 8xy = 41$$

Solving differential equations by this method requires recognition of the correct combination of variables. Rearrangement of terms is usually necessary before recognition is possible. Finally, we must keep in mind that many differential equations do not contain a combination of variables that leads to easy solution.

Exercise 6.4. Calculate a general solution to the differential equations in problems 1 through 7.

1. $x dx + y dx + x dy = 0$
2. $x dy + y^2 dx = y dx$
3. $y dx + x^3 dx - 2 dx = x dy$
4. $(x^2 + y^2 + x)dx + y dy = 0$
5. $y dy + (y^2 - x^2)dx = x dx$

6. $x\,dy + 4xy^3\,dy = -y\,dx$

7. $x^3\,dy + x^2y\,dx + y\,dx = x\,dy$

Calculate an exact solution to the following differential equations.

8. $y\,dx = x\,dy + y^3dx + y^2x\,dy$, if $x = 2$ when $y = 4$.

9. $e^{x/y}(x\,dy - y\,dx) - y^4\,dy = 0$, if $x = 0$ when $y = 2$.

6.4 FIRST-ORDER LINEAR DIFFERENTIAL EQUATIONS

A linear differential equation is one in which the dependent variable and its derivatives appear only in the first degree. The general form of a first-order linear differential equation is:

$$\frac{dy}{dx} + yF(x) = G(x) \tag{6.9}$$

where $F(x)$ and $G(x)$ are functions of x only. If in (6.9) $G(x) = 0$, then the D.E. is said to be *homogeneous*, or *reduced*. Differential equations in the form of (6.9) appear often in technical applications.

Examples of first-order differential equations are:

(a) $\dfrac{dy}{dx} + x^2y = e^x$

(b) $\dfrac{dy}{dx} + 2y = x^2$

(c) $\dfrac{dy}{dx} + y \sin x = \cos x$

A general solution for (6.9) is started by rewriting:

$$dy + yF(x)\,dx = G(x)\,dx \tag{6.10}$$

Now if we multiply through by $e^{\int F(x)dx}$ we arrive at the general solution:

$$y = e^{-\int F(x)dx} \int e^{\int F(x)dx}\,G(x)\,dx + Ce^{-\int F(x)dx} \tag{6.11}$$

Example 6.13. Solve $dy/dx + 3y = x$.
    From (6.9) $F(x) = 3$ and $G(x) = x$, so

$$y = e^{-\int 3dx} \int e^{\int 3dx}\,x\,dx + Ce^{-\int 3dx}$$

$$= e^{-3x} \int e^{3x}\,x\,dx + Ce^{-3x}$$

From integral tables we find

$$\int xe^{ax}\,dx = \frac{e^{ax}}{a^2}(ax - 1)$$

so

$$\int e^{3x} x\,dx = \frac{e^{3x}}{9}(3x - 1)$$

and

$$y = e^{-3x}\left(\frac{e^{3x}}{9}(3x - 1)\right) + Ce^{-3x}$$

$$= \tfrac{1}{9}(3x - 1) + Ce^{-3x}$$

Example 6.14.   Solve $dy/dx + y = x$.

Here $F(x) = 1$ and $G(x) = x$ and, multiplying through by dx, we have $dy + y\,dx = x\,dx$, and from (6.11)

$$y = e^{-\int dx}\int e^{\int dx} x\,dx + Ce^{-\int dx}$$

$$= e^{-x}e^{+x}(x - 1) + Ce^{-x}$$

$$= x - 1 + Ce^{-x}$$

Example 6.15.   Solve $dy/dx + 2y = x^3$.

Multiplying through by dx:

$$dy + 2y\,dx = x^3\,dx$$

Here $F(x) = 2$ and $G(x) = x^3$. From (6.11):

$$y = e^{-\int 2\,dx}\int e^{\int 2\,dx} x^3\,dx + Ce^{-\int 2\,dx}$$

therefore:

$$y = e^{-2x}\int e^{2x} x^3\,dx + Ce^{-2x}$$

From integral tables:

$$\int x^m e^{ax}\,dx = \frac{x^m e^{ax}}{a} - \frac{m}{a}\int x^{m-1} e^{ax}\,dx$$

so

$$\int e^{2x} x^3\,dx = \frac{x^3 e^{2x}}{2} - \frac{3}{2}\int x^2 e^{2x}\,dx$$

$$= \frac{x^3 e^{2x}}{2} - \frac{3e^{2x}}{2} = \frac{1}{2}(x^3 - 3)\,e^{2x}$$

and

$$y = e^{-2x}\tfrac{1}{2}(x^3 - 3)\,e^{2x} + Ce^{-2x}$$

$$= \tfrac{1}{2}(x^3 - 3) + Ce^{-2x}$$

Example 6.16.   Solve $dy + (2/x)y\,dx = 4x\,dx$.

Here $F(x) = 2/x$ and $G(x) = 4x$, so from (6.11)

$$y = e^{-2\int dx/x} \int e^{2\int dx/x} 4x\,dx + Ce^{-2\int dx/x}$$

$$= e^{-2\ln x} \int e^{2\ln x} 4x\,dx + Cx^{-2\ln x}$$

$$= x^{-2} \int (x^2) 4x\,dx + Cx^{-2}$$

$$= x^{-2} \int 4x^3\,dx + Cx^{-2}$$

$$= x^{-2} \frac{4x^4}{4} + Cx^{-2}$$

Therefore

$$y = x^2 + \frac{C}{x^2}$$

or

$$yx^2 = x^4 + C$$

Example 6.17.   Solve $x^2\,dy + 2xy\,dx = \sin x\,dx$.

Dividing through by x^2 puts the D.E. in the form of (6.10):

$$dy + \frac{2}{x} y\,dx = \frac{1}{x^2} \sin x\,dx$$

Here $F(x) = 2/x$ and $G(x) = (1/x^2)\sin x$, and from (6.11)

$$y = e^{-2\int dx/x} \int e^{2\int dx/x} \frac{1}{x^2} \sin x\,dx + Ce^{-2\int dx/x}$$

$$= x^{-2} \int x^2 \frac{1}{x^2} \sin x\,dx + Cx^{-2}$$

$$= x^{-2} \int \sin x\,dx + Cx^{-2}$$

$$= x^{-2} (-\cos x) + Cx^{-2}$$

$$= -\frac{1}{x^2} \cos x + \frac{C}{x^2}$$

or

$$x^2 y = -\cos x + C$$

Exercise 6.5.   In problems 1 through 14 find a general solution to the given differential equations.

1. $dy/dx = x^2$
2. $dy/dx = y^2$
3. $dy + y\,dx = e^{-x}\,dx$
4. $x\,dy + 3y\,dx = dx$
5. $dy = x^2 y^2\,dx$
6. $x\,dy = -y\,dx$

7. $dy + y\,dx = e^{-x}\cos x\,dx$ 8. $dy + 2xy\,dx = x\,dx$
9. $dy = xe^{4x}\,dx + 4y\,dx$ 10. $dy + y\tan x\,dx = -\sin x\,dx$
11. $dy/dx + y = 3$ 12. $dy = x^2y\,dx + 3x^2\,dx$
13. $x\,dy = y\,dx + (x^2 - 1)^2\,dx$ 14. $(1 + x^2)\,dy + xy\,dx = x\,dx$

In problems 15 through 19 find an exact solution to the given differential equations.

15. $dy = \sin x\,dx$, when $x = 0$ and $y = 0$.
16. $dy = x^2\,dx + dx$, when $x = 0$ and $y = 1$.
17. $dy = y(dx/x)$, when $x = 1$ and $y = 1$.
18. $(\sin x)(dy/dx) + y = \tan x$, when $x = \pi/4$ and $y = 0$.
19. $dy + 2y\,dx = e^{-x}\,dx$, when $x = 0$ and $y = 1$.

6.5 LAPLACE TRANSFORMS

The last method for solving differential equations that we shall discuss uses the Laplace transforms. The use of Laplace transforms lends itself quite well to the electronics field because initial conditions are usually known or given and are required for the use of Laplace transforms.

In order to write, discuss, and use Laplace transforms, functional notation will be quite important. The student should review the discussion on functions in the Precalculus Mathematics Review section before proceeding.

Recall that if $y = x^2$, then y is a function *of* x or, symbolically, $y = f(x)$. If we are concerned about a particular value of y corresponding to a given value of x, we say y equals the functional value *at* x, or $y = f[x]$.

Thus $y = f(x) = x^2$ shows y to be an "f" of x function. And $y = f[3] = 3^2 = 9$ shows the functional value of $y = x^2$ when $x = 3$ to be 9.

From our experience with the derivative we know that if $y = f(x) = x^2$, then $y' = g(x) = 2x$. In words this says if y is a function "f" of x or x^2, then the derivative of y or y' is some different function "g" of x or $2x$.

If $y = f(x) = x^2$

then $y' = g(x) = 2x$

and $y[3] = f[3] = 3^2 = 9$

while $y'[3] = g[3] = 2 \cdot 3 = 6$

The idea of transforms in mathematics is not new and is not new to the student, although he may not realize he has been exposed to it.

Mathematically, if given a situation, expression, or function and you wish an answer or new expression or new variable function, you can proceed in one of two ways:

1. Attack the problem directly, arriving at a satisfactory conclusion. This is the usual method.

2. Use the detour or transform method which changes the given to some new situation that is attacked and brought to an intermediate conclusion which is then transformed back to the original situation, thus producing the same result as the first method.

An example of this detour or transform method that is familiar to the student is the use of logarithms in a multiplication problem. Say the given problem is to multiply 20 by 3. The direct attack would be to multiply 20 by 3, producing the correct answer or product 60.

The detour or transform method is to transform the 20 to its equivalent logarithm and the 3 to its equivalent logarithm, yielding:

$$\text{logarithm } 20 = 1.3010$$

and $$\text{logarithm } 3 = 0.4771$$

These logarithms are then added, producing the logarithm of $3 \cdot 20$ or 1.7781. Note that so far we have transformed two real numbers 3 and 20 into two different real numbers 0.4771 and 1.3010. Also the manipulation or operation was changed from multiplication to addition.

All that is left to do now is to inverse transform this addition result back to the original kind of real numbers (in this case antilog 1.7781), which yields the answer 60. Figure 6.1 illustrates the two methods graphically.

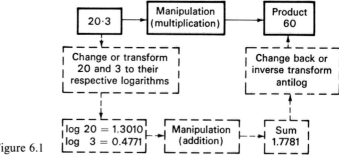

Figure 6.1

Let us now see how the Laplace transform is used to solve a differential equation. If given a differential equation, the direct method is to attack it in any of the ways we have thus far learned, hopefully producing a solution. In this method the variable or variables do not change. The detour method requires transforming the given functions of x into different functions in a new variable. Manipulation in this new variable is usually algebraic, producing an answer in the new variable. The answer then is changed back to the original variable by inverse transformation. Figure 6.2 illustrates these two methods.

The transform we shall use to accomplish our detour route in Figure 6.2 is the Laplace transform. The Laplace transform used will depend on the type of differen-

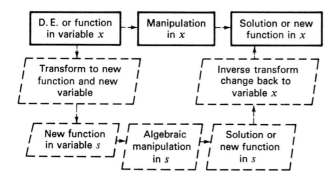

Figure 6.2

tial equation presented. Let us look at a specific situation to see how the Laplace transform is derived and also learn some new symbols.

If we are given some function of t, $f(t)$, and we desire to define a new function F in a different variable, $F(s)$, we use (6.12):

$$F(s) = \int_0^\infty e^{-st} f(t)\, dt \tag{6.12}$$

From this we see that integration of the right side of (6.12) results in a function of the variable s. In order to show symbolically that $F(s)$ is the Laplace transform of $f(t)$, the notation $\mathscr{L}(f)$ is used:

$$\mathscr{L}(f) = F(s) = \int_0^\infty e^{-st} f(t)\, dt \tag{6.13}$$

Example 6.18. Calculate the Laplace transform for the function defined by $f(t) = t$ when $t > 0$.

From (6.13):

$$\mathscr{L}(f) = \mathscr{L}(t) = \int_0^\infty e^{-st} t\, dt$$

Integration here is accomplished by consulting the integration tables. From the tables

$$\int xe^{ax}\, dx = \frac{e^{ax}}{a^2}(ax - 1)$$

so

$$\int_0^\infty te^{-st}\, dt = \left. \frac{e^{-st}}{s^2}(-st - 1) \right]_0^\infty$$

evaluation produces

$$\left\{ \frac{e^{-s(\infty)}}{s^2}[-s(\infty) - 1] \right\} - \left\{ \frac{e^{-s(0)}}{s^2}[-s(0) - 1] \right\}$$

Evaluation for the upper limit (∞) as shown is impossible, but if we think of the limit of e^{-st} as t approaches an extremely large number, we see that e^{-st} will approach zero. Symbolically:

$$\text{as } t \to \infty \Rightarrow e^{-st} \to 0$$

therefore the upper-limit evaluation approaches zero. The lower-limit (0) evaluation becomes:

$$-\left\{ \frac{e^0}{s^2}(0 - 1) \right\} = -\frac{1}{s^2}(-1) = \frac{1}{s^2}$$

From all of this then:

$$\text{if } f(t) = t, \qquad \text{then } \mathscr{L}(f) = \mathscr{L}(t) = \frac{1}{s^2}$$

Example 6.19.   Calculate the Laplace transform for the function defined by $f(t) = \cos at$.
   From (6.13):

$$F(s) = \mathscr{L}(f) = \mathscr{L}(\cos at) = \int_0^\infty e^{-st} \cos at \, dt$$

From integration tables:

$$\int e^{ax} \cos px \, dx = \frac{e^{ax}(a \cos px + p \sin px)}{a^2 + p^2}$$

Therefore:

$$\int_0^\infty e^{-st} \cos at \, dt = \frac{e^{-st}(-s \cos at + a \sin at)}{s^2 + a^2} \bigg]_0^\infty$$

$$= (0) - \left(\frac{1(-s \cos (a \cdot 0) + a \sin (a \cdot 0))}{s^2 + a^2} \right)$$

$$= \frac{s}{s^2 + a^2}$$

So,

$$\text{if } f(t) = \cos at, \qquad \text{then } \mathscr{L}(\cos at) = \frac{s}{s^2 + a^2}$$

Note in both Examples 6.18 and 6.19 that functions of x were transformed to new functions of a new variable s, and that the transformed functions operations were algebraic.
   Laplace transforms of sums or differences of functions become the sums or differences of their transforms. That is,

$$\mathscr{L}[f(x) + g(x)] = \mathscr{L}(f) + \mathscr{L}(g) \tag{6.14}$$

$$\mathscr{L}[f(x) - g(x)] = \mathscr{L}(f) - \mathscr{L}(g) \tag{6.15}$$

In words, (6.14) says that the Laplace transform of the sum of the function f of x and the function g of x becomes the Laplace transform of the function f of x plus the Laplace transform of the function g of x. Whenever the student becomes disenchanted with mathematical symbolism, he should compare (6.14) symbolically with the words.

The student should now realize that most Laplace transforms can be derived, but we will not do so. We shall use the table of Laplace transforms given in Figure 6.3, which will provide for all our needs in this book. More extensive tables of Laplace transforms are available.

	$f(t) = \mathcal{L}^{-1}(F)$	$F(s) = \mathcal{L}(f)$
1	1	$1/s$
2	t	$1/s^2$
3	$t^{(n-1)}/(n-1)!$	$1/s^n$ n a positive integer
4	e^{-at}	$1/(s+a)$
5	$1 - e^{-at}$	$a/s(s+a)$
6	e^{at}	$1/(s-a)$
7	te^{at}	$1/(s-a)^2$
8	$\cos(at)$	$s/(s^2+a^2)$
9	$(1/a)\sin(at)$	$1/(s^2+a^2)$
10	$(1/a^2)[1 - \cos(at)]$	$1/s(s^2+a^2)$
11	$(1/a^3)[at - \sin(at)]$	$1/s^2(s^2+a^2)$
12	$e^{at}\cos(bt)$	$(s-a)/[(s-a)^2+b^2]$
13	$e^{-at} - e^{-bt}$	$(b-a)/(s+a)(s+b)$
14	$ae^{-at} - be^{-bt}$	$s(a-b)/(s+a)(s+b)$
15	te^{-at}	$1/(s+a)^2$
16	$t^{n-1}e^{-at}$	$(n-1)!/(s+a)^n$
17	$e^{-at}(1-at)$	$s/(s+a)^2$
18	$[(b-a)t + 1]e^{-at}$	$(s+b)/(s+a)^2$
19	$\sin(at) - at\cos(at)$	$2a^3/(s^2+a^2)^2$
20	$t\sin(at)$	$2as/(s^2+a^2)^2$
21	$\sin(at) + at\cos(at)$	$2as^2/(s^2+a^2)^2$
22	$t\cos(at)$	$(s^2-a^2)/(s^2+a^2)^2$
23	$e^{-at}\sin(bt)$	$b/[(s+a)^2+b^2]$
24	$e^{-at}\cos(bt)$	$(s+a)/[(s+a)^2+b^2]$

Figure 6.3

The Laplace transform table in Figure 6.3 has two columns. The first column is headed $f(t) = \mathscr{L}^{-1}(F)$ and the second heading is $F(s) = \mathscr{L}(f)$.

$F(s) = \mathscr{L}(f)$ says in words the function F of s is the transform of the function f of t.

$f(t) = \mathscr{L}^{-1}(F)$ says in words the function f of t is the inverse transform of the function F of s.

To use the table then, the function $f(t)$ is located in column 1 and its Laplace transform $F(s)$ on the same line in column 2. Thus, if $f(t) = e^{-at}$, then $\mathscr{L}(f) = F(s) = 1/(s + a)$; and if $F(s) = s/(s^2 + a^2)$, then $\mathscr{L}^{-1}(F) = \cos at$. Or if $f(t) = (1/a) \sin at$, then $\mathscr{L}(f) = F(s) = 1/(s^2 + a^2)$; and if $F(s) = 1/(s - a)$, then $\mathscr{L}^{-1}(F) = f(t) = te^{at}$.

Since

$$\mathscr{L} Kf(t) = K\mathscr{L}(f) \tag{6.16}$$

the Laplace transform of $4t$ is $4(1/s^2)$ from line 2, and the Laplace transform of $3te^{-at}$ is $3[1/(s + a)]$ from line 4.

Example 6.20.   What is the inverse Laplace transform $\mathscr{L}^{-1}(F)$ of the function $F(s) = 1/s(s - 2)$?

From line 5, column 2, we find the function $F(s) = a/s(s + a)$, which is quite similar to our function. If the numerator of our function was -2, then our function would be the same as $a/s(s + a)$ with $a = -s$. To make the numerator -2 we must multiply by (-2) and to compensate for the -2 multiplier we multiply by $-\frac{1}{2}$, therefore

$$F(s) = \frac{1}{s(s - 2)} = -\frac{1}{2}\left(\frac{-2}{s(s - 2)}\right)$$

and $\mathscr{L}^{-1}(F) = -\frac{1}{2}(1 - e^{2t})$ according to line 5 and (6.16).

Exercise 6.6.   In problems 1 through 10 establish $\mathscr{L}(f)$ for the given $f(t)$.

1. $f(t) = 1$ 2. $f(t) = 2$
3. $f(t) = 6$ 4. $f(t) = 10$
5. $f(t) = e^{3t}$ 6. $f(t) = 1 - \cos 2t$
7. $f(t) = t^3 e^{-2t}$ 8. $f(t) = 3e^{-2t} \sin 4t$
9. $f(t) = \cos 2t - \sin 2t$ 10. $f(t) = 3t \sin 2t + e^{-2t} \cos 3t$

In problems 11 through 24 establish $\mathscr{L}^{-1}(F)$ for the given $F(s)$.

11. $F(s) = 1/s$ 12. $F(s) = 2/s^2$
13. $F(s) = 3/s^4$ 14. $F(s) = 4/(s + 2)$
15. $F(s) = 2/s(s + 3)$ 16. $F(s) = 2/s(s - 3)$
17. $F(s) = 3/(s - 2)^2$ 18. $F(s) = 3s/(s^2 + 4)$
19. $F(s) = s/(s^2 + 6s + 9)$ 20. $F(s) = (s + 2)/(s + 3)^2$
21. $F(s) = 1/(s + 5)$ 22. $F(s) = 3/(s^4 + 4s^2)$
23. $F(s) = (s + 2)/(s^2 + 9)^2$ 24. $F(s) = (s^2 - 1)/(s^4 + 2s^2 + 1)$

In order to use Laplace transforms to solve differential equations, we will need some additional information and symbols.

If $y = f(x)$ is a given function and $y' = g(x)$ is the function obtained by differentiation of $f(x)$, then symbolically $y' = f'(x) = g(x)$.

We now wish to calculate the Laplace transform of the first derivative of a function $f(t)$. By (6.13):

$$\mathcal{L}(f') = \int_0^\infty e^{-st} f'(t)\, dt$$

Letting $u = e^{-st}$ and $dv = f'(t)$, then $du = -se^{-st}\, dt$ and $v = f(t)$, and integrating by parts

$$\mathcal{L}(f') = e^{-st} f(t) \Big]_0^\infty + s \int_0^\infty e^{-st} f(t)\, dt$$

$$= 0 - f[0] + s\mathcal{L}(f)$$

therefore

$$\mathcal{L}(f') = s\mathcal{L}(f) - f[0] \qquad (6.17)$$

Using a similar approach it can be shown that:

$$\mathcal{L}(f'') = s^2 \mathcal{L}(f) - sf[0] - f'[0] \qquad (6.18)$$

Note that (6.17) and (6.18) allow us to express the transform of a derivative of a function in terms of s and the transform of the given function itself.

Example 6.21. Calculate the Laplace transform of $f''(t) - 2f'(t)$ if $f[0] = 0$ and $f'[0] = 1$.

According to (6.15)

$$\mathcal{L}[f''(t) - 2f'(t)] = \mathcal{L}(f'') - 2\mathcal{L}(f')$$

and by (6.18):

$$\mathcal{L}(f'') = s^2 \mathcal{L}(f) - sf[0] - f'[0]$$

$$= s^2 \mathcal{L}(f) - s(0) - 1$$

And by (6.17):

$$-2\mathcal{L}(f') = -2\left[s\mathcal{L}(f) - f[0] \right]$$

$$= -2\left[s\mathcal{L}(f) - 0 \right]$$

$$= -2s\mathcal{L}(f) + 0$$

Therefore:

$$\mathcal{L}(f'') - 2\mathcal{L}(f') = s^2 \mathcal{L}(f) - 1 - 2s\mathcal{L}(f)$$

$$= (s^2 - 2s)\mathcal{L}(f) - 1$$

Example 6.22. Calculate the Laplace transform of $f''(t) + f'(t)$, if $f[0] = 0$ when $f'[0] = 0$.

From (6.15):

$$\mathcal{L}[f''(t) + f'(t)] = \mathcal{L}(f'') + \mathcal{L}(f')$$

From (6.18):

$$\mathcal{L}(f'') = s^2\mathcal{L}(f) - sf[0] - f'[0]$$
$$= s^2\mathcal{L}(f) - s \cdot 0 - 0$$
$$= s^2\mathcal{L}(f)$$

And from (6.17):

$$\mathcal{L}(f') = s\mathcal{L}(f) - f[0]$$
$$= s\mathcal{L}(f) - 0$$
$$= s\mathcal{L}(f)$$

Therefore

$$\mathcal{L}[f''(t) + f'(t)] = s^2\mathcal{L}(f) + s\mathcal{L}(f)$$
$$= (s^2 + s)\mathcal{L}(f)$$

Exercise 6.7. Calculate the Laplace transforms of the given functions with given conditions as stated.

1. $2y'' - y' + y$, if $f[0] = 1$ and $f'[0] = 0$.
2. $y'' - 3y'$, if $f[0] = 2$ and $f'[0] = -1$.
3. $f''(t) - 2f'(t)$, if $f[0] = 0$ and $f'[0] = 1$.
4. $y'' - 3y' + 2y$, if $f[0] = -1$ and $f'[0] = 2$.
5. $2y' - y = 0$, if $y[0] = 1$.
6. $y' + 3y = e^{-3t}$, if $y[0] = 1$.

We are now ready to apply our knowledge of Laplace transforms to finding a particular solution to certain differential equations when initial conditions are given.

Example 6.23. Solve $2y' - y = 0$, if $y[0] = 1$.

$$\mathcal{L}(2y') - \mathcal{L}(y) = \mathcal{L}(0)$$
$$2\mathcal{L}(y') - \mathcal{L}(y) = 0$$
$$2\mathcal{L}(y') = 2(s\mathcal{L}(y) - y[0])$$
$$= 2(s\mathcal{L}(y) - 1)$$
$$= 2s\mathcal{L}(y) - 2$$

Therefore

$$2s\mathscr{L}(y) - 2 - \mathscr{L}(y) = 0$$

$$2s\mathscr{L}(y) - \mathscr{L}(y) = 2$$

$$(2s - 1)\mathscr{L}(y) = 2$$

$$\mathscr{L}(y) = \frac{2}{2s - 1}$$

$$= \frac{1}{s - (1/2)}$$

Therefore

$$\mathscr{L}(y) = F(s) = \frac{1}{s - (1/2)}$$

and

$$\mathscr{L}^{-1}(F) = f(t) = e^{t/2}$$

From all of this then the particular solution to the given differential equation is $y = e^{t/2}$.

Example 6.24. Solve $y' + 3y = e^{-3t}$, if $y[0] = 1$.

$$\mathscr{L}(y') + 3\mathscr{L}(y) = \mathscr{L}(e^{-3t})$$

$$\mathscr{L}(y') = s\mathscr{L}(y) - y[0]$$

$$\mathscr{L}(e^{-3t}) = \frac{1}{s + 3}$$

$$s\mathscr{L}(y) - y[0] + 3\mathscr{L}(y) = \frac{1}{s + 3}$$

$$(s + 3)\mathscr{L}(y) - 1 = \frac{1}{s + 3}$$

$$(s + 3)\mathscr{L}(y) = 1 + \frac{1}{s + 3}$$

$$= \frac{s + 3}{s + 3} + \frac{1}{s + 3} = \frac{s + 4}{s + 3}$$

$$F(s) = \mathscr{L}(y) = \frac{s + 4}{(s + 3)^2}$$

$$10^{-2}s\mathscr{L}(i) + 2\mathscr{L}(i) = \frac{600}{s^2 + (200)^2}$$

$$(10^{-2}s + 2)\mathscr{L}(i) = \frac{600}{s^2 + (200)^2}$$

$$10^{-2}(s + 200)\mathscr{L}(i) = \frac{600}{s^2 + (200)^2}$$

$$\mathscr{L}(i) = \frac{600}{10^{-2}(s + 200)[s^2 + (200)^2]}$$

$$= \frac{10^2 \cdot 600}{[(s + 200)][s^2 + (200)^2]}$$

$$= \frac{60000}{[s + 200][s^2 + (200)^2]}$$

By partial fractions:

$$\frac{60000}{(s + 200)(s^2 + 200^2)} = \frac{A}{s + 200} + \frac{Bs + C}{s^2 + 200^2}$$

and $60000 = A(s^2 + 200^2) + Bs(s + 200) + C(s + 200)$

When $s = -200 \Rightarrow 60000 = A(200^2 + 200^2) + Bs(0) + C(0)$

$$60000 = 80000A$$

$$A = \frac{60000}{80000} = \frac{3}{4}$$

$$\mathscr{L}^{-1}(F) = [(4 - 3)t + 1]e^{-3t}$$

$$= (t + 1)e^{-3t}$$

Example 6.25.   Solve $y'' + 4y = \sin 2t$, if $y[0] = 0$ and $y'[0] = 0$.

$$\mathscr{L}(y'') + 4\mathscr{L}(y) = \mathscr{L}(\sin 2t)$$

$$\mathscr{L}(y'') = s^2\mathscr{L}(y) - sy[0] - y'[0]$$

$$\mathscr{L}(\sin 2t) = 2\mathscr{L}(\tfrac{1}{2}\sin 2t) = 2\frac{1}{s^2 + 4} = \frac{2}{s^2 + 4}$$

$$s^2\mathscr{L}(y) - s \cdot 0 - 0 = \frac{2}{s^2 + 4}$$

$$F(s) = \mathscr{L}(y) = \frac{2}{s^2(s^2 + 4)} = 2\left(\frac{1}{s^2(s^2 + 4)}\right)$$

$$\mathscr{L}^{-1}(F) = f(t) = \frac{2}{8}[2t - \sin 2t] = \frac{t}{2} - \frac{1}{4}\sin 2t$$

$$y = \frac{t}{2} - \frac{1}{4}\sin 2t$$

Example 6.26.   Solve $10^{-2}(di/dt) + 2i = 3\sin 200t$, if $t = 0$ when $i = 0$.
Rewriting: $10^{-2}(i)' + 2i = 3\sin 200t$

$$10^{-2}\mathscr{L}(i') + 2\mathscr{L}(i) = 3\mathscr{L}(\sin 200t)$$

$$10^{-2}[s\mathscr{L}(i) - i[0]] + 2\mathscr{L}(i) = 3\left(\frac{200}{s^2 + (200)^2}\right)$$

When $s = 0 \Rightarrow 60000 = 200^2 A + B(0)(200) + C(200)$

$$60000 = 40000A + 200C$$

$$60000 = 40000(\tfrac{3}{4}) + 200C$$

$$60000 = 30000 + 200C$$

$$30000 = 200C$$

$$C = \frac{30000}{200} = 150$$

When $s = 200 \Rightarrow 60000 = 80000A + 80000B + 400C$

$$60000 = 80000(\tfrac{3}{4}) + 80000B + 400 \cdot 150$$

$$60000 = 60000 + 80000B + 60000$$

$$80000B = -60000$$

$$B = -\frac{60000}{80000} = -\frac{3}{4}$$

Therefore:

$$\mathscr{L}(i) = \frac{3/4}{(s + 200)} - \frac{(3/4)s - 150}{s^2 + 200^2}$$

$$= \frac{3/4}{s + 200} - \frac{(3/4)s}{s^2 + 200^2} + \frac{150}{s^2 + 200^2}$$

$$= \frac{3}{4}\left(\frac{1}{s^2 + 200}\right) - \frac{3}{4}\left(\frac{s}{s^2 + 200^2}\right) + \frac{3}{4}\left(\frac{200}{s^2 + 200^2}\right)$$

$$F(s) = \mathscr{L}(i) = \frac{3}{4}\left\{\left(\frac{1}{s + 200}\right) - \left(\frac{s}{s^2 + 200^2}\right) + \left(\frac{200}{s^2 + 200^2}\right)\right\}$$

and

$$\mathscr{L}^{-1}(F) = i = \tfrac{3}{4}(e^{-200t} - \cos 200t + \sin 200t)$$

Example 6.27.   Solve $q'' + 100q' + 2500q = 50$ if $q[0] = 0$ when $t = 0$ and $q'[0] = 0$.

$$\mathscr{L}(q'') = s^2\mathscr{L}(q) - s \cdot q[0] - q'[0]$$

$$100\mathscr{L}(q') = 100s\mathscr{L}(q) - 100q[0]$$

$$s^2\mathscr{L}(q) + 100s\mathscr{L}(q) + 2500\mathscr{L}(q) = \frac{50}{s}$$

$$s(s^2 + 100s + 2500)\mathscr{L}(q) = 50$$

$$\mathscr{L}(q) = \frac{50}{s(s^2 + 100s + 2500)}$$

$$F(s) = \mathscr{L}(q) = \frac{50}{s(s + 50)^2}$$

By partial fractions:

$$\mathscr{L}(q) = \frac{1/50}{s} + \frac{A}{(s + 50)^2} + \frac{B}{s + 50}$$

$$F(s) = \mathscr{L}(q) = \frac{1}{50}\left\{\frac{1}{s} - \frac{50}{(s + 50)^2} - \frac{1}{s + 50}\right\}$$

$$\mathscr{L}^{-1}(q) = q = \tfrac{1}{50}(1 - 50te^{-50t} - e^{-50t})$$

Exercise 6.8.   Solve the following differential equations.

1. $y' + y = 0$, if $y[0] = 1$.
2. $y' - 2y = 2$, if $y[0] = 2$.
3. $2y' - 3y = 0$, if $y[0] = -1$.
4. $y' + 2y = 1$, if $y[0] = 0$.
5. $y'' + 2y' + 2y = 0$, if $y[0] = 0$ when $y'[0] = 1$.
6. $y' + 2y = te^{-2t}$, if $y[0] = 0$.
7. $y'' + 4y = 0$, if $y[0] = 0$ when $y'[0] = 1$.
8. $(1/500)i' + 4i = 0$, if $i = 20$ when $t = 0$.
9. $Li' + Ri = 0$, if $i = E/R$ when $t = 0$.
10. $q' + 500q = 10$, if $q = 0$ when $t = 0$.
11. $y' - 10y = 3e^{-4x}$, if $x = 0$ when $y[0] = 2$.
12. $i' + 100i = 200e^{-100t}$, if $i = 0$ when $t = 0$.
13. $y'' + 2y' = 0$, if $y[0] = 0$ when $y'[0] = 2$.
14. $y'' + 2y' + y = 0$, if $y[0] = 0$ when $y'[0] = -2$.
15. $y'' - 4y' + 5y = 0$, if $y[0] = 1$ when $y'[0] = 2$.
16. $y'' + 4y = \sin 2t$, if $y[0] = 0$ when $y'[0] = 0$.

Appendix

Many proofs have been purposely omitted from Unit 2 because the author has found they tend to slow down and even frighten some students.

The proofs that are not difficult are presented here for the interested student or concerned instructor.

(2.1) Page 38

$$\text{If } y = kx^n + C \Rightarrow \frac{dy}{dx} = nkx^{n-1}$$

For this proof we shall use the delta method outlined on page 35 to obtain the average slope $\Delta y/\Delta x$, and then take the limit of $\Delta y/\Delta x$ as Δx approaches zero to obtain the instantaneous slope or first derivative dy/dx.

In $y = kx^n + C$, k is a multiplicative constant, C is an additive constant, and we shall assume the exponent n to be a positive integer. A short proof following this one will show that in fact n may be positive, negative, integral or fractional, rational or irrational.

If we are given $y = kx^n + C$, let us take a point $[(x + \Delta x),(y + \Delta y)]$ and substitute it into our equation, yielding:

$$y + \Delta y = k(x + \Delta x)^n + C$$

Now if we expand the right side by use of the binomial expansion (see page 2 of the Precalculus Mathematical Review section), we obtain:

$$y + \Delta y = k\left[x^n + nx^{n-1}(\Delta x) + \frac{n(n-1)}{2!} x^{n-2}(\Delta x)^2 \right.$$

$$\left. + \frac{n(n-1)(n-2)}{3!} x^{n-3}(\Delta x)^3 + \cdots + (\Delta x)^n \right] + C$$

Multiplying through by the k yields:

$$y + \Delta y = kx^n + knx^{n-1}(\Delta x) + \frac{kn(n-1)}{2!} x^{n-2}(\Delta x)^2$$

$$+ \frac{kn(n-1)(n-2)}{3!} x^{n-3}(\Delta x)^3 + \cdots + k(\Delta x)^n + C$$

From this we subtract the original equation, producing:

$$\Delta y = knx^{n-1}(\Delta x) + \frac{kn(n-1)}{2!} x^{n-2}(\Delta x)^2$$

$$+ \frac{kn(n-1)(n-2)}{3!} x^{n-3}(\Delta x)^3 + \cdots + k(\Delta x)^n$$

And dividing both sides by Δx we get:

$$\frac{\Delta y}{\Delta x} = knx^{n-1} + \frac{kn(n-1)}{2!} x^{n-2}(\Delta x) + \frac{kn(n-1)(n-2)}{3!} x^{n-3}(\Delta x)^3$$

$$+ \cdots + k(\Delta x)^{n-1}$$

from which:

$$\lim_{\Delta x \to 0} \frac{\Delta y}{\Delta x} = nkx^{n-1} = \frac{dy}{dx}$$

if n is a positive integer.

We shall now show that n need not be restricted to being a positive integer. If $y = x^n$ and we take the logarithm of both sides, we obtain:

$$\ln y = \ln x^n \quad \text{or} \quad \ln y = n \ln x$$

which is true for n even though it be negative, positive, fractional, integral, rational, or irrational. Now if we differentiate both sides using equation (2.31), page 71, we obtain:

$$\frac{1}{y} \cdot \frac{dy}{dx} = \frac{n}{x}$$

Multiplying both sides by y produces:

$$\frac{dy}{dx} = \frac{n}{x} \cdot y$$

But since we have given $y = x^n$, we substitute x^n for y:

$$\frac{dy}{dx} = \frac{n}{x} x^n$$

or

$$\frac{dy}{dx} = n(x^{-1})(x^n) = nx^{n-1}$$

which is true for all values of n mentioned above. So obviously then:

$$\text{If } y = kx^n + C \Rightarrow \frac{dy}{dx} = nkx^{n-1}$$

(2.3) **Page 42**

If $y = ku^n + C \Rightarrow y' = nku^{n-1}\dfrac{du}{dx}$

Given $y = u^n$ where u is a function of x, from $y = u^n$ we calculate

$$\frac{dy}{du} = nu^{n-1}$$

But we are seeking dy/dx and not dy/du, so to obtain a connection, we assert:

$$\frac{\Delta y}{\Delta x} = \frac{\Delta y}{\Delta x} \qquad\qquad \text{Identity}$$

$$= \frac{\Delta y}{1} \cdot \frac{1}{\Delta x} \qquad\qquad \text{Fraction multiplication}$$

$$= \left(\frac{\Delta y}{1} \cdot \frac{1}{\Delta x}\right)\frac{\Delta u}{\Delta u} \qquad \text{Multiplication by one}$$

$$= \frac{\Delta y}{\Delta u} \cdot \frac{\Delta u}{\Delta x} \qquad\qquad \text{Fraction multiplication}$$

Therefore $\Delta y/\Delta x = (\Delta y/\Delta u)\cdot(\Delta u/\Delta x)$ and taking the limit as Δx approaches zero (if the limit exists), we obtain

$$\frac{dy}{dx} = \frac{dy}{du}\frac{du}{dx}$$

Thus, substituting our previously calculated dy/du, we obtain:

$$y' = nu^{n-1}\frac{du}{dx}$$

(2.20) **Page 64**

If $y = k\sin u + C \Rightarrow y' = k\cos u\dfrac{du}{dx}$

If $y = \sin u$, where u is a function of x, we have: If $y = \sin u \Rightarrow (dy/du) = \cos u$. See (2.18), page 62. But from page 283 we see that $dy/dx = (dy/du)(du/dx)$, so by substitution, if $y = \sin u \Rightarrow dy/dx = \cos u\,(du/dx)$ and if $y = k\sin u + C \Rightarrow (dy/dx) = k\cos u\,(du/dx)$.

(2.21) **Page 64**

If $y = k\cos u + C \Rightarrow y' = -k\sin u\dfrac{du}{dx}$

If $y = k \cos u + C$, where u is a function of x, we have: If $y = \cos u \Rightarrow dy/dx = -\sin u$. See (2.19), page 00. But once again $dy/dx = (dy/du)(du/dx)$ from page 000, so by substitution, if $y = \cos u \Rightarrow dy/dx = -\sin u \, (du/dx)$ and if $y = k \cos u + C \Rightarrow dy/dx = -k \sin u \, (du/dx)$.

(2.24)   *Page 66*

$$\text{If } y = uv \Rightarrow y' = u\frac{dv}{dx} + v\frac{du}{dx}$$

If $y = uv$, where u and v are functions of x, then we will use the delta method and substitute $(y + \Delta y)$, $(u + \Delta u)$ and $(v + \Delta v)$ into the given equation, yielding:

$$y + \Delta y = (u + \Delta u)(v + \Delta v)$$

and expanding we get:

$$y + \Delta y = uv + v(\Delta u) + u(\Delta v) + (\Delta u)(\Delta v)$$

From this we subtract the original equation which yields:

$$y = v(\Delta u) + u(\Delta v) + (\Delta u)(\Delta v)$$

Dividing both sides by Δx, produces:

$$\frac{\Delta y}{\Delta x} = v\frac{\Delta u}{\Delta x} + u\frac{\Delta v}{\Delta x} + \frac{\Delta u}{\Delta x}(\Delta v)$$

$$= u\frac{\Delta v}{\Delta x} + v\frac{\Delta u}{\Delta x} + \frac{\Delta u}{\Delta x}(\Delta v)$$

from which:

$$\lim_{\Delta x \to 0} \frac{\Delta y}{\Delta x} = \frac{dy}{dx} = u\frac{dv}{dx} + v\frac{du}{dx}$$

provided we can show that $(\Delta v)(\Delta u/\Delta x)$ goes to zero in the limiting process. Since v is a function of x we write $v = g(x)$, and $v + \Delta v = g(x + \Delta x)$. Subtracting the $v = g(x)$ we get

$$v = g(x + \Delta x) - g(x)$$

and in the limiting process above $\Delta x \to 0$, and $g(x + \Delta x) \to g(x)$ which yields:

$$v = g(x) - g(x) = 0$$

and thus $(\Delta u/\Delta x)(\Delta v)$ must go to zero.

(2.25)   *Page 67*

$$\text{If } y = \frac{u}{v} \Rightarrow y' = \frac{v\,du/dx - u\,dv/dx}{v^2}$$

If $y = u/v$, where u and v are functions of x, then we will substitute $(y + \Delta y)$, $(u + \Delta u)$, and $(v + \Delta v)$ into the given equation:

$$y + \Delta y = \frac{u + \Delta u}{v + \Delta v}$$

and then subtracting the original equation we have:

$$y = \frac{u + \Delta u}{v + \Delta v} - \frac{u}{v}$$

And changing each fraction to its equivalent using a common denominator we have:

$$\Delta y = \frac{v(u + \Delta u)}{v(v + \Delta v)} - \frac{u(v + \Delta v)}{v(v + \Delta v)}$$

$$= \frac{uv + v(\Delta u) - uv - u(\Delta v)}{v(v + \Delta v)}$$

$$= \frac{v(\Delta u) - u(\Delta v)}{v(v + \Delta v)}$$

Now dividing through by Δx we get:

$$\frac{\Delta y}{\Delta x} = \frac{v(\Delta u/\Delta x) - u(\Delta v/\Delta x)}{v(v + \Delta v)}$$

and $$\lim_{\Delta x \to 0} \frac{\Delta y}{\Delta x} = \frac{dy}{dx} = \frac{v(du/dx) - u(dv/dx)}{v^2}$$

(2.27)   Page 69

$$\text{If } y = ke^u + C \Rightarrow y' = ke^u \frac{du}{dx}$$

If $y = e^u$ then $dy/dx = e^u$. From (2.26) we know that $dy/dx = (dy/du)(du/dx)$, so by substitution $dy/dx = e^u \, du/dx$ and if $y = ke^u + C \Rightarrow y' = ke^u \, (du/dx)$.

(2.31)   Page 71

$$\text{If } y = k \ln u + C \Rightarrow y' = \frac{k}{u} \frac{du}{dx}$$

If $y = \ln u$ then $dy/du = 1/u$ from (2.29). We know though that $dy/dx = (dy/du)$ (du/dx), so by substitution $dy/dx = (1/u)(du/dx)$ and if $y = k \ln u + C \Rightarrow y' = (k/u)(du/dx)$.

(2.32) Page 72

$$\text{If } y = ka^u + C \Rightarrow y' = ka^u \frac{du}{dx} \ln a$$

Here a is a positive constant and u is a function of x. Since a is a positive constant it may be expressed as some power b of e, or $a = e^b$. By substitution then, if $y = a^u$ we have

$$y = (e^b)^u = e^{bu}$$

From this then $dy/du = e^{bu}$ and $du/dx = b(dy/dx)$. Our basic equation, however, states $dy/dx = (dy/du)(du/dx)$, so $dy/dx = e^{bu} b(du/dx) = be^{bu}(du/dx) = b(e^b)^u(du/dx)$, but if $a = e^b$ this becomes $dy/dx = ba^u(du/dx)$, or $dy/dx = a^u(du/dx)b$.

If $a = e^b$, from the laws of natural logarithms, $b = \ln a$. Making this substitution we have:

$$\frac{dy}{dx} = a^u \frac{du}{dx} \ln a$$

Or if $y = ka^u + C$ then $dy/dx = ka^u(du/dx) \ln a$.

Simpson's Rule   Pages 168–9

Given three points in a plane. Through these points it is possible to pass one and only one parabola of the form $y = ax^2 + bx + c$. Figure A.1 shows three points

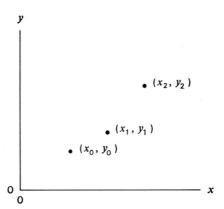

Figure A.1

whose coordinates are (x_0,y_0), (x_1,y_1) and (x_2,y_2). To determine the equation of the unique parabola through x_0,y_0,x_1,y_1,x_2, and y_2, we write:

$$y_0 = ax_0^2 + bx_0 + c$$

$$y_1 = ax_1^2 + bx_1 + c$$

$$y_2 = ax_2^2 + bx_2 + c$$

Three simultaneous equations in three unknowns allow us to solve for the a, b, and c that determines our $y = ax^2 + bx + c$ which passes through the three given points.

In Figure A.2 the plot of $y = ax^2 + bx + c$ is shown. Now if perpendiculars are dropped at x, $x + h$, and $x + 2h$, their lengths will be respectively y_0, y_1, and y_2 as shown.

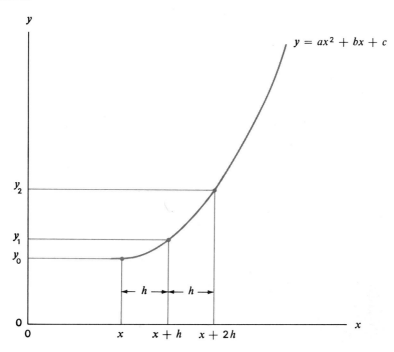

Figure A.2

Now to calculate the area under $y = ax^2 + bx + c$ between x and $(x + 2h)$:

$$A \underset{x \to (x + 2h)}{} = \int_x^{x + 2h} (ax^2 + bx + c)\,dx = \frac{ax^3}{3} + \frac{bx^3}{2} + cx \Big]_x^{x + 2h}$$

$$= \left[\frac{a(x + 2h)^3}{3} + \frac{b(x + 2h)^2}{2} + c(x + 2h) \right]$$

$$- \left[\frac{ax^3}{3} + \frac{bx^2}{2} + cx \right]$$

$$= \frac{a}{3}(x^3 + 6hx^2 + 12h^2x + 8h^3) + \frac{b}{2}(x^2 + 4hx + 4h^2)$$

$$+ cx + 2ch - \frac{a}{3}x^3 - \frac{b}{2}x^2 - cx$$

$$= \frac{ax^3}{3} + \frac{6ahx^2}{3} + \frac{12ah^2x}{3} + \frac{8ah^3}{3} + \frac{bx^2}{2} + \frac{4bhx}{2} + \frac{4bh^2}{2}$$

$$+ cx + 2ch - \frac{ax^3}{3} - \frac{bx^2}{2} - cx$$

$$= \frac{6ahx^2}{3} + \frac{12ah^2x}{3} + \frac{8ah^3}{3} + \frac{6bhx}{3} + \frac{6bh^2}{3} + \frac{6ch}{3}$$

$$= \frac{h}{3}(6ax^2 + 12ahx + 8ah^2 + 6bx + 6bh + 6c)$$

$$= \frac{h}{3}[(ax^2 + 4ax^2 + ax^2) + (8ahx + 4ahx) + (4ah^2$$

$$+ 4ah^2) + (bx + 4bx + bx) + (4bh + 2bh)(c + 4c + c)]$$

$$= \frac{h}{3}(ax^2 + bx + c + 4ax^2 + 8ahx + 4ah^2 + 4bx + 4bh$$

$$+ 4c + ax^2 + 4axh + 4ah^2 + bx + 2bh + c)$$

$$= \frac{h}{3}[(ax^2 + bx + c) + (4ax^2 + 8ahx + 4ah^2 + 4bx$$

$$+ 4bh + 4c) + (ax^2 + 4axh + 4ah^2 + bx + 2bh + c)]$$

$$= \frac{h}{3}[(ax^2 + bx + c) + 4(ax^2 + 2ahx + ah^2 + bx + bh$$

$$+ c) + (ax^2 + 4axh + 4ah^2 + bx + 2bh + c)]$$

$$= \frac{h}{3}\{(ax^2 + bx + c) + 4[a(x + h)^2 + b(x + h) + c]$$

$$+ [a(x + 2h)^2 + b(x + 2h) + c]\} \quad \text{(A.1)}$$

From $y = ax^2 + bx + c$ we write:

$$y_0 = ax^2 + bx + c \quad \text{(A.2)}$$

$$y_1 = a(x + h)^2 + b(x + h) + c \quad \text{(A.3)}$$

$$y_2 = a(x + 2h)^2 + b(x + 2h) + c \quad \text{(A.4)}$$

Now substituting A.2, A.3, and A.4 into A.1 we obtain:

$$A = \frac{h}{3}(y_0 + 4y_1 + y_2) \quad \text{(A.5)}$$

We could also have shown that (A.5) would result if the original equation for the parabola was:

$$x = ay^2 + by + c$$

Let us now proceed with a nonparabolic curve as pictured in Figure A.3. The area A_1 will approximately equal the area under a parabola passed through p_0, p_1, and p_2. This area under the parabola will be closer to A_1 than the area under

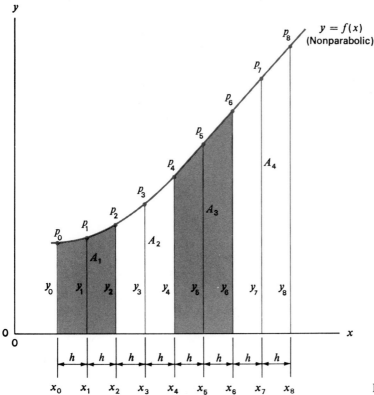

Figure A.3

a straight line through p_0 and p_2. Area A_2 will approximate the area under a parabola through p_2, p_3, and p_4. Similarly the areas A_3 and A_4 can be approximated, which allows us to say that the total area will approximately equal the sum of the area A_1, A_2, A_3, and A_4, or

$$A \underset{x_0 \to x_8}{\approx} A_1 + A_2 + A_3 + A_4$$

Applying (A.5) to the areas in Figure A.3, we have:

$$A_1 \approx \frac{h}{3}(y_0 + 4y_1 + y_2)$$

$$A_2 \approx \frac{h}{3}(y_2 + 4y_3 + y_4)$$

$$A_3 \approx \frac{h}{3} (y_4 + 4y_5 + y_6)$$

$$A_4 \approx \frac{h}{3} (y_6 + 4y_7 + y_8)$$

And

$$A \approx \frac{h}{3} (y_0 + 4y_1 + 2y_2 + 4y_3 + 2y_4 + 4y_5 + 2y_6 + 4y_7 + y_8)$$

which becomes very close to the exact area when h is held small.

Simpson's rule then is based on the premise that the area under a curve be divided into an even number of equal-width vertical strips. If we use Figure A.3 as a guide, we let h be the width of the strips and $y_0, y_1, y_2, \ldots, y_n$ the ordinates, the area under the curve closely approximates:

$$A \approx \frac{h}{3} (y_0 + 4y_1 + 2y_2 + 4y_3 + 2y_4 + \cdots + 4y_{(n-1)} + y_n)$$

in which y_0 is the ordinate at x_0 and y_n the ordinate at x_n. From all of this then:

$$A \underset{x_0 \to x_n}{=} \int_{x_0}^{x_n} y \, dx = \frac{h}{3} (y_0 + 4y_1 + 2y_2 + 4y_3 + 2y_4 \\ + \cdots + 4y_{(n-1)} + y_n)$$

(4.24)   Translation Formula Page 227

$$I_p = I_c + AD^2$$

In Figure A.4, we have area A with its centroidal axis yy, the parallel axis pp and the distance between them D. From all of this:

$$dI_p = (D - x)^2 \, dA$$

Integrating both sides we have:

$$I_p = \int (D^2 - 2Dx + x^2) \, dA$$

$$= \int D^2 \, dA - \int 2Dx \, dA + \int x^2 \, dA$$

$$= D^2 \int dA - 2D \int x \, dA + \int x^2 \, dA$$

$$= D^2 A - 2D \int x \, dA + \int x^2 \, dA$$

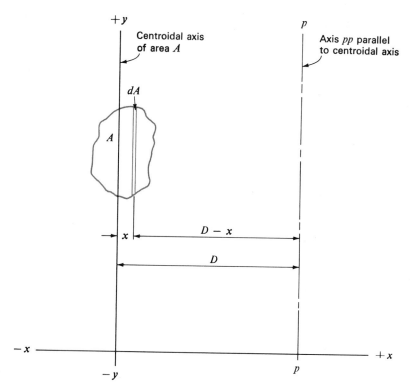

Figure A.4

In the second term $-2 \int x \, dA$, $\int x \, dA$ is the expression for the first moment of an area about its centroidal axis, which is by definition zero. Therefore $-2D \int x \, dA = 0$, and

$$I_p = D^2 A + \int x^2 \, dA$$

which is an expression of the relationship between the moment of inertia about a centroidal axis and the moment about a parallel axis. However,

$$\int x^2 \, dA = I_c$$

So:

$$I_p = I_c + D^2 A$$

Abbreviated Integral Table

1. The integration constant is not shown.
2. All logarithms (ln) are natural or base $e = 2.71818 \cdots$.
3. All angles are in radians.
4. In all cases u and v are functions of x. That is, $u = f(x)$ and $v = g(x)$.

Elementary Forms

1. $\int k\, dx = kx$

2. $\int ku\, du = k \int u\, du$

3. $\int (u + v)\, dx = \int u\, dx + \int v\, dx$

4. $\int u\, dv = u \int dv - \int v\, du = uv - \int v\, du$

5. $\int kx^n\, dx = \dfrac{kx^{n+1}}{n+1} \qquad n \neq -1$

6. $\int ku^n\, du = \dfrac{ku^{n+1}}{n+1} \qquad n \neq -1$

7. $\displaystyle\int_a^b f(x)\, dx = g(x)\Big]_a^b = g[b] - g[a]$

8. $\int \dfrac{k\, du}{u} = k \ln u$

9. $\int e^x\, dx = e^x$

10. $\int e^{ax}\, dx = \dfrac{e^{ax}}{a}$

11. $\int \ln x\, dx = x \ln x - x$

Forms Containing $(a + bx)$

12. $\int \dfrac{dx}{a + bx} = \dfrac{1}{b} \ln (a + bx)$

13. $\int \dfrac{u\, du}{a + bu} = \dfrac{1}{b^2}[(a + bu) - a \ln (a + bu)]$

14. $\int \dfrac{dx}{x(a + bx)} = -\dfrac{1}{a} \ln \left(\dfrac{a + bx}{x}\right)$

15. $\int \dfrac{du}{u(a + bu)} = -\dfrac{1}{a} \ln \left(\dfrac{a + bu}{u}\right)$

16. $\displaystyle\int \frac{dx}{(a + bx)^2} = -\frac{1}{b(a + bx)}$

17. $\displaystyle\int \frac{u\,du}{(a + bu)^2} = \frac{1}{b^2}\left[\frac{a}{a + bu} + \ln(a + bu)\right]$

18. $\displaystyle\int \frac{dx}{x(a + bx)^2} = \frac{1}{a(a + bx)} - \frac{1}{a^2 n}\left(\frac{a + bx}{x}\right)$

19. $\displaystyle\int \frac{du}{u(a + bu)^2} = \frac{1}{a(a + bu)} - \frac{1}{a^2}\ln\left(\frac{a + bu}{u}\right)$

Forms Containing $\sqrt{a + bu}$

20. $\displaystyle\int u\sqrt{a + bu}\,du = -\frac{2(2a - 3bu)(a + bu)^{3/2}}{15b^2}$

21. $\displaystyle\int \frac{u\,du}{\sqrt{a + bu}} = -\frac{2(2a - bu)\sqrt{a + bu}}{3b^2}$

22. $\displaystyle\int \frac{du}{u\sqrt{a + bu}} = \frac{1}{\sqrt{a}}\ln\left(\frac{\sqrt{a + bu} - \sqrt{a}}{\sqrt{a + bu} + \sqrt{a}}\right) \qquad a > 0$

23. $\displaystyle\int \frac{\sqrt{a + bu}}{u}\,du = 2\sqrt{a + bu} + a\int \frac{du}{u\sqrt{a + bu}}$

Forms Containing $(u^2 \pm a^2)$, $\sqrt{u^2 \pm a^2}$, and $\sqrt{a^2 - u^2}$

24. $\displaystyle\int \frac{du}{u^2 - a^2} = \frac{1}{2a}\ln\left(\frac{u - a}{u + a}\right)$

25. $\displaystyle\int \frac{du}{\sqrt{u^2 \pm a^2}} = \ln(u + \sqrt{u^2 \pm a^2})$

26. $\displaystyle\int \frac{du}{u\sqrt{u^2 + a^2}} = -\frac{1}{a}\ln\left(\frac{a + \sqrt{u^2 + a^2}}{u}\right)$

27. $\displaystyle\int \frac{du}{u\sqrt{u^2 - a^2}} = \frac{1}{a}\sec^{-1}\frac{u}{a}$

28. $\displaystyle\int \frac{du}{u\sqrt{a^2 - u^2}} = -\frac{1}{a}\ln\left(\frac{a + \sqrt{a^2 - u^2}}{u}\right)$

29. $\displaystyle\int \sqrt{u^2 \pm a^2}\, du = \frac{u}{2}\sqrt{u^2 \pm a^2} \pm \frac{a^2}{2}\ln\left(u + \sqrt{u^2 \pm a^2}\right)$

30. $\displaystyle\int \sqrt{a^2 - u^2}\, du = \frac{u}{2}\sqrt{a^2 - u^2} + \frac{a^2}{2}\sin^{-1}\frac{u}{a}$

31. $\displaystyle\int \frac{\sqrt{u^2 + a^2}}{u}\, du = \sqrt{u^2 + a^2} - a\ln\left(\frac{a + \sqrt{u^2 + a^2}}{u}\right)$

32. $\displaystyle\int \frac{\sqrt{u^2 - a^2}}{u}\, du = \sqrt{u^2 - a^2} - a\sec^{-1}\frac{u}{a}$

33. $\displaystyle\int \frac{\sqrt{a^2 - u^2}}{u}\, du = \sqrt{a^2 - u^2} - a\ln\left(\frac{a + \sqrt{a^2 - u^2}}{u}\right)$

34. $\displaystyle\int (u^2 \pm a^2)^{3/2}\, du = \frac{u}{4}(u^2 \pm a^2)^{3/2} \pm \frac{3a^2 u}{8}\sqrt{u^2 \pm a^2}$

$$+ \frac{3a^4}{8}\ln\left(u + \sqrt{u^2 \pm a^2}\right)$$

35. $\displaystyle\int (a^2 - u^2)^{3/2}\, du = \frac{u}{4}(a^2 - u^2)^{3/2} + \frac{3a^2 u}{8}\sqrt{a^2 - u^2} + \frac{3a^4}{8}\sin^{-1}\frac{u}{a}$

36. $\displaystyle\int \frac{(u^2 + a^2)^{3/2}}{u}\, du = \frac{1}{3}(u^2 + a^2)^{3/2} + a^2\sqrt{u^2 + a^2} - a^3\ln\left(\frac{a + \sqrt{u^2 + a^2}}{u}\right)$

37. $\displaystyle\int \frac{(u^2 - a^2)^{3/2}}{u}\, du = \frac{1}{3}(u^2 - a^2)^{3/2} - a^2\sqrt{u^2 - a^2} + a^3\sec^{-1}\frac{u}{a}$

38. $\displaystyle\int \frac{(a^2 - u^2)^{3/2}}{u}\, du = \frac{1}{3}(a^2 - u^2)^{3/2} - a^2\sqrt{a^2 - u^2} + a^3\ln\left(\frac{a + \sqrt{a^2 - u^2}}{u}\right)$

39. $\displaystyle\int \frac{du}{(u^2 \pm a^2)^{3/2}} = \pm\frac{u}{a^2\sqrt{u^2 \pm a^2}}$

40. $\displaystyle\int \frac{du}{(a^2 - u^2)^{3/2}} = \frac{u}{a^2\sqrt{a^2 - u^2}}$

41. $\displaystyle\int \frac{du}{u(u^2 + a^2)^{3/2}} = \frac{1}{a^2\sqrt{u^2 + a^2}} - \frac{1}{a^3}\ln\left(\frac{a + \sqrt{u^2 + a^2}}{u}\right)$

42. $\displaystyle\int \frac{du}{u(u^2 - a^2)^{3/2}} = -\frac{1}{a^2\sqrt{u^2 - a^2}} - \frac{1}{a^3}\sec^{-1}\frac{u}{a}$

43. $\int \dfrac{du}{u(a^2 - u^2)^{3/2}} = \dfrac{1}{a^2 \sqrt{a^2 - u^2}} - \dfrac{1}{a^3} \ln\left(\dfrac{a + \sqrt{a^2 - u^2}}{u}\right)$

Trigonometric Forms

44. $\int \sin u \, du = -\cos u$

45. $\int \cos u \, du = \sin u$

46. $\int \tan u \, du = \ln (\sec u)$

47. $\int \sin^2 u \, du = \tfrac{1}{2}x - \tfrac{1}{4}\sin 2x$

48. $\int \sin^3 u \, du = -\cos u + \tfrac{1}{3}\cos^3 u$

49. $\int \sin^n u \, du = -\dfrac{1}{n} \sin^{n-1} u \cos u + \dfrac{n-1}{n} \int \sin^{n-2} u \, du$

50. $\int \cos^2 u \, du = \dfrac{u}{2} + \dfrac{1}{2} \sin u \cos u$

51. $\int \cos^3 u \, du = \sin u - \tfrac{1}{3}\sin^3 u$

52. $\int \cos^n u \, du = \dfrac{1}{n} \cos^{n-1} u \sin u + \dfrac{n-1}{n} \int \cos^{n-2} u \, du$

53. $\int \tan^n u \, du = \dfrac{\tan^{n-1} u}{n-1} - \int \tan^{n-2} u \, du$

54. $\int \cot^n u \, du = -\dfrac{\cot^{n-1} u}{n-1} - \int \cot^{n-2} u \, du$

Miscellaneous Forms

55. $\int u e^{au} \, du = \dfrac{e^{au}(au - 1)}{a^2}$

56. $\int u^2 e^{au} \, du = \dfrac{e^{au}}{a^3} (a^2 u^2 - 2au + 2)$

57. $\int u^n \ln u \, du = u^{n+1} \left(\dfrac{\ln u}{n + 1} - \dfrac{1}{(n + 1)^2} \right)$

58. $\int u \sin u \, du = \sin u - u \cos u$

59. $\int u \cos u \, du = \cos u + u \sin u$

60. $\int e^{au} \sin bu \, du = e^{au} \left(\dfrac{a \sin bu - b \cos bu}{a^2 + b^2} \right)$

Answers to
Selected Problems

Page 18   Exercise 1.1

1. The slope of a straight line is defined as the ratio of rise over run, or change in y divided by change in x.

3. $-\frac{8}{5}$ 5. 1   7. $-\frac{8}{5}$

Page 23   Exercise 1.4

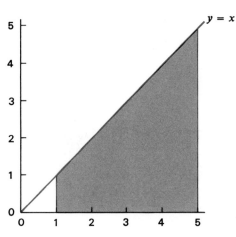

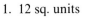

1. 12 sq. units

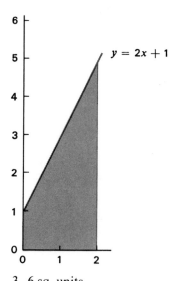

3. 6 sq. units

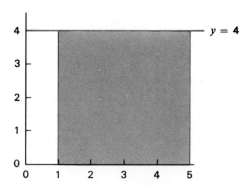

5. 16 sq. units

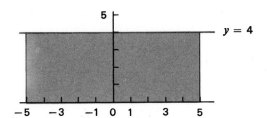

7. 40 sq. units

Page 25   Exercise 1.6

1. Slope of a straight line is defined as the ratio of rise to run, or change in y, (Δy), divided by change in x, (Δx).
3. Instantaneous slope of a curved line is defined as the slope of the line tangent to the curve at the point in question.
5. Area under a curved-line segment is defined as the area between the curved-line segment and the x axis.
7. Plot the curve accurately. Make the plot as large as possible. Make unit squares as small as practical.

Page 29   Exercise 2.1

1. 5
3. No value
5. No value
7. No value
9. 0
11. No value
13. No value
15. 0

Page 33   Exercise 2.2

1. -13
3. -6
5. Undefined
7. Undefined
9. Undefined
11. Undefined

Page 36   Exercise 2.3

1. $(\Delta y)/(\Delta x) = 2x + (\Delta x)$
3. $(\Delta y)/(\Delta x) = 4x + (\Delta x)$
5. $(\Delta y)/(\Delta x) = 3/[(x + 3)(x + \Delta x + 3)]$
7. $(\Delta y)/(\Delta x) = 3x^{\frac{1}{2}} - \frac{3}{4}x^{-\frac{3}{4}}(\Delta x) + \frac{3}{8}x^{-\frac{5}{2}}(\Delta x)^2 + \cdots$
9. $(\Delta y)/(\Delta x) = -3/[x(x + \Delta x)]$
11. $(\Delta A)/(\Delta r) = 2\pi r + \pi(\Delta r)$

Page 38   Exercise 2.4

1. $dy/dx = 2x = 6$
3. $dy/dx = 4x = 4$
5. $dy/dx = 3/(x + 3)^2 = \frac{3}{16}$
7. $dy/dx = 3x^{\frac{1}{2}} = 6$
9. $dy/dx = -3/x^2 = -\frac{3}{4}$

Page 40   Exercise 2.5

1. $dy/dx = 2x$
5. $dy/dx = 3/\sqrt{6x} = \sqrt{6x}/3$
7. $dy/dx = -3/x^2$
11. $dy/dx = 14x^6$
13. $dy/dx = 1/\sqrt[5]{x^4}$
19. $dy/dx = -8/3 \sqrt[3]{x^7}$

3. $dy/dx = 4x$

9. $dy/dx = 3(k+1)x^k$
15. $dy/dx = -4\pi/3 \sqrt[3]{x^7}$
17. $dy/dx = 2/\sqrt{x^3}$

Page 41   Exercise 2.6

1. $dy/dx = 2Ax + B$
5. $dy/dx = \sqrt{x}/(2x)$
11. $dy/dx = 2/\sqrt{x} - 2/\sqrt{x^3}$
13. $dy/dx = -12/x^4$
17. $dy/dx = -3\pi/2x^4$

3. $dy/dx = 35x^4 - 60x^2$
9. $dy/dx = 8x - 8/x^2$

15. $dy/dx = -104/x^5$
19. $dy/dx = 2x - 3$

Page 42   Exercise 2.7

1. $dy/dx = -24x(5 - x^2)$
5. $dy/dx = 5x/\sqrt{100 - x^2}$
9. $dy/dx = 16x/\sqrt[3]{x^2 + 16}$

3. $dy/dx = 4x/[3(x^2 + 9)^{\frac{2}{3}}]$
7. $dy/dx = 17x/(6 - x^2)^{\frac{3}{2}}$

Page 49   Exercise 2.8

1. The ordinal value $f[2]$ is greater than any other $f[x]$ for all x's close to $x = 2$.
3. Maximum, minimum, inflection point. .
5. Calculate the slope of the curve a little to the left of the given critical point, then calculate the slope a little to the right of the critical point. If the slope varies $+, 0, -$ then a maximum exists. If $-, 0, +$ then a minimum exists. If $+, 0, +$ or $-, 0, -$ then an inflection point exists.
7. $dy/dx = 4x^3 + 6x^2 - 6x$. Critical points: $x = (-3 - \sqrt{33})/4$ min, $x = 0$ max, $x = (-3 + \sqrt{33})/4$ min.
9. $dy/dx = 3x^2 - 6x - 9$. Critical points: $x = -1$ max, $x = 3$ min.
11. $(9x^2 - 6)/(2\sqrt{3x^3 - 6x + 20})$. Critical points: $x = -\sqrt{6}/3$ max, $x = \sqrt{6}/3$ min.
13. $dy/dx = -4x^3 + 48x$. Critical points: $x = -2\sqrt{3}$ infl., $x = 0$ min, $x = 2\sqrt{3}$ max.
15. $dy/dx = 1 - (4/x^2)$. Critical points: $x = -2$ max, $x = 2$ min.
17. $\dfrac{dy}{dx} = \dfrac{-10(4x^3 - 9x)}{(2x^4 - 9x^2)^2}$. Critical points: $x = -\frac{3}{2}$ min, $x = 0$ max, $x = \frac{3}{2}$ min.

19. $5\sqrt{2}/2$ by $5\sqrt{2}/2$.
21. No. Some do, but it is not necessary, since only a change in direction is needed for an inflection point. It is not necessary for the slope to be zero.

Page 51   Exercise 2.9

1. 7 cps   3. 42.9 mph
5. $t = 1$, $ds/dt = 19$; $t = 2$, $ds/dt = 23$; $t = 10$, $ds/dt = 55$
7. $ds/dt = 400 + 600t$
9. Straight line passing through the origin with slope $2k$.
11. $\theta = 0$, max; $\theta = 11° 18'$, min.

Page 56   Exercise 2.10

1. $i = dq/dt = 6t$ amp; $t = 0.01$, $i = 0.06$ amp; $t = 0.03$, $i = 0.18$ amp; $t = 0.05$, $i = 0.30$ amp.
3. $e_{ind} = (-100)(0.003) = -0.3$ volts.
5. $P = dw/dt = 6t^2 + 3$, $t = 0.02$, $P = 3.0024$ watts.
7. $de/dt = 900t^2$; $i = 1800 \times 10^{-4} t^2$
9. $e_{ind} = -40/\sqrt{t}$ volts.
11. $e_{ind} = -2.4$ volts.

Page 59   Exercise 2.11

1. $i = (t^3 + 60t + 3000)/600000$
5. $e = 1060$ volts

Page 65   Exercise 2.13

1a. $y = (\sin x)^2$
1c. $y = \sin (x)^2$
1e. $y = 2(\sin x)^2$
1g. $y = 2[\sin (2x)]$
3. $y' = 2 \cos 2x$
7. $y' = -9 \sin x \cos^2 x$
11. $y' = 4x \sec^2 x^2$
15. $y' = 2x \csc^2 x^2$
19. $y' = -(\sin \sqrt{x})/2\sqrt{x}$
21. $y' = (\cos \sqrt{1-x})/(2\sqrt{1-x})$
23. $y' = -(\cos \sqrt{1-x})/(2\sqrt{1-x})$
25. $y' = -\omega \sin (\omega x + \pi/2)$
27. $y' = -(2/x^2) \cos (2/x)$
29. $y' = -(9/2x^{1/4}) \cos x^{3/4}$

1b. $y = \sin (2x)$
1d. $y = 2(\sin x)$
1f. $y = a[\sin (x)^2]$
1h. $y = 2\{[\sin (2x^2)]^2\}$
5. $y' = -3x^2 \sin x^3$
9. $y' = 4 \sec^2 2x$
13. $y' = 2 \csc^2 2x$
17. $y' = -16 \sin (2x + 3)$

Page 69   Exercise 2.14

1. $y' = \dfrac{x^3}{\sqrt{2x+1}} + \dfrac{3x^2(2x+1)}{\sqrt{2x+1}} = \dfrac{7x^3 + 3x^2}{\sqrt{2x+1}}$

3. $y' = x(2x) + (x^2+1)(1) = 3x^2 + 1$

5. $y' = 2x^3(6)(2x+1) + (2x+1)^3(6x^2) = 12x^3(2x+1) + 6x^2(2x+1)^3$

7. $y' = \dfrac{(x^2+1)(1) - x(2x)}{(x^2+1)^2} = \dfrac{1 - x^2}{(x^2+1)^2}$

9. $y' = \dfrac{(1-x)(2x) - x^2(-1)}{(1-x^2)} = \dfrac{2x - x^2}{(1-x)^2}$

11. $y' = \dfrac{(1-x^2)(2) - (2x+3)(-2x)}{(1-x^2)^2} = \dfrac{2x^2 + 6x + 2}{(1-x^2)^2}$

Page 72   Exercise 2.15

1. $y' = (2x+3)\,e^{(x^2+3x+5)}$

3. $y' = e^{\sqrt{x}}/2\sqrt{x}$

5. $y' = -e^{\sqrt{1-x}}/2\sqrt{1-x}$

7. $y' = e^{(x+8)}$

9. $y' = 1.3029/x$

11. $y' = (6/x) - 3\cos x + e^x$

13. $y' = 65.145/x$

15. $y' = (8x)/(x^2+3)$

17. $y' = -1/x$

19. $y' = -0.8686x/(4-x^2)$

21. $y' = \dfrac{.4343\cos(x+\pi)}{\sin(x+\pi)}$

22. $y' = 0$

25. $y' = 5\,e^{(x+1)}$

27. $y' = \cos x - 2\sin 2x$

29. $y' = -2e^x \sin 2x + e^x \cos 2x$

31. $y' = -1/x$

Page 72   Exercise 2.16

1. $y' = \cot x$

3. $y' = 15\cos(5x)\sin^2(5x)$

5. $y' = -3\sin^2 3x + 3\cos^2 3x = 3(\cos^2 3x - \sin^2 3x)$

7. $y' = \dfrac{x + \sqrt{x^2 - a^2}}{x^2 + x\sqrt{x^2 + a^2} - a^2}$

9. $y' = (\cos x - e^{2x}\sin x)/e^{2x}$

11. $y' = -4/(e^x - e^{-x})^2 = -4e^{2x}/(e^{2x} - 1)^2$

13. $y' = \frac{1}{2}\tan(\pi/4 + x/2) + 2\cot(\pi/4 + x/2)$

15. $y' = (1 + \cos(x/2))/2$

17. $y' = \tan^3 x$

19. $y' = \ln x$

Page 77   Exercise 2.17

1. 150π fpm

3. 200π fpm

5. $V_x = 153.2\pi$ fpm; $V_y = 128.56\pi$ fpm

Page 82   Exercise 2.18

1. $x = 0$, min
3. $x = 0$, infl
5. $x = \pi/2$, max; $x = 3\pi/2$, min
7. $x = -3$ infl
9. $x = 1$, max; $x = 13$, min
11. $x = 0$, max; $x = \pi/2$, *min*; $x = \pi$, max
13. $x = \pi/2$, max; $x = 3\pi/2$, min
15. $x = -\frac{1}{2}$, max
17. $5 + 5 = 10$; $5 \times 5 = 25$

Page 85   Exercise 2.19

1. $dy/dx = 1/y$
3. $dy/dx = -y/x$
5. $\dfrac{dy}{dx} = \dfrac{6xy(x^2 + 1)^2}{(x^2 + 1)^3 + 6}$
7. $dy/dx = -5x/3y$
9. $dy/dx = 15/2y$
11. $dy/dx = 3x^2/(1 - 6y)$

Page 86   Exercise 2.20

1. $dy = 15x^4\,dx$
3. $dy = 5\,dx$
5. $dy = 2\,dx/\sqrt{x}$
7. $dy = -x^3\,dx$
9. $dy = 5\cos \pi\,dx$
11. $dy = (\cos x + \sin x)e^x\,dx$
13. $dy = \sqrt{6x}\,dx/2x$
15. $dy = (\cos x + 2\cos 2x)\,dx$

Page 97   Exercise 2.21

1. $t = 1$ sec
3. $i = 1.041 \times 10^{-4}$ amp
5. $e_{\text{ind}} = -5.62$ volts

Page 98   Review problems

5. Second derivative
7. Undefined
9. Undefined
11. No critical points
13. Slope is zero at all critical points.
15. $-4/\pi$
17. $x = 1, x = 2, x = 3, x = -2$
    $y' = 27, y' = 24, y' = 15, y' = 0$
19. $dy/dx = (2x - 5y)/(3y^2 + 5x - 1)$

Page 102   Exercise 3.1

1. $x^3/3 + C$
3. $x^3 + C$
5. $4x^{1/2} + C$
7. $x + C$
9. $-10x + C$
11. $x^2 + C$

13. $3x^{4/3}/4 + C$ 15. $x^2/2 + C$

17. $9x^{2/3}/2 + C$ 19. $-\frac{2}{5}x^{5/3} + C$

Page 104   Exercise 3.2

1. $y = x^3 - 1$ 3. $y = \frac{3}{4}x^{4/3}$

5. $y = x^2$ 7. $y = 3x^{2/3} + 2$

Page 107   Exercise 3.3

1. $-1/5x^5 + C$ 3. $(2x^2 + 1)^{3/2}/6 + C$

5. $(200x^4 + 2)^{3/2}/1200 + C$

7. $-(3 - x)^5/5 + C$ 9. $-(3 - x^4)^6/4 + C$

11. $\frac{3}{4}(4x^2 - 9)^{5/2} + C$ 13. $\frac{1}{6}(4\phi - 1)^{3/2} + C$

15. $\frac{1}{3}(x^2 - 6x - 7)^{3/2} + C$

Page 112   Exercise 3.4

1. $\frac{13}{3}$ 3. $\frac{14}{3}$

5. $\frac{199}{200}$ 7. $\frac{68}{3}$

9. 76 11. $-\frac{32}{3}$

13. -12 15. $\frac{448}{3}$

Page 122   Exercise 3.6

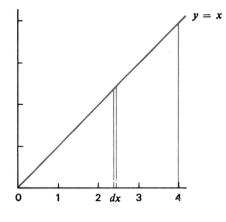
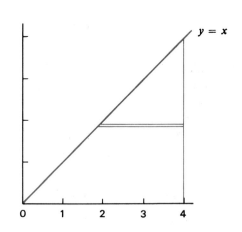

1. $A = 8$

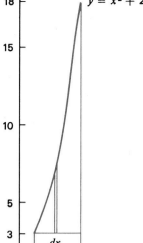

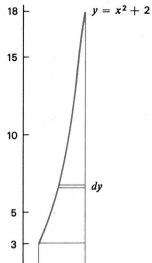

3. $A = 36$

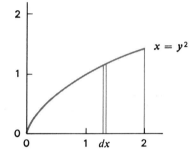

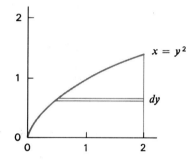

5. $A = 2$

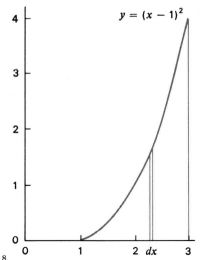

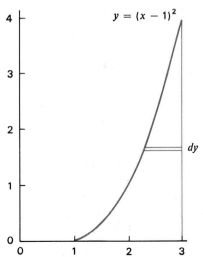

7. $A = \frac{8}{3}$

Page 123   Exercise 3.7

1. Av. ord. = 2   3. Av. ord. = 12
5. Av. ord. = 1   7. Av. ord. = $\frac{4}{3}$

Page 127   Exercise 3.8

1. 0   3. -3
5. $2 \sin 2x + C$ 7. $-\sin(4-x) + C$
9. $-\frac{1}{4}e^{1-4x} + C$ 11. $-e^{-x} + C$
13. $\frac{1}{3}e^{3x+1} + C$ 15. $\frac{1}{12}$
17. 9.6   19. 0.585

Page 132   Exercise 3.9

1. $s = 16t^2 ; v = 32t$ 3. $v = 32t - 50$
$\qquad\qquad\qquad\qquad\quad s = 16t^2 - 50t + 400$

Page 142   Exercise 3.10

1. $r = 6''$, $v = 288\pi$ in^3
$\quad r = 12''$, $v = 2304\pi$ in^3
$\quad r = 18''$, $v = 7776\pi$ in^3
$\quad r = 20''$, $v = 32000\pi/3$ in^3
3. 488 in^3 5. 2091.24π in^3

Page 152   Exercise 3.11

1. $m^2 a^2 \pi/3$ 3. $v = 4\pi/3$
5. $v = 32\pi/2 = 16\pi$ 7. $v = 40\pi$
9. $v = 128\pi/5$

Page 155   Exercise 3.12

1. 12 amp   3. $t = 0.337$ sec
5. $i = -(t^3/15) + (3t^2/10) + C$
7. $w = 162\sqrt{3}$

Page 158   Exercise 3.14

1. $(e^x/2)(\sin x + \cos x) + C$
3. $-x^2 \cos x + 2x \cos x + 2 \sin x + C$
5. $(x^3/9)(3 \ln x - 1) + C$
7. $x \sin x + \cos x + C$

9. $\dfrac{\sec^3 x \tan x}{4} + \dfrac{3}{8} \sec x \tan x + \dfrac{3}{8} \ln |\sec x + \tan x| + C$

11. $\dfrac{(x-1)\sqrt{2x+1}}{3} + C$

13. $\dfrac{e^{-x}(-\cos x + \sin x)}{2} + C$

15. $x \ln (x^2 + 1) - 2x + 2 \tan^{-1} x + C$

Page 162   Exercise 3.15

1. $\dfrac{-1}{13(2x+3)} + \dfrac{7}{13(x-5)}$

3. $\dfrac{-5}{x-1} + \dfrac{2}{(x+3)^2}$

5. $\dfrac{-3}{(x+2)^3} + \dfrac{8}{(x+2)^2} + \dfrac{1}{(x+2)}$

7. $\dfrac{8}{x^2+3} - \dfrac{4}{x^2-2}$

Page 169   Exercise 3.16

1. $\dfrac{x-3}{2\sqrt{6}} \tan^{-1} \dfrac{\sqrt{6}\,x}{3}$ 3. $\frac{1}{3} \sin x (\cos^2 x + 2)$

5. $(-x^5 + 20x^3 - 120x) \cos x + (5x^4 - 60x^2 + 120) \sin x$

7. 166.6   9. 98.97

11. 0.03475   13. $\frac{1}{45}(2+3x)^5 - \frac{1}{18}(2+3x)^4$

15. $[(16 - 24x + 30x^2)\sqrt{(1+x)^3}]/105$

17. $-2\sqrt{2} \cos (x/2)$

19. $3x/8 + (\sin 2x)/4 + (\sin 4x)/32$

Page 173   Exercise 3.17

1. $\frac{2}{27}(37^{3/2} - 1)$ 3. $\frac{14}{3}$

5. 64.16   7. 2.262

Page 177   Exercise 3.18

1. $16R^3/3$ 3. $abc/6$

5. $\pi/32$ 7. $4x^{3/2} + C$

9. $\frac{15}{4}x^{4/5} + C$ 11. $-\frac{1}{2} \cos (x^2 + 1) + C$

13. $-\frac{1}{20}(5 - x^5)^4 + C$ 15. 216

17. $\pi/4$ $\qquad$ 19. $-\sqrt{25-x^2}/25x + C$

21. $(\pi - 2)/4$

Page 188   Exercise 4.1

a. $\bar{x} = \frac{13}{6}, \bar{y} = \frac{11}{6}$ $\qquad$ c. $\bar{x} = \frac{29}{14}, \bar{y} = \frac{39}{14}$

e. $\bar{x} = -\frac{5}{32}, \bar{y} = \frac{51}{22}$ $\qquad$ g. $\bar{x} = \frac{13}{4}, \bar{y} = \frac{31}{8}$

Page 192   Exercise 4.2

a. $\bar{x} = \frac{23}{14}, \bar{y} = \frac{17}{14}$ $\qquad$ c. $\bar{x} = 0, \bar{y} = 0$

e. $\bar{x} = \frac{10}{21}, \bar{y} = \frac{131}{105}$

Page 213   Exercise 4.4

1. Centroid lies on axis $\frac{1}{4}$ of the altitude from the base.

3. $V = \frac{2}{3}\pi \times 10^{3/2}$ $\qquad$ 5. $\bar{y} = 3$

7. $\bar{y} = 6$ $\qquad$ 9. $\bar{y} = \frac{10}{3}$

11. $\bar{y} = \frac{14}{9}$ $\qquad$ 13. $\bar{x} = \frac{135}{144}$

15. $\bar{y} = \frac{9}{8}$ $\qquad$ 17. $\bar{y} = 0.8591$

19. $\bar{y} = \frac{20}{9}$

Page 218   Exercise 4.6

1. $\bar{x} = \bar{y} = 40/\pi$

Page 234   Exercise 4.7

1. $r_x = 2.94, r_y = 1.35$ $\qquad$ 3. $r_x = 5.89, r_y = 1.16$

5. $r_x = 1.5, r_y = 0.93$ $\qquad$ 7. $r_y = 4.88, r_x = 21.32$

Page 235   Exercise 4.8

1. $I_c = 125, r = 2.88675$ $\qquad$ 3. $I_{xx} = 303.75, r = 3.67425$

5. $I_{xx} = 1250\pi$ $\qquad$ 7. $I_{xx} = \frac{64}{3}, r = 1.15472$

Page 235   Exercise 4.10

1. $I_{xx} = 151.875\pi$ in^4 $\qquad$ 3. $I_c = 38266.56$ in^4

5. $I_{xx} = 574$ in^4 $\qquad$ 7. $I_{xx} = 763.47$ in^4

9. $I_{xx} = 2520$ in^4

Page 237   Exercise 4.11

1. $I_{yy} = 24.3$ in^4 $\qquad$ 3. $I_{xx} = 78.1$ in^4

Page 238   Exercise 5.1

1. 8, 10, 12, 14, 16; $a = 2, d = 2$
3. 17, 21, 25, 29, 33; $a = 5, d = 4$
5. 15, 11, 7, 3, -1; $a = 5, d = -4$
7. $a + 9, a + 12, a + 15, a + 18, a + 21$; $a = a, d = 3$
9. $-5b, -7b, -9b, -11b, -13b$; $a = b, d = -2b$
11. $\frac{1}{2}(\frac{2}{3})^8$
13. 0.00000000001

Page 243   Exercise 5.2

1. $\frac{4}{3}$ 3. 1
5. 18   7. 0
9.0

Page 247   Exercise 5.3

1. $f(x) = \sin 2x = 2x - \dfrac{8x^3}{3!} + \dfrac{32x^5}{5!} - \dfrac{128x^7}{7!} + \cdots$

3. $f(x) = \sqrt{1 + x} = 1 + \frac{1}{2}x - \frac{1}{8}x^2 + \frac{1}{16}x^3 + \cdots$
5. $f(x) = e^x \sin x = a + x + (2x/2!) + (2x^3/3!) + \cdots$

7. $f(x) = 1 - \dfrac{9x^2}{2!} + \dfrac{81x^4}{4!} - \dfrac{729x^6}{6!} + \cdots$

9. $f(x) = x + x^2 + \cdots$ 13. $f(x) = x + x^2 + \cdots$
11. $f(x) = 1 + (x^2/2!) + \cdots$
15. $f(x) = 1 - 2x^6 + (2x^{12}/3) - (4x^{18}/45) + \cdots$

Page 249   Exercise 5.4

1. 3.32   3. 2.049   5. 0.4848
7. $e^{-2}\left[1 - (x - 2) + \dfrac{(x - 2)^2}{2!} - \cdots\right]$

9. $\dfrac{1}{2}\left[\sqrt{3} + \left(x - \dfrac{\pi}{3}\right) - \dfrac{\sqrt{3}}{2!}\left(x - \dfrac{\pi}{3}\right)^2 - \cdots\right]$
11. $2 + \frac{1}{2}(x - 8) - \frac{1}{288}(x - 8)^2 + \cdots$

Page 255   Exercise 5.5

1. $f(x) = \dfrac{1}{2} - \dfrac{2}{\pi}\sin x - \dfrac{2}{3\pi}\sin 3x - \cdots$

3. $f(x) = \dfrac{3}{2} + \dfrac{2}{\pi} \sin x + \dfrac{2}{3\pi} \sin 3x + \cdots$

5. $f(x) = \dfrac{2}{\pi} - \dfrac{4}{3\pi} \cos 2x - \dfrac{4}{15\pi} \cos 4x - \cdots$

7. $f(x) = \dfrac{l}{L} + \dfrac{2}{\pi}\left[-\sin \dfrac{\pi l}{L} \cos \dfrac{\pi x}{L} + \dfrac{1}{2} \sin \dfrac{2\pi l}{L} \cos \dfrac{2\pi x}{L} \right.$

$\quad\quad\quad - \dfrac{1}{3} \sin \dfrac{3\pi l}{L} \cos \dfrac{3\pi x}{L} + \dfrac{1}{4} \sin \dfrac{4\pi l}{L} \cos \dfrac{4\pi x}{L} - \dfrac{1}{5} \sin \dfrac{5\pi l}{L} \cos \dfrac{5\pi x}{L} + \cdots \left.\right]$

9. $f(x) = \dfrac{9}{\pi^2}\left[\sin \dfrac{\pi}{3} \sin \dfrac{\pi x}{L} + \dfrac{1}{4} \sin \dfrac{2\pi}{3} \sin \dfrac{2\pi x}{L} + \dfrac{1}{9} \sin \pi \sin \dfrac{3\pi x}{L} \right.$

$\quad\quad\quad + \dfrac{1}{16} \sin \dfrac{4\pi}{3} \sin \dfrac{4\pi x}{L} + \dfrac{1}{25} \sin \dfrac{5\pi}{3} \sin \dfrac{5\pi x}{L} + \cdots \left.\right]$

Page 261   Exercise 6.2

1. $-\frac{1}{2} \cos t + C$

3. $\frac{1}{2} \sin 4x + 3 \ln x + C$

5. $-\frac{1}{2} e^{-x^2 - 5} + C$

7. $x \sqrt{9 - 4x^2} + \sin^{-1}(2x/3) + C$

9. $7x + \ln y = C$

11. $50t - \sin^{-1}(i) = C$

13. $y = (\sqrt{3}/6) \tan^{-1}(\sqrt{3}/2)t - 2$

15. $x = \frac{1}{5} \ln(y/2)$

Page 262   Exercise 6.3

1. $x^2 - y^2 = C$

3. $\ln(y/x) = C$

5. $\ln y + 3x = C$

7. $\ln[(x - 1)/(y + 2)] = C$

9. $x + \ln(3 - y) = C$

11. $3x + \ln(5 - 3y) = C$

13. $\ln(4 + y^2) - x = C$

15. $2x - \ln(4 - y^2) = C$

17. $\sin 2y - 4 \tan(x/2) = C$

19. $3xe^{-x} - 3e^{-x} - e^{-3y} = C$

21. $t = 0.001 \ln[4/(4 - 2i)]$

23. $\theta - \sin^{-1}(v/2) = \pi/3$

25. $x - \sin^{-1}(y/3) = 1$

Page 265   Exercise 6.4

1. $2xy + x^2 = C$

3. $x^3 - 2y - Cx = -4$

5. $\ln(y^2 - x^2) + 2x = C$

7. $x^2y - y = Cx$

9. $2x = 2xy^2 - 15y$

Page 268   Exercise 6.5

1. $y = (x^3/3) + C$

3. $ye^x = x + C$

5. $(1/y - (x^3/3) + C$ 7. $ye^x = \sin x + C$

9. $2y = e^{4x}(x^2 + C)$ 11. $y = 3 + Ce^{-x}$

13. $3y = x^4 - 6x^2 - 3 + Cx$

15. $y = -\cos x + 1$ 19. $y = e^{-x}$

17. $y = x$

Page 274 Exercise 6.6

1. $\mathscr{L}(f) = 1/s$ 3. $\mathscr{L}(f) = 6/s$

5. $\mathscr{L}(f) = 1/(s - 3)$ 7. $\mathscr{L}(f) = 6/(s + 2)^4$

9. $\mathscr{L}(f) = (s - 2)/(s^2 - 4)$ 11. $f(t) = 1$

13. $f(t) = (3t^3)/3!$ 15. $f(t) = 1 - e^{-3t}$

17. $f(t) = 3te^{2t}$ 19. $f(t) = e^{-3t}(1 - 3t)$

21. $f(t) = e^{-5t}$

23. $f(t) = \frac{1}{54}(9t \sin 3t + 2 \sin 3t - 6t \cos 3t)$

Page 276 Exercise 6.7

1. $(2s^2 - s + 1)\mathscr{L}(f) - 2s + 1$

3. $(s^2 - 2s)\mathscr{L}(f) - 1$

5. $\mathscr{L}(y) = 1/(s - \frac{1}{2})$

Page 280 Exercise 6.8

1. $y = e^{-t}$ 3. $y = -e^{3t/2}$

5. $y = e^{-t} \sin t$ 7. $y = \frac{1}{2} \sin 2t$

9. $i = (E/R)(1 - e^{-Rt/L})$

11. $y = (31e^{10x} - 3e^{-4x})/14$

13. $y = 1 - e^{-2t}$ 15. $y = e^{2t} \cos t$

Index

Differential equations *continued*
  general solution, 259
  solving, by integration, 263
    by Laplace transforms, 269
    by separation of variable, 261
Differentials, 85
Differentiating circuits, L, 60
  RC, 60
Divergence, 240
Domain of a function, 12
Double integration, 124

e, 2
Effective ordinate of sine function, 164
Equations, differential, 257
  first-order linear, 266
Expansions, binomial, 2, 165
Exponents, laws of, 2

Factorial notation, 1
Falling bodies, 50
Flux required, 154
Fourier series, 249
Functions, 12
  inverse, 13

Geometric sequence, 239
Graph, of inverse trigonometric functions, 6
  of trigonometric functions, 5, 6
Graphical differentiation, 20
Graphical integration, 24
Gyration, radius of, 220

Henry, 56
Hyperbola, 9

Indefinite integral, 100
Identities, trigonometric, 7
Impedence, 89
Implicit functions,
  differentiation, 83
Induced voltage, 53, 55
Inductance, mutual, 56
Inertia, moment of, 219
Inflection point, 46
Instantaneous power, 54
Instantaneous slope, 20
Integral, definite, 112
  double, 124
  indefinite, 100
  of $k \cos u \, du$, 126
  of $k \, e^u \, du$, 126
  of $k \sin u \, du$, 126

Integral *continued*
  of $k \tan u \, du$, 126
  of $k \, u^n \, du$, 104
  of $k \, u^{-1} \, du$, 126
  summary of, 179
  triple, 173
Integrating circuits, 155
Integration, constant, 102
  double, 124
  fundamental theorem of, 115
  by partial fractions, 158
  by parts, 156
  tables, 163, 179, 291
Inverse trigonometric functions, graph of, 6

j operator, 2

Kirchoff's law, current, 57
  voltage, 58

Laplace transforms, 269
Length of curved line, 169
Limit, defined, 28
  theorems, 31
Limits of integration, 112
Linear differential equations, 266
Logarithms, 8

Maclaurin series, 243
Maxima, 42
Minima, 42
Moment arm, 184
Moment of inertia, 219
  by double integration, 237
  summary of, 232
  translation of, 227
Moments, 181
  first, 184
  second, 219
Motion, angular, 73
  linear, 50
Mutual inductance, 56

Natural logarithm (base *e*), 1
  differentiation of, 71
Negative slope, 16

Octant, 175
Ordinate, average, 122

Pappus, theorem of, 214
Parabola, 9, 10
Parallel-axis theorem, 227

71 72 73   12 11 10 9 8 7 6 5 4 3 2 1